PROPULSION SYSTEMS FOR SPACE FLIGHT

PROPULSION SYSTEMS
FOR SPACE FLIGHT

WILLIAM R. CORLISS

The Martin Company; Formerly of
The General Electric Company

McGRAW-HILL BOOK COMPANY, INC.

New York   Toronto   London

1960

PROPULSION SYSTEMS FOR SPACE FLIGHT

13175

THE MAPLE PRESS COMPANY, YORK, PA.

PREFACE

The design, development, and construction of reaction engines for use in outer space has engendered a new technology. The most appropriate name for this assemblage of diverse techniques is *space propulsion*. In treating this "spanking" new subject, this book runs the gamut from turbojets to photon propulsion. An effort has been made to emphasize the more advanced or "exotic" space engines. The focus of interest has therefore been shifted from chemical rockets to the nuclear and electrical propulsion systems. The longest chapter of the book is devoted to the different methods of generating power in space, which spotlights the most critical problem in space propulsion: *space power*.

This book is at once a survey and an evaluation of the manifold schemes that have been proposed for transporting matter about the universe. Space propulsion is a rapidly expanding and changing field. The literature is overgrown with ideas, concepts, and brainstorms. Some weeding of this prolific garden will be evident in the book.

The bulk of the subject matter originated in a survey course on advanced propulsion concepts that the author presented at General Electric in the spring of 1958. The course material has been expanded considerably and brought up to date (a challenging job in itself), but the survey character remains. The primary function of this book is that of integrating a fragmented technology into some semblance of order. In attempting to reach this goal, every nook and cranny of science and pseudoscience was investigated. Some of the subjects treated, *antigravity*, for example, still have an aura of black magic about them. However, when the field is examined for perspective, using common measures of performance, some order and reason can be seen. Space propulsion, as the phrase goes, is "settling down." With the romance removed, the real problems are the same ones we had yesterday, those of translating rather fuzzy concepts into reliable operational hardware.

The author hopes that both technical and nontechnical people will find something of interest in the panorama of space engines displayed here. Which propulsion system will power the first manned spaceship to Mars, we cannot honestly say. There is a challenge, however, in setting down the energy resources available to mankind to see if they lead to the planets.

Many people at General Electric have aided me in reviewing the manuscript and clearing it for publication. I wish to express my thanks to M. Zipkin, H. Brown, H. Nichols, E. Schnetzer, A. Sherman, A. Beverage, R. Edwards, J. Cullen, D. McGinnis, and especially to my wife, Virginia Corliss, for her encouragement, patience, and assistance in typing the final manuscript.

William R. Corliss

CONTENTS

Preface v

1. Introduction 1

1-1. Expansion into Space; 1-2. The History of Space Technology; 1-3. Definition of the Propulsion System; 1-4. The Role of Power; 1-5. Other Critical Problems in Space Travel; 1-6. Horizons in Time and Space

2. Propulsion-system Performance and Space Missions 7

2-1. Mission Requirements and Propulsion-system Capabilities. FUNDAMENTALS OF REACTION ENGINES: 2-2. The Reaction Engine; 2-3. Other Applications of Reaction Theory; 2-4. Relativity and Photons; 2-5. Force Fields in Space; 2-6. Other Environmental Interactions; 2-7. Generalized Performance of Reaction Engines. PERFORMANCE OF SPACE PROPULSION SYSTEMS: 2-8. The Factors That Make Up Performance; 2-9. Relations between Propulsion Parameters; 2-10. Optimization of the Parameters. SPACE MISSIONS: 2-11. Mission Classes and Maneuvers; 2-12. Mission and Engine Parameters; 2-13. Planetary Surface Missions; 2-14. Satellite Missions; 2-15. Interplanetary Missions; 2-16. Interstellar Missions; 2-17. The Energetics of Space Travel. PROPULSION-SYSTEM SELECTION: 2-18. The Process of Selection

3. The Environment of Space 54

3-1. Elements of the Void. PARTICULATE MASS: 3-2. The Mass Spectrum; 3-3. Stars to Asteroids; 3-4. Meteoroids, Micrometeoroids, and Cosmic Dust; 3-5. Atoms and Atomic Particles; 3-6. Planetary Atmospheres; 3-7. Utilization of the Mass Spectrum. ELECTROMAGNETIC RADIATION: 3-8. The Electromagnetic Spectrum; 3-9. Effects of Electromagnetic Radiation. FORCE FIELDS IN SPACE: 3-10. Action-at-a-distance Fields; 3-11. Control of the Space Environment

4. Power Generation in Space 71

4-1. Power Requirements in Outer Space; 4-2. The Power-plant Spectrum; 4-3. A General Approach. TRANSPORTABLE ENERGY SOURCES: 4-4. Chemical Sources of Power; 4-5. Radioisotopes; 4-6. Nuclear Fission and Fusion; 4-7. Mechanical and Electrical Energy Storage. ENVIRONMENTAL ENERGY SOURCES: 4-8. Basis of Environmental Energy Sources; 4-9. Solar Power Sources; 4-10. Free Radical Energy from the Atmosphere; 4-11. Utilization of the Earth's Magnetic Field; 4-12. Wireless Transmission of Power. THERMAL-MECHANICAL-ELECTRICAL ENERGY CONVERSION: 4-13. Heat to Electricity; 4-14. Thermodynamic Cycles; 4-15. Heat to Mechanical Energy; 4-16. Electrical Generators. DIRECT CONVERSION: 4-17. Direct Conversion of Heat to Electricity; 4-18. The Thermionic Converter; 4-19. Thermoelectric Generators; 4-20. Fuel Cells; 4-21.

Chemical Batteries; 4-22. Solar Cells. HEAT REJECTION IN OUTER SPACE: 4-23. Heat Disposal; 4-24. The Temperature Problem; 4-25. Physical Construction; 4-26. Meteoroid Punctures. SYNTHESIS AND EVALUATION: 4-27. Intercomparison of Power Supplies; 4-28. Final Evaluation

5. Thermal Propulsion Systems 134

5-1. Principles of Thermal Propulsion Systems; 5-2. Thermodynamics of Thermal Engines. AIR-BREATHING BOOSTERS: 5-3. A New Application for the Turbojet Engine; 5-4. Turbojet Booster Performance; 5-5. Evaluation of Air-breathing Boost. CHEMICAL ROCKETS: 5-6. The Conventional Space Engine; 5-7. Evaluation of Chemical Rockets. THE RECOMBINATION RAM JET: 5-8. Energy from the Ionosphere; 5-9. Drag versus Thrust; 5-10. Thermodynamics; 5-11. Evaluation of the Recombination Ram Jet. NUCLEAR-FISSION ROCKETS: 5-12. The Application of Nuclear Power to Rockets; 5-13. Heat-transfer Nuclear Rockets; 5-14. Low-pressure Nuclear Heat-transfer Rockets; 5-15. The Consumable Nuclear Rockets; 5-16. Nuclear Bomb Propulsion. THERMONUCLEAR ENGINES: 5-17. Power from Fusion Reactions; 5-18. Propulsion-system Design Considerations; 5-19. Systems with External Working Fluids; 5-20. The Leaky Magnetic Bottle. PLASMA JETS: 5-21. Introduction to the Plasma Jet; 5-22. Description of Operation; 5-23. Plasma-jet Physics; 5-24. Plasma-jet Performance; 5-25. Auxiliaries and Barrier Problems of the Plasma Jet; 5-26. Evaluation of the Plasma Jet; 5-27. A Nuclear-electric Hybrid Space Engine. EVALUATION OF THERMAL ENGINES: 5-28. Final Comparisons

6. Electrical Propulsion Systems 186

6-1. Introduction to Electrical Propulsion Systems; 6-2. Electromagnetic Fields; 6-3. Magnetohydrodynamics (MHD). ION DRIVES: 6-4. Introduction to Ion Propulsion; 6-5. The Basic Ion Drive; 6-6. The Emitter; 6-7. The Accelerator Section; 6-8. The Beam Neutralizer; 6-9. The Integrated Propulsion Unit; 6-10. Propulsion Parameters; 6-11. The Typical Ion Drive; 6-12. Auxiliaries and Barrier Problems in Ion Propulsion. PLASMA ACCELERATORS: 6-13. Plasma Acceleration; 6-14. Plasmoid Guns; 6-15. Traveling-wave Accelerators; 6-16. Plasma Pumps or $E \times H$ Accelerators; 6-17. Kolb Tubes; 6-18. Transient Magnetic Field Accelerators; 6-19. Evaluation of Plasma Propulsion Systems. EVALUATION OF ELECTRICAL PROPULSION SYSTEMS: 6-20. Final Summary

7. Nuclear-particle Generators 229

7-1. Nuclear-particle Emitters for Propulsion; 7-2. Fission Reactors as Particle Emitters; 7-3. Radioisotope Particle Sources; 7-4. Magnetic Focusing of Charged Particles; 7-5. Thermonuclear-particle Generators; 7-6. Summary of Nuclear-particle Generators

8. Photonic Propulsion Systems 238

8-1. Introduction to Photonic Propulsion Systems; 8-2. Physics of Photon Engines. PHOTON DRIVES: 8-3. Propulsion Parameters for Photonic Engines; 8-4. Practical Aspects of Photonic Propulsion; 8-5. Evaluation of Photon Rockets. SOLAR SAILS: 8-6. The Operation of Solar Sails; 8-7. The Design of Solar Sails; 8-8. Evaluation of Solar Sails; 8-9. Summary and Evaluation of Photonic Propulsion

9. Propulsion Systems Using Natural Force Fields 255

9-1. Natural Force Fields; 9-2. Magnetic Fields; 9-3. The Use of Electrostatic Fields in Space; 9-4. Antigravity; 9-5. Miscellaneous Concepts; 9-6. Evaluation of Propulsion Using Force Fields

10. Summary and Evaluation 262

10-1. Review of Space Propulsion Techniques; 10-2. Comparison of Performance and Missions Requirements; 10-3. The Difficulties Ahead; 10-4. What Lies Beyond?

Glossary of Terms 273

Table of Symbols 278

Bibliography 282

Index 295

PROPULSION SYSTEMS FOR SPACE FLIGHT

CHAPTER 1

INTRODUCTION

1-1. Expansion into Space. The propulsion systems to be described in the following pages have already penetrated into nearby space. Barring the unexpected, they will carry man himself to the reaches of the solar system. Nature and technology may be capricious and unpredictable, but interplanetary travel now seems to be a reasonable extrapolation of current scientific and engineering achievements.

Such a venture outside of the protective atmosphere of our planet is magnificent in its scope. The common superlatives hardly seem adequate to describe the huge quantities of energy, money, manpower, and materials that will eventually be consumed in this endeavor. Yet, these things constitute only a part of the whole picture. Space travel demands many other ingredients: the will for space exploration; the basic technology; the natural resources; and, finally, some sort of catalysis is needed to accelerate the process.

The will or desire for space travel has always been with us. The fundamental thoughts on travel to the planets and stars are far from new. In their thoughts, the Greeks and Romans have preceded us to the moon. After several hundred years of careful cultivation, we have finally acquired a technological base that is adequate for space exploration. At our disposal are vast industrial complexes, millions of skilled workers, immense supplies of natural resources and capital. Practical space travel is made from such things as these. The path of development from the wheel to the nuclear rocket is a long one. We stand today at the pyramid of an increasingly sophisticated* technology. Each physical law and industrial process is an indispensible building block. Fortunately, we also have the wealth necessary to do the job at hand. Given the proper stimulus, it is possible for us to divert large segments of labor and capital to space travel. The stimulus or catalysis is mandatory, for nations will not invest their wealth in extraterrestrial experiments too questionable or too unlikely to provide a good return on their investments. It is this factor that explains why we did not immediately push out into space following World War II when most of the other essential constituents for space conquest were present.

* See Glossary of Terms at the back of the book.

1

It is somewhat ironical that the first real extraterrestrial efforts had to await the catalytic action of international competition. Such competition carries with it the implication of military operations, both hot and cold. And it is true that, not only is space technology dependent upon military funds, but much of the groundwork upon which we now rely originated in war projects. It appears certain that space, like the land, sea, and air, will also become a battlefield. This is favorable for the hastening of space flight but difficult for taxpayers and the direct participants in the military actions.

The purpose of this book is not to dwell on the reasons and justifications for space exploration. Instead, the objective is to study the various possible means of locomotion between the planet earth and the nearby astronomical objects. As for the philosophy, suffice it to say that many reliable level-headed people now believe that this new adventure is neither trivial nor futile. All other rationalizing is left as an exercise for the reader.

1-2. The History of Space Technology. It is customary to include a lengthy historical treatment of rocketry and the beginnings of space flight in a book such as this. Indeed, the history really is fascinating. The space age did not burst into bloom without much thinking, fumbling, and many trials and tribulations. We are where we are today because the race collectively has made a million mistakes but was yet able to score a few victories. In this latter-day epic, there are science heroes like Newton, Ziolkowski, and Goddard, and inspirers like Verne, Wells, and Ley. Then, there are those who are rarely mentioned, like the engineer who designed the prosaic bolt that held the rocket together, the draftsman, and the rest of the unsung contributors. Such people and events really deserve more than these few paragraphs in passing. For those so inclined, a number of excellent historical summaries are available, and the reader is referred to them (Refs. 1-1, 1-6, and 1-11[*]).

The changing flavor of space technology is worth a jotting or two. The time is not far past when space was the exclusive property of those we might collectively call "the enthusiasts." This category includes the spectrum from the crackpots to the serious scientists. These people were, and still are, convinced as only enthusiasts can be convinced of the worth of space flight. It is impossible to be derogatory about them. Nurtured by the journals of the British Interplanetary Society and the American Rocket Society, and, it must be admitted, some excellent science fiction, they created most of the ideas and concepts we work with today. None of the propulsion systems to be discussed in this book are really new. Almost every idea conjured in today's brain-storm sessions will be found residing somewhere in the astronautical literature. And

[*] References are listed in the Bibliography at the back of the book.

frequently the men who were mentally out in space yesterday are the hardware project leaders of today.

The flavor has changed, though.   At some indefinable time, even before the satellites, space technology changed from an avocation to a vocation. In short, people became serious about it.   This change was undoubtedly conditioned by the A-bombs and the advances in supersonic flight.   The launchings of the satellites, of course, delivered the *coup de grâce* to the bulk of the skeptics.   Today, hundreds of millions of dollars are allotted to space technology, and, what is most important, there is an aura of respectability about the work.   Crackpots and doubters are still with us,

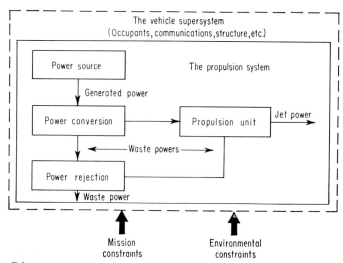

FIG. 1-1. Schematic of the space propulsion system and its components.   The space-vehicle supersystem is indicated by the enclosing dotted box.   The influences of mission and environmental constraints are shown by the arrows.

but space has become respectable, fit for respectable people and congressional appropriations.

1-3. Definition of the Propulsion System.   In spite of the overuse of the word "system," it is still convenient to use.   Our reference point in defining the term will be the complete set of space propulsion equipment, including the necessary power-producing machinery.   Figure 1-1 illustrates how the propulsion system is related to the vehicle, a supersystem, and the components of the propulsion system, the subsystems.   The scope of this book begins with the power source, and follows the progress of the energy through the conversion and rejection phases to the propulsion unit where the power is transformed into thrust.   The application of the systems approach to space propulsion expands the area of interest to include the power supply, the space environment, and the constraints imposed by the mission itself. In electrical and photonic thrust generators, the production of power is particularly critical in its influence on ultimate system performance. As Fig. 1-1 implies, it is impossible to talk intelligently about space propulsion without including the source of power.

1-4. The Role of Power. We have indicated that power is a key factor in interplanetary flight. It must be available in large quantities over long periods of time. The successful application of many space propulsion systems depends upon the development of lightweight power sources. At the present time, space technology revolves around the chemical rocket. In this system, chemical combustion produces thousands of megawatts for less than five minutes in the normal impulse applications. Nuclear rockets will consume 10 times as much power for comparable periods of time. Looking farther ahead to steady-state space propulsion, plasma and ion drives will demand megawatts of power for possibly years at a time. Everything boils down to one fundamental point, good propulsion-system performance requires immense supplies of energy generated by a lightweight source. We shall show later that the faster we wish to travel to Mars and the larger the payload desired, the greater the power level of the propulsion system.

In space, energy will also be necessary for human survival. Away from the relatively kind environment that exists at the earth's surface, man must create livable conditions. He will also wish to communicate, energize instruments, and possibly engage in warfare. These things will provide an additional drain on any power source aboard the space craft. In many cases, the same power supply will suffice for both propulsion and the auxiliaries.

As the various space propulsion systems are analyzed, it will become apparent that the power-plant specific mass, measured in kilograms per kilowatt, is an essential parameter in space performance calculations. Intrinsic in this single factor are the sizes and efficiencies of the power source, power converters, and the waste-heat rejector. There is no intention here to deemphasize the propulsion unit itself but rather to properly divide the responsibility for good performance between the power supply and propulsion unit.

Searching the future, when we shall wish to explore nearby stellar systems, and when the engines described in this book are well on their way toward obsolescence, the fundamental problem will still be one of energy and power. To move from one astronomical body to another means overcoming gravitational forces. This, in turn, infers the expenditure of energy, and the faster the trip, the more energy required.

1-5. Other Critical Problems in Space Travel. The great importance of energy in space flight has already been treated. There are several other factors just as critical but not so apparent. Satellite operations and interplanetary flight will involve the continuous operation of space vehicles for time periods on the order of years. True, we shall eventually wish to travel to Mars in a few days along short-time high-energy paths, but the longer duration trips, which are more economical of energy, will come first. When we speak of running machinery continuously and keeping people alive in an alien environment for years at a time, we have an endurance problem of a new order of magnitude. How many of today's machines will operate for a year continuously? Some long-lived equipment, like large steam turbines, can run year in and year out with little maintenance, but most contemporary mobile equipment has a trouble-free operating lifetime between 100 and 1,000 hr. Three key words in this vein are reliability, vulnerability, and design lifetime. These factors are not generally emphasized in assessing the performance of propulsion systems conceived for use in space. In the final analysis, we must know not only the easily measured engine parameters like thrust and weight, but there also must be included an objective analysis of the probability that the system will run at a satisfactory performance level for the intended time period.

It is no enviable job to try and attach numbers to the elusive qualitative factors just mentioned. The more conceptual the design of the machine, the less simple the task. We know that to design a turbine for 10,000 hrs of life rather than 1,000 means considerable strengthening of the mechanical design. Long-term creep of the metal then becomes a critical factor. The addition of the adjective "unattended" also introduces a whole new design philosophy. In the study of the various space propulsion systems, it is mandatory that we attend to these time-dependent variables. The reliability of a system, its vulnerability to the space environment, may sound the death knell to many an otherwise promising engine.

One last factor, too frequently glossed over, is the "state of the art." In using this phrase, we refer to the time period when it would be possible to build and successfully operate the system being examined. To put all propulsion systems on the same footing, some effort to evaluate each system's state of the art must be made. In short, we cannot plan trips to the moon in 1970 via an antigravity machine with the same assurance that we have with chemical rockets. Certainly, in the brief discussion above, we have not run the full course of the critical problems involved in space flight. This section is rather a notice that we intend to examine space propulsion systems with a critical and objective eye in the subsequent chapters.

Considering the imminence of space travel, the time for careful appraisals is at hand. The objective of this book is simple. It is to give a realistic, comprehensive survey of all space propulsion schemes, what is presently known about each, their states of the art, and their present and potential performances. As far as possible, contemporary technology and realistic projections of it will be used in predicting the performance of the engines to be studied. Such a tack will make many a propulsion system look comparatively very poor indeed. For it is quite obvious that today's machinery is too heavy and inefficient for most space applications. Few technical break-throughs are in sight in this area. It is hoped that this book's approach will be healthy for space propulsion technology, although perhaps it will discourage those ready to buy tickets to Mars.

1-6. Horizons in Time and Space. Of one thing we can be sure, progress will eventually surpass the wildest conjectures of the space enthusiasts. Discoveries will visit us from the most unexpected quarters. Inventions in the area of gravity control could obsolete all reaction engines for the earth-escape operation. Looking even farther ahead, if the science-fiction stories are true precursors, the conquest of space by such crude means as flight through the three spatial and single temporal dimensions we know now will surely be transitory. Beyond space propulsion, we have teleportation, the conquest of hyperspace, and faster-than-light space drives, although these visions are not the subject of this book.

We have grown accustomed to rapid progress. Already we have visited the moon and the planets in the mind's eye. If this pyramid of technical accomplishments, with space flight presently at its peak, is a stable configuration in time, and if nuclear war does not bring the whole edifice down about our ears, then assuredly we will pass beyond the planets to the farther stars, new galaxies, and dimensions. A Whitman-like vista of the universe lies before us; however, it is still somewhat uncertain what our method of locomotion will be.

CHAPTER 2

PROPULSION-SYSTEM PERFORMANCE AND
SPACE MISSIONS

2-1. Mission Requirements and Propulsion-system Capabilities. One of the central problems in space technology is the matching of the mission* requirements with the capabilities of the multitude of space propulsion systems that have been proposed. To provide a convincing solution to this problem, a careful groundwork must first be constructed. In this chapter, we investigate the parameters which describe the performance of space propulsion systems and how they are related to the factors that measure the objectives of the space mission.

In this discussion, the fact that the engine is but a component of a larger entity, the spaceship, becomes an essential consideration. It is discovered that the mission and its demands upon the spaceship ultimately dominate the final selection and design of the engine. Engine design and vehicle design are inseparable. They are both subservient to the mission. The major problem of the propulsion-equipment designer becomes the determination of the mission requirements and their translation into engine capabilities.

In elaborating on these points, the basic principles of reaction engines will first be reviewed. Then, some of the factors which describe engine performance will be investigated. In order to provide goals and reference points for the propulsion-system designer, a survey will be made of the major missions of interest in space travel and their demands on the engine. Finally, there will be a brief discussion of engine selection for space applications.

FUNDAMENTALS OF REACTION ENGINES

2-2. The Reaction Engine. All reaction engines are based on the law of conservation of momentum. Although there are skeptics, we shall assume this law to be valid throughout the universe.

In actuality, any propulsion system is a reaction engine in the sense that there is a net transfer of momentum from the vehicle to the reference

* See Glossary of Terms at the back of the book.

7

frame containing the external observer. A ship's propeller imparts velocity to the water, a jet engine exchanges momentum with the air, and an automobile transfers momentum to the earth itself through the traction of its tires. Space propulsion only asks that we apply a familiar law to a less familiar situation.

To calculate the thrust produced by the continuous expulsion of matter from a vehicle operating in a vacuum, we use Newton's second law

$$\mathbf{F} = \frac{d(m\mathbf{v}_e)}{dt} \tag{2-1}$$

where $\mathbf{F}$ = propulsion-system thrust*

$m\mathbf{v}_e$ = momentum of jet exhaust in the reference frame of the vehicle

t = time

Note that this equation does not apply to air-breathing engines like the turbojet. The initial momentum of the fluid extracted from the environment must be included for such engines. Since the bulk of the space propulsion systems carry their own propellant, Eq. (2-1) will be adequate for our purposes. Carrying out the differentiation indicated in Eq. (2-1) we have

$$\mathbf{F} = \mathbf{v}_e \frac{dm}{dt} + m \frac{d\mathbf{v}_e}{dt} \tag{2-2}$$

However, the last term on the right of Eq. (2-2) is zero in most reaction engines since a constant exhaust velocity usually prevails. This assumption leads to the well-known

$$\mathbf{F} = \dot{m}\mathbf{v}_e \tag{2-3}$$

where $\dot{m}$ = the rate at which propellant mass is consumed by the engine.

Even though a thrust may be generated by a propulsion system, it is important to recognize that an acceleration of the vehicle may not inevitably result. To cite an example, at the earth's surface a rocket may produce a thrust equal to or less than the vehicle weight without causing gross motion. In situations like this, the propulsion system generates a thrust which only partially compensates for action-at-a-distance forces already acting on the spaceship. Practical uses of such "nonaccelerating" engines include satellite attitude control in the presence of perturbing torques, satellite orbit sustaining, and atmospheric-drag compensation.

In spite of the legality of applying the term "reaction engine" to all propulsive devices, whether automobiles or spacecraft, custom reserves this designation primarily for jet engines and rockets. The only basis for this distinction seems to be that the jet of expelled matter, and thus

---

* See Glossary of Symbols at the back of the book.

the reaction principle, is more easily discerned in such engines. In most space propulsion systems, it will also be quite apparent that mass is ejected from the engine. This mass may be in the form of ions, nuclear fragments, or more conventional working fluids. A possible exception might be an antigravity machine which would nullify or somehow distort the gravitational field. Momentum would be conserved, though, regardless of the type of propulsion system.

The conventional reaction engines, the air-breathing jet and the chemical rocket, consist of a pump, a combustion section, and a nozzle. These components are shown schematically in Fig. 2-1. This diagram

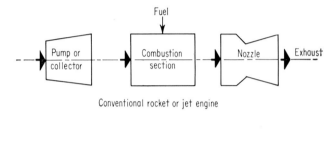

Conventional rocket or jet engine

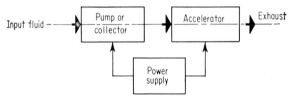

Generalized space propulsion system

FIG. 2-1. Propulsion-system schematics for conventional reaction engines and generalized space propulsion systems. The usual combustion chamber and nozzle are replaced by the accelerator section of the space drive.

is not satisfactory in space propulsion, where power may be supplied from a source external to the propulsion unit, and where combustion and expansion of gases may be unnecessary to the generation of thrust. The ion drive is a good example of a combustor-less, nozzle-less machine. (Chap. 6). In this instance, an ionized fluid is accelerated by electrostatic fields. Considerations such as these lead to the more generalized picture of the reaction engine also shown in Fig. 2-1.

2-3. Other Applications of Reaction Theory. There are several conclusions that are useful in discussions of space vehicles that may be derived from reaction theory. In Fig. 2-2, an admittedly strange variety of rocket is illustrated. It operates in a conventional manner except that its exhaust is caught by an imaginary collector attached rigidly to the main rocket body. Obviously this ridiculous object will go nowhere.

This diagram is included to illustrate an important point: In a region free of action-at-a-distance forces, there can be no vehicle acceleration unless there is some net amount of momentum transferred out of the system including the vehicle and propulsion system. Restating the law of conservation of momentum: If we surround a space vehicle with an imaginary box, there can be no net acceleration relative to an external reference frame unless some net amount of momentum leaves the system through the surface of the box. For example, the ions from an ion drive which impinge on and adhere to any part of the spaceship surface cannot contribute to the propulsion system thrust.

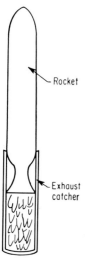

Rocket

Exhaust catcher

Fig. 2-2. A rocket with an exhaust catcher. No thrust can be generated by the vehicle as a whole since no momentum leaves the system.

Another application of this law is shown in Fig. 2-3. Here, we have a space vehicle in a region free from force fields. The power supply or some other type of rotating machinery contributes a mass which is free to rotate relative to the vehicle framework. If this mass is the rotor of a generator or turbine, it will be connected to the main vehicle body through the bearing friction, the forces exerted through the electromagnetic fields, and the working fluid. When such a machine starts up in space, the interplay of torques will cause the vehicle shell to accelerate until an angular momentum equal to and opposite from that of the rotor is built up. The application of the imaginary-box principle shows that no momentum has escaped through the box surface if it encompasses the entire vehicle. Therefore, the total momentum inside the box remains unchanged despite the starting of the rotating equipment. In many applications, it will be desirable to have the shell fixed or rotating at a controlled velocity (for the creation of artificial gravity) relative to some external inertial frame. Unwanted vehicle spin may be eliminated by an impulse from the propulsion system. As long as the exhaust leaves the system through the box, we are free to adjust the spin of the vehicle shell at will. When the thrust is shut off and equilibrium once again attained, any forces transmitted by the bearings, electromagnetic fields, and aerodynamic action must balance one another out. Angular momentum will once more be conserved within the imaginary box.

2-4. Relativity and Photons. Some of the more radical space engines will transfer momentum from the spaceship to the environment by the radiation of photons or the expulsion of relativistic particles. In either case, the equations developed above will not apply.

When mass is ejected at velocities which, relative to the spaceship, approach that of light, Einstein's special theory of relativity must be employed to derive a new equation for thrust. To an observer on the space vehicle, the high-velocity-exhaust particles will appear to have

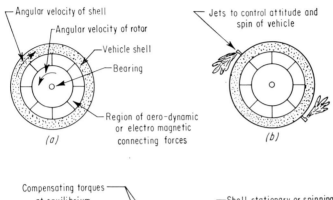

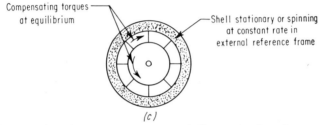

FIG. 2-3. Conservation of momentum among rotating parts aboard space vehicles. (a) At start-up, the vehicle shell accelerates until its angular momentum is equal and opposite to that of the rotating parts. (b) Vehicle spin may be controlled by a propulsion system which ejects mass from the system. (c) At equilibrium, all internal torques add up to zero and no acceleration of the vehicle shell can take place.

higher masses than they did at rest. This relativistic increase in mass is described by

$$m = \frac{m_0}{(1 - v^2/c^2)^{1/2}} \qquad (2\text{-}4)$$

where m_0 = rest mass of the particle
m = apparent mass of the particle
c = velocity of light
Using this relationship, the new equation for the thrust is

$$\mathbf{F} = \frac{\dot{m}_0 \mathbf{v}_e}{(1 - v_e^2/c^2)^{1/2}} \qquad (2\text{-}5)$$

As $v_e \rightarrow c$, the thrust increases rapidly, but, as we shall show in Sec. 2-7, the power required also rises toward infinity.

When photons are emitted instead of physical particles, as in the case of the photon drive, momentum is carried off with the velocity of light.

Photons, or electromagnetic quanta of energy, do not carry any intrinsic mass. They may be thought of as discrete packets of radiant energy. The amount of energy that they carry is proportional to the frequency of the electromagnetic energy and is given by

$$E = hf \qquad (2\text{-}6)$$

where E = photon energy
$\quad h$ = Planck's constant
$\quad f$ = frequency of radiation

The photons also carry momentum to the amount hf/c. Considering the fact that photons are massless, the assignment of momentum to the photon contradicts the usual association of that quantity with mass and velocity. A rationalization may be made to preserve some vestige of our conventional ideas. When a photon is created in an engine, mass disappears. The amount of mass lost is given by Einstein's equation

$$m = \frac{E}{c^2} \qquad (2\text{-}7)$$

This same amount of mass reappears when the photon is absorbed by interstellar gas or some object somewhere in the universe. Mass, then, really is transferred from the vehicle to the environment just as in any other reaction engine. The thrust of a photon emitter is still given by the time derivative of the momentum. Using Eq. (2-6), we obtain

$$F = \frac{d(hf/c)}{dt} = \frac{1{,}000P_e}{c} \qquad (2\text{-}8)$$

where P_e equals the directed power in the jet in kilowatts.

The Eqs. (2-3), (2-5), and (2-8) are sufficient for computation of thrust levels for all of the common reaction engines encountered in space propulsion.

2-5. Force Fields in Space. It has already been pointed out (Sec. 1-4) that the purpose of the reaction engine is to provide a force to overcome gravitational fields that exist in outer space. So far as we can determine, the force due to gravitation is the only important action-at-a-distance force that will materially affect the spaceship. Regardless of the origin of the force which prevents us from traveling freely from one planet to another, whenever such a force is overcome either by brute force (the reaction engine) or by some shrewder means (antigravity), the law of conservation of momentum still applies. Drawing an imaginary box about the entire solar system, if a spaceship penetrates the surface of the box, it must be concluded that the whole solar system has been given an increment of momentum equal and opposite to that of the spaceship. Likewise, when an antigravity machine leaves the earth, it pushes the planet itself away according to the same law.

The gravitational fields centered at the planets may be regarded as a distinct hindrance during the first phases of space travel. However, as interplanetary navigators become more proficient, they may find ways to take advantage of the many gravitating objects in the solar system. Figure 2-4 illustrates how a change in direction, ordinarily requiring a burst of thrust, may be accomplished by a close brush with a planet or asteroid. It is possible that a spacecraft may gain or lose energy in maneuvers where momentum is transferred solely through the gravitational fields connecting the vehicle and the planet.

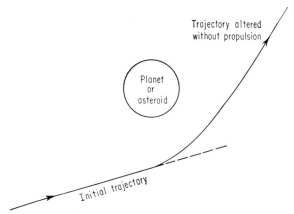

FIG. 2-4. Gravitational fields may be used to aid space flight. A change in spaceship direction may be accomplished by a close brush with a planet or asteroid.

2-6. Other Environmental Interactions. Space is far from being empty (Chap. 3). Copious quantities of matter and energy pervade the regions between the planets and the stars, particularly in the vicinity of massive bodies. If any of this material or electromagnetic energy impinges on the spaceship, then an enhancement or degradation of thrust may result. As discussed in Chap. 3, these effects will usually be very small. To the optimist, though, there is an opportunity here to take advantage of this "free" interstellar material and energy. The ram-jet principle, where mass and energy is ingested by the engine and used as propellant or power source, may be employed in space propulsion (see Chaps. 5 and 8 for propulsion systems of this type). In addition, propulsive thrust may be obtained directly through pressure effects, as in the case of the solar sail (Chap. 8). The space environment may not be an unmixed tragedy to the astronaut.

2-7. Generalized Performance of Reaction Engines. Many of the important parameters describing reaction engines may be incorporated

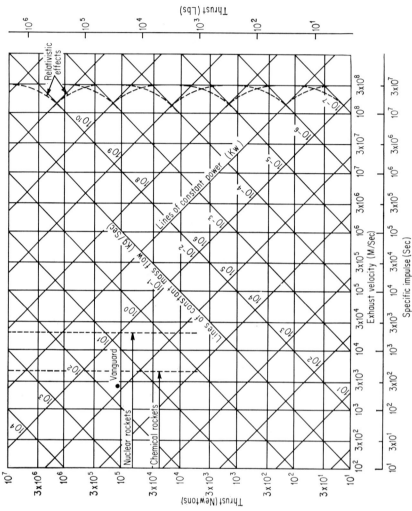

FIG. 2-5. A generalized performance chart for reaction engines which carry their own propellant.

14

in a single graph, Fig. 2-5. The three parameters already defined are the thrust F, the rate at which propellant mass flows $\dot{m}$, and the exhaust velocity v_e. To these, we add the directed power in the jet P_e and the specific impulse I_{sp}, a derived quantity. The defining equations are

$$1{,}000P_e = \frac{\dot{m}v_e^2}{2} + \frac{3\dot{m}v_e^4}{8c^2} + \cdots \tag{2-9}$$

$$I_{sp} = \frac{F}{g_0\dot{m}} = \frac{v_e}{g_0} \tag{2-10}$$

Equation (2-9) is an infinite series. The first term on the right side parallels the usual definition of kinetic energy, while the additional terms add the relativistic effects. Note that v_e must be defined in such a way that it is the average velocity of the exhaust particles projected onto the engine axis. In Eq. (2-10), we see that, in most cases, the specific impulse is directly proportional to the exhaust velocity. In physical terms, the specific impulse is the engine thrust divided by the propellant weight flow $g_0\dot{m}$, referred to the earth's surface. It has the units of seconds and is numerically equal to the number of newtons of thrust generated per newton of propellant consumed per second. It is a fundamental propulsion parameter. For pure environmental propulsion systems, where all of the propellant is extracted from the environment, $\dot{m} = 0$ and the specific impulse equals infinity.

Some more equations relating the five fundamental variables are

$$F = \dot{m}v_e = \dot{m}g_0I_{sp} \tag{2-11}$$

$$P_e = \frac{\dot{m}g_0^2I_{sp}^2}{2{,}000} = \frac{Fg_0I_{sp}}{2{,}000} \tag{2-12}$$

Once two of the four independent parameters are known, a point may be fixed on Fig. 2-5 and the remaining variables determined. Any point on this graph represents a propulsion system. By plotting the capabilities of known engines, areas representing the different types of space propulsion systems may be outlined on Fig. 2-5. In the way of a preview of coming chapters, this has been done for chemical and nuclear rockets. Simple though this chart may be, it serves to point out a number of facts pertinent to space propulsion.

1. Proceeding along a line of constant thrust, it is apparent that lower mass flows of propellant and, therefore, higher specific impulses, are purchased only at the price of higher power requirements.

2. At a given power level, one can produce any desired thrust, although the specific impulse may suffer accordingly.

3. As the velocity of light is approached, very large quantities of power are needed to generate even small thrusts.

4. A historical trend in propulsion technology is noted in that there is a continual pressure to force the specific-impulse barrier. The tendency is to move across the chart to the right with time as better techniques and materials are discovered.

5. The highest specific impulse shown on the chart, 30,000,000 sec for the photon drive, is the limit for all systems that carry their own propellant supplies. From the definition of the specific impulse, Eq. (2-10), $\dot{m} = 0$ would infer an infinite specific impulse for environmental engines. This condition actually prevails with the solar sail and a few other space engines.

PERFORMANCE OF SPACE PROPULSION SYSTEMS

2-8. The Factors That Make Up Performance. When we speak of performance, we refer to the ability of a machine (or a human being) to accomplish some assigned task. Performance usually implies some degree of excellence so that a graded scale can be set up. The descriptive terms used to specify performance are as endless and varied as the machines and applications themselves. Taking the automobile as an example, the average motorist is concerned with reliability, style, and the number of miles obtained for each gallon of fuel. A racing car, however, may better be measured by its top speed and a truck by its load-carrying capabilities. Granted that these are all facets of the crucial quality of performance, how are space propulsion systems to be measured? What measures of excellence are significant in this case?

To begin, let us make a list of the variables which might be used to describe the intrinsic properties of a space propulsion system. This is done in Table 2-1. Most of the factors listed are carried over from our knowledge of jet and rocket engines. We must be cautious in applying the results of such narrow experience to a broad and unexplored field like space flight. The factors used in subsequent analysis should be sufficiently general to describe any space mission, space vehicle, and any type of propulsion system.

Figure 2-6 will be helpful in this quest. It is a more detailed version of Fig. 1-1, where some of the relationships between the power and efficiencies assigned to each of the various components have been added.

It is immediately apparent from Table 2-1 and Fig. 2-6 that there are two major classes of parameters: those to which numbers can easily be assigned, and those which are difficult or impossible to measure numerically. The fact that the assignment of numbers to a parameter may be easy or difficult has no bearing on the importance of the factor. The qualitative factors, as well as the quantitative measures, are vital to the description of the space engine.

TABLE 2-1. PROPULSION-SYSTEM PARAMETERS

Symbol	Name	Remarks

Intrinsic or engine-oriented parameters

Symbol	Name	Remarks
F	Thrust	The force exerted by the engine, newtons
I_{sp}	Specific impulse	A measure of propellant economy, sec
F_{sp}	Specific thrust	The thrust generated per unit of power consumed, newtons/kw
M_{sp}	Specific mass	The mass of the power supply per unit of power delivered to the propulsion unit, kg/kw
M_{PS}	Propulsion-system mass	Sum of propulsion-unit and power-supply masses, kg
e	Power-supply efficiency	Ratio of the power delivered to the propulsion unit to the total generated
e'	Propulsion-unit efficiency	Ratio of the useful jet power to the power delivered to the propulsion unit
ΔE_{PS}	Propulsion-system-energy increment*	Total useful energy delivered to the jet during the mission, joules
P	Power level of the source	Total power generated, kw
P_e	Exhaust power	Useful power in the jet, kw
$\dot{m}$	Propellant-mass flow	kg/sec
No symbol	Reliability	The probability that the propulsion system will function satisfactorily over a given time period
No symbol	Vulnerability	The probability that interaction with the environment will abort the mission
No symbol	State of the art	The time period when all essential components, materials, and techniques are expected to be developed
No symbol	Development risk	The probability of encountering insoluble development problems
No symbol	Flexibility	A measure of the ease with which a system can be altered to perform other missions

Vehicle-oriented parameters

Symbol	Name	Remarks
M_0	Initial gross mass	Sum of all vehicle masses, kg
F/W	Thrust-to-weight ratio	As measured at the earth's surface
M_{PL}	Payload mass	Crew, supplies, instruments, etc., kg
M_{PP}	Propellant mass	Fuel and working fluid, kg
M_{ST}	Structure mass	A catchall, kg
P_V	Auxiliary power	Power diverted to vehicle, kw

Mission-oriented parameters

Symbol	Name	Remarks
ΔV	Velocity increment	Sum† of all velocity increments given to the vehicle, m/sec

TABLE 2-1. PROPULSION-SYSTEM PARAMETERS (*Continued*)

Symbol	Name	Remarks
		Mission-oriented parameters
ΔE_M	Mission energy increment	Sum of all energy changes, kinetic and potential, required by the mission, joules
ΔE_V	Vehicle energy increment	Sum of all energy changes actually imparted to the vehicle, joules
$\int F\,dt$	Total impulse	The integrated product of the thrust and mission time, newton-sec
t	Time, duration	Mission duration, sec

* The interrelations among the various energy increments are discussed in Sec. 2-12.
† Actually, the square root of the sum of the velocities squared in some cases.

All of the parameters listed in Table 2-1 may be divided into three groups. The propulsion-system-oriented parameters are listed first. Following these are the vehicle-oriented factors. They incorporate some of the vehicle characteristics as well as those of the propulsion system. The impossibility of separating propulsion system from the vehicle

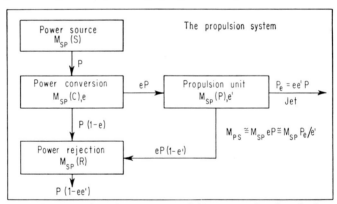

FIG. 2-6. Detailed schematic of the space propulsion system showing the flow of power, component efficiencies, and component specific masses.

supersystem is further illustrated by this list. Finally, Table 2-1 is completed with a tabulation of mission-oriented performance parameters. This list describes the end results of the action of the propulsion system. These factors are, so to speak, two steps away from the actual engine parameters which concern us directly. The great challenge in engine performance analysis is the search for the connecting links between the engine and mission-performance factors, so that accurate comparisons can be made between the mission goals and the propulsion-system capabilities.

2-9. Relations between Propulsion Parameters. The parameters listed in Table 2-1 are neither unique nor independent. In fact, we may immediately proceed to write several equations relating them. Since most of the mathematical relationships are matters of definition or are quite obvious, little discussion has been included.

$$M_{PP} = \frac{Ft}{g_0 I_{sp}} \tag{2-13}$$

$$M_0 = M_{PL} + M_{PP} + M_{ST} + M_{PS} \tag{2-14}$$

$$F_{sp} = \frac{F}{eP} \tag{2-15}$$

$$P_e = ee'P \tag{2-16}$$

The reader should refer to the back of the book for a complete table of symbols and units used. If the assumption is made that the propulsion-unit mass is negligible and the power-plant mass is proportional to the power level delivered to the propulsion unit, the following equation results:

$$M_{PS} = eM_{sp}P \tag{2-17}$$

This equation is not valid for all space propulsion systems; however, the electrical space engines follow this relationship fairly accurately.

Eliminating P, P_e, and e from Eqs. (2-12), (2-16), and (2-17) we obtain

$$M_{PS} = \frac{M_{sp}Fg_0 I_{sp}}{2{,}000e'} \tag{2-18}$$

Equation (2-18) illustrates the strong influence of the specific impulse upon the propulsion-system mass. By making the further and usually dangerous assumption that the power-supply mass dominates the entire vehicle mass, we derive

$$\frac{F}{W} = \frac{F}{g_0 M_0} \cong \frac{F}{g_0 M_{PS}} = \frac{2{,}000e'}{M_{sp}g_0{}^2 I_{sp}} \tag{2-19}$$

If the several assumptions made in deriving Eq. (2-19) hold, and they do fairly well for electrical space propulsion systems, it is evident that the thrust-to-weight ratio is inversely proportional to the specific impulse. This is a valuable generalization for electrical space engines and illustrates very forcefully the performance penalties paid for high specific impulses.

Using the relationships developed above, an expression for the energy increment generated by the propulsion system may be written in terms of the propulsion-system parameters

$$\Delta E_{PS} = 1{,}000 P_e t = \frac{Fg_0 I_{sp}t}{2} \tag{2-20}$$

The velocity increment and the other energy increments defined in Table 2-1 cannot be written exclusively in terms of the engine parameters because of the environmental forces which will partially control their magnitudes. To illustrate, the gravitational fields of the astronomical objects near the vehicle, which are obviously unrelated to the engine performance, will enter into the determination of the velocity and energy increments.

2-10. Optimization of the Parameters.   The space-propulsion-system designer will want to achieve the highest performance for the least cost. The preceding compilation of relations holding among the factors affecting performance gives little hint on how to obtain this objective. No guideposts have yet been presented which show how to select the best values of the engine parameters for a given mission. In attacking this problem, we define the goal of the mission in terms of the mission-oriented parameters of Table 2-1, ΔV, ΔE_V, and the total impulse. In opposition to the customary use of ΔV, ΔE_V seems to hold more promise as a general indicator of performance for all of the different types of space missions. A more detailed discussion of this problem follows in Sec. 2-12. Once some desirable commodity is defined as a measure of excellence, some determination of its cost in mass and energy must be fixed. The unit of currency varies with the mission. Two basic measures of cost for any portion of a specific mission are the propulsion-system-energy increment ΔE_{PS} and the total initial mass of the system at the outset of the mission. The total energy expended is proportional to the fuel costs, the expense incurred in sustaining and protecting the human cargo, transmitting information, and performing other mission functions. The total system mass, whether the mission begins from the earth's surface or a satellite orbit, is a measure of the mission's cost in materials, facilities, and launching equipment. If an attempt is made to minimize the cost of a specific mission, some meaningful relationships among the propulsion parameters will result. In such an approach, it is convenient to bypass the equally crucial matters of reliability and vulnerability. This is done only because these qualitative factors are not yet amenable to mathematical treatment.

Perhaps the most interesting and most common criterion used in optimizing propulsion-system parameters is that which requires a minimum initial gross mass. By minimizing the gross mass for a fixed payload, we obviously maximize the payload-to-gross-weight ratio. The derivation is begun by writing Eq. (2-14) with each component expressed in terms of the specific impulse

$$M_0 = M_{PL} + \frac{M_{sp}Fg_0I_{sp}}{2{,}000e'} + \frac{Ft}{g_0I_{sp}} \tag{2-21}$$

The structural mass is ignored in Eq. (2-21). It should also be noted that this analysis applies only to systems where the propulsion-unit mass is negligible in comparison with the power-supply mass, and where the power-supply mass is proportional to the power level. These conditions hold best for the electrical propulsion systems. By differentiation, we find that the optimum specific impulse occurs, using the minimum-gross-mass criterion, at

$$\frac{Ft}{g_0 I_{sp}} = \frac{M_{sp}F g_0 I_{sp}}{2{,}000e'} \tag{2-22}$$

In terms of the mass components, Eq. (2-22) is equivalent to $M_{PP} = M_{PS}$.

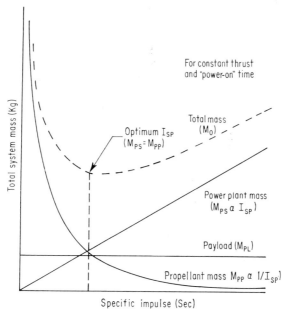

Fig. 2-7. Space-system mass breakdown when specific impulse is optimized using the criterion of minimum initial gross mass. The minimum occurs when $M_{PP} = M_{PS}$.

A particularly appealing physical interpretation is discovered by plotting the separate terms on Eq. (2-21) as functions of the specific impulse. This has been done in Fig. 2-7. A minimum in the gross mass occurs when the curve representing the rapidly dropping propellant mass intersects the rising power-plant mass curve. Both are plotted for a given thrust level and mission duration. The optimum specific impulse occurs at the minimum in the curve. The power-plant mass actually is not a strict linear function of the specific impulse. In Chap. 4, the actual behavior of the specific mass as a function of power and, thus, specific impulse, will be treated more fully.

Solving Eq. (2-22) for the specific impulse we get

$$I_{sp} = \sqrt{\frac{2{,}000te'}{M_{sp}g_0{}^2}} \qquad (2\text{-}23)$$

Equation (2-23) indicates that the optimum specific impulse is proportional to the square root of the mission duration or *thrust-on time*. It is also inversely proportional to the square root of the power-plant specific mass. The relationship between these three factors is illustrated in

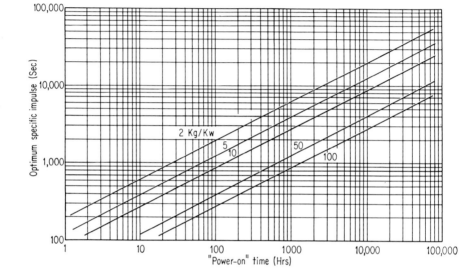

FIG. 2-8. Optimum specific impulse versus "power on" time using the criterion of minimum initial gross mass.

Fig. 2-8. Apparently, the mission duration has a strong effect on the optimum specific impulse and, therefore, upon the final choice of the propulsion system. In the way of illustration, a 10,000-hr mission combined with a specific mass of approximately 10 kg/kw leads to an optimum specific impulse of about 10,000 sec. A 1,000-hr or 40-day mission would optimize with a specific impulse of about 3,000 sec. Such results are significant, for they reveal a method by which propulsion-system parameters can be related to mission parameters. The results just given apply, of course, only to electrical space engines using the criterion of minimum gross mass.

Only the gross aspects of performance have been treated here. The equations show that once four of the five parameters M_{PL}, t, F, M_{sp}, and I_{sp} have been selected, the fifth can be uniquely determined if some figure of merit for the mission is selected and optimized. Although such techniques may be used as guides in the design of space propulsion systems, they leave many things unsaid. For example, one may wish to minimize system vulnerability to meteoroids or maximize reliability at the sacrifice of specific impulse or of minimum-mission-energy increment. In addition, a time-modulated thrust may lead to better performance for some missions. In the last analysis, the designer must carefully examine the mission, select the criteria which best suit the purpose, and optimize the parameter which has the most meaning for the particular mission at hand. The simple illustration given above does not demonstrate the real difficulty of this task.

SPACE MISSIONS

2-11. Mission Classes and Maneuvers. The more romantic missions for the spaceship will be the long anticipated voyages to the moon, Mars, and Venus. Unfortunately, there are many missions of the work-horse variety which must be completed before we can walk the supposed deserts of Mars. The first real problem is that of getting off the earth's surface, of overcoming the pull of gravity and placing large payloads out in space. Second, we wish to establish large satellites, not only to serve as staging platforms for more ambitious space projects but also for a variety of peaceful and military purposes. A portion of this book will be devoted to propulsion for these less spectacular space missions.

Just which propulsion systems are going to be attractive out in space? The popular literature abounds with space engines of all descriptions. In order to compare mission requirements with propulsion-system capabilities, it is first necessary to know just what is demanded by the space missions. What energies, accelerations, and specific impulses are needed for each mission phase and maneuver?

No space atlas yet exists to give ready and complete information on thrusts and energies for each potential space trip. Gradually the data will be accumulated, but, for the present, the analysis must remain crude. Descriptions of several broad classes of missions will be given in sufficient detail to establish the magnitude of the propulsion problem. An outline of the maneuvers required and some possible applications of these classes is given below. More thorough discussion follows this summary.

Class 1. *Planetary Surface Missions.* In this class, enough thrust must be generated to overcome the surface gravitational force of the planet or moon under consideration. On the earth itself, a thrust-to-weight ratio greater than 1 is inferred, while on Mars or the moon, lesser values would be sufficient.

MANEUVERS. (*a*) Acceleration from surface; (*b*) deceleration and descent onto surface.

EXAMPLES. (*a*) Launching of satellites, spaceships, and probes; (*b*) missile launching.

Class 2. *Satellite Missions.* Here gravitational forces are largely compensated for by centrifugal forces. Low thrust-to-weight ratios ($<10^{-2}$) are adequate for many maneuvers.

MANEUVERS. (*a*) Drag compensation at low altitude, (*b*) orbit trimming, (*c*) orbit transfer, (*d*) creation of artificial gravity, (*e*) attitude control, (*f*) rendezvous with other satellites, (*g*) compensation of gyroscopic torques.

EXAMPLES. (*a*) Meteorological satellite, (*b*) astronomical satellite, (*c*) lunar and interplanetary staging platform, (*d*) military reconnaissance satellite, (*e*) geodetic satellite, (*f*) TV and radio repeater, (*g*) scientific satellite station.

Class 3. *Interplanetary Missions.* These missions consist of flights from one planetary orbit to another. The thrust-to-weight ratio required depends to a large extent upon how much time is allotted for the trip. The lunar trip is considered a special case in this class.

MANEUVERS. (*a*) Acceleration out of satellite orbit, (*b*) acceleration into satellite orbit, (*c*) trajectory correction, (*d*) possible evasion of meteor swarms.

APPLICATIONS. (*a*) Spaceships and probes.

Class 4. *Interstellar Missions.* In this class, vehicles will travel from some point in the solar system, probably from a satellite orbit about a planet, to a similar point in another star system. Again the allowable thrust-to-weight ratio depends on the duration allowed for the trip.

Other specialized missions and combinations of those mentioned above are possible. As an example, the planetary surface and interplanetary missions might easily be accomplished using the same vehicle and propulsion system.

2-12. Mission and Engine Parameters. Superficially, space-voyage calculations should be simple. One has a vehicle with a certain mass, which may decrease with time as propellant and fuel are consumed, and a thrust acting upon it. The vehicle will wend its way through the gravitational fields of the planets, whose positions are known as functions of time. The difficulty is not in the setting up of the problem but rather in the solution of the resulting equations. The so-called "ballistic-space-flight problems," where bursts of thrust are employed, are easy to solve when only two bodies are present, and the vehicle is so small that it does not perturb the gravitational fields. Whenever the vehicle thrust is applied over a significant portion of the mission, say, when an electrical, low-thrust engine is used, the mathematics become vastly more complex. The same thing occurs when more than two gravitationally important bodies are present. Today's philosophy is to relegate these more difficult situations to the automatic computer rather than search for analytical solutions.

In the past work on space missions, a bewildering variety of parameters have been used to describe the orbits and their relationships to the engine and vehicle.   When considering the propulsion system, it is desirable to use terms which are closely related to the engine parameters discussed in the preceding sections.   The ultimate objective would be a set of easily understood parameters which conveniently and uniquely describe both the mission requirements and the propulsion-system capabilities.

Given a specific mission and vehicle, there will be numerous thrust and specific-impulse programs which will permit completion of the objectives within the specified time.   The difficulties come about in deciding which propulsion systems are capable of producing the desired thrust program, and, next, which one will do the best job according to the particular figure of merit established for the mission.

The most common parameter used to describe space missions is the total velocity increment ΔV.   It is the square root of the sum of the squares of all velocity increments which are given to the vehicle during the mission.   Another factor which may be used is the sum of all the energy increments given to the vehicle.   The minimum energy increment just sufficient to complete the mission ΔE_M may be much smaller than the actual energy imparted to the vehicle ΔE_V.   Usually, the greater the difference between the two, the faster the mission.   A third energy increment ΔE_{PS} is the energy associated with the directed velocity of the jet. It is larger than either ΔE_V or ΔE_M, since the energy appearing in the jet will not all be transferred to the vehicle.   If one views the system containing the rocket and its exhaust from an external reference frame, the law of conservation of energy permits complete transfer of the exhaust kinetic energy to the spaceship only if the velocity of ejection is equal to the spaceship velocity.   If this condition is not true, the exhaust particles will have some residual kinetic energy in the external reference frame and the ratio $\Delta E_V/\Delta E_{PS}$, sometimes called the propulsive efficiency, will be less than one.

There are several drawbacks to the use of ΔV as a mission parameter. In describing a space mission, we may have the following situation existing.   Taking the Venus trip for illustration (Ref. 2-2),* the separate velocity increments are:

Maneuver	Velocity increment
Escape from earth	11.2 km/sec
Entry into transfer orbit	2.5
Exit from transfer orbit	2.7
Descent to the surface of Venus	10.4
Total	26.8 km/sec

* References are listed in the Bibliography at the back of the book.

With ballistic spaceships, where the duration of the impulse is short compared to the mission time, these velocities correspond to the increments added when the propulsion system is fired. The shortcomings of the velocity-increment concept involve, first, the fact that these velocity increments really are derived from kinetic-energy increment and cannot always be added as they are above. For example, if the first and second pairs of maneuvers are accomplished with single impulses, the total velocity increment may be reduced to 22.2 km/sec. Here, velocities must be squared, added, and the square root of the sum extracted. Perhaps the most important reason for not using ΔV extensively in this book is the desire to pave the way for the nonballistic systems of the future. When adequate amounts of energy become available, spaceships will often be powered by engines which produce thrust over most of the mission. In these instances, the velocity increment will be an anachronism. Take, as an illustration, the problem of escaping from the earth. This can be done with a single impulse, if the escape velocity can be achieved. It can also be done by a continuous-thrust system, in which case, velocities much less than 11.2 km/sec can be used.

The energy budget of the mission ΔE_V, including both the potential and kinetic energies given to the vehicle, appears to be the best alternative to the velocity-increment concept. It will be used as the common thread tying together the many diverse space missions under scrutiny.

The conventional velocity increments will be supplanted by the sums of all the energy increments required during the different segments of the mission. These will be added without regard to sign. Dissipative effects like atmospheric drag will be ignored. It is implicit in this assumption that surface launchings and descent maneuvers require the same amounts of energy. Atmospheric braking may alter the situation somewhat, but the conservative approach utilizing propulsion-system braking will be adopted in this book. A possible pitfall in the use of energy increments occurs where satellite attitude control is desired. Here no work is actually done on the vehicle, although the value of ΔE_{PS} is certainly greater than zero. In spite of this exception, the energy approach is the most general one available. It will be used throughout this book to assess the performance required by each class of missions.

Assuming that an energy budget can be specified for each mission, how can we make use of the energy techniques developed in the first part of this chapter? In subsequent sections, each of the four broad mission classes will be surveyed and an attempt made to specify the *characteristic* ΔE_M for some of the typical maneuvers. The three energy increments may then be compared, as they are for the hypothetical mission shown in Fig. 2-9.

Figure 2-9 is of value in illustrating the difference between the vehicle and mission energy increments. Suppose the mission is the transfer of the spaceship from the surface of planet A to the surface of planet B. The solid line in Fig. 2-9 represents the energy-level changes that a spaceship would take on a minimum energy trajectory. First, there is the escape from planet A into an orbit around the sun at approximately A's radius from the sun. The interplanetary orbit transfer then occurs, increasing the total energy of the spaceship, if the movement is away from the sun, and decreasing it toward the sun. When the orbit transfer is

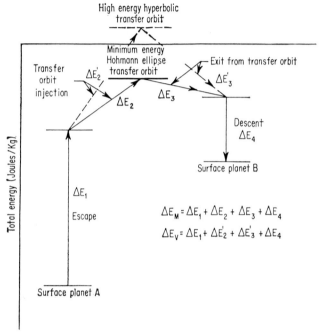

FIG. 2-9. Energy-level diagram for a typical interplanetary trip. The maneuvers include escape from earth, injection into the transfer orbit, exit from the transfer orbit, and powered descent to the target planet. Fast and minimum-energy transfer orbits are indicated.

complete, the spaceship is in an orbit about the sun at approximately the same radius as planet B. The intermediate energy level indicated is that possessed by the vehicle in the transfer orbit. Finally, there is the descent onto the surface of planet B. All of these energy increments must be added, since they all require the expenditure of energy by the propulsion system. Even if the total energy is decreased, thrust must be applied to slow the vehicle down. A high-energy short-time transfer orbit is indicated by the dotted lines. Almost all space missions can be treated with energy-level diagrams like this one. The mission energy increment ΔE_M is the minimum energy change which will allow successful completion of the mission regardless of time duration. The actual vehicle energy increment ΔE_V may be much larger, if fast trips are desired. Figure 2-9 may be used to illustrate the velocity-increment philosophy as well. Each energy increment also represents a velocity increment. Obviously, velocity increments cannot always be added like energy increments as we have indicated previously. It is also apparent that the whole trip could be made with only two energy increments by combining the launching and descent with the interplanetary-orbit-transfer maneuver.

The energy concept is a powerful one. With it one can measure both energy of velocity and position. Except for spaceships moving at relativistic velocities, the kinetic energy E_k is given by

$$E_k = \frac{MV^2}{2}$$

The potential energy E_p of an object in a gravitational field is expressed by this equation

$$E_p = -\frac{\gamma M M_p}{r}$$

where M_p is the mass of the astronomical body and r is the distance of the spaceship. The total energy per unit mass will be

$$\frac{E_t}{M} = \frac{V^2}{2} - \frac{\gamma M_p}{r} \tag{2-24}$$

The reference level chosen for potential-energy measurements is at infinity, where E_p is fixed at zero. The coordinate system will always be centered on the principal gravitating body. In the cases of planetary surface and satellite missions, the origins will be at the centers of the planets under consideration. For interplanetary and interstellar missions, we shall use the sun as the reference point.

2-13. Planetary Surface Missions. The surface of any gravitating body—planet, star, or asteroid—is at the bottom of a potential-energy well created by the gravitational field. Planetary surface missions deal with the problem of moving payloads safely into and out of these wells. In missions involving escape or powered descent, ΔE_M will be given by the depth of the well in energy units. In escape, this amount of energy is just that kinetic energy calculated using the escape velocity. Escape or its reverse, powered descent, may be accomplished either by the impulse rocket so familiar today or by some more powerful engine which climbs at a steady speed, quite possibly less than the escape value for the planet. ΔE_M is identical for both methods. If the velocity of climb in the latter example is slow, ΔE_M will be only slightly less than

ΔE_V, but ΔE_{PS} would be very great because of the energy used in *hovering* or, equivalently, balancing gravity's force with engine thrust.   In Fig. 2-10, the potential-well concept is shown by plotting the potential energy per unit mass versus the distance from the center of the gravitating object, the earth in this case.   For escape, the vehicle must be boosted from the bottom of the well to the top.   Placing a satellite in orbit

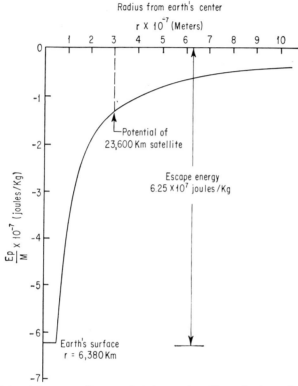

Radius from earth's center

$r \times 10^{-7}$ (Meters)

Potential of 23,600 Km satellite

Escape energy
6.25×10^7 joules/Kg

$\frac{E_p}{M} \times 10^{-7}$ (joules/Kg)

Earth's surface
$r = 6,380$ Km

FIG. 2-10. Potential-energy diagram for the earth.   Note the large fraction of the escape energy required to launch an object to 23,600 km.

involves climbing only part way up the potential hill and giving it orbital velocity.   The depth of any gravitational well may be calculated from Eq. (2-25).

$$E_p = -\frac{\gamma M M_p}{R}\tag{2-25}$$

where R = radius of the planet, moon, or asteroid
      M_p = its mass
Table 2-2 presents well depths for some of the planets and asteroids in the solar system.   It is interesting to note that the potential wells are

quite shallow for some of the moons and asteroids.   Low thrust-to-weight ratio propulsion systems might escape from Eros, for example.

TABLE 2-2. POTENTIAL WELLS IN THE SOLAR SYSTEM

Object	Mass, kg	Radius, m	Well depth, joules/kg	Escape velocity, m/sec
Sun.............	1.99×10^{30}	6.96×10^8	1.91×10^{11}	6.18×10^5
Mercury........	3.17×10^{23}	2.42×10^6	8.74×10^6	4.18×10^3
Venus..........	4.87×10^{24}	6.20×10^6	5.24×10^7	1.02×10^4
Earth..........	5.98×10^{24}	6.38×10^6	6.25×10^7	1.12×10^4
Mars...........	6.40×10^{23}	3.40×10^6	1.25×10^7	5.0×10^3
Jupiter.........	1.90×10^{27}	7.14×10^7	1.77×10^9	5.97×10^4
Saturn.........	5.69×10^{26}	6.04×10^7	6.28×10^8	3.54×10^4
Uranus.........	8.70×10^{25}	2.38×10^7	2.44×10^8	2.2×10^4
Neptune........	1.03×10^{26}	2.23×10^7	3.08×10^8	2.48×10^4
Pluto..........	5.4×10^{24}	7.2×10^6	5.0×10^7	1.0×10^4
Moon...........	7.34×10^{22}	1.74×10^6	2.81×10^6	2.37×10^3
Phobos.........	1×10^{15}	8×10^3	8.3×10^1	4×10^0
Ceres..........	8×10^{20}	3.7×10^5	1.4×10^5	5×10^2
Eros...........	1×10^{16}	1×10^4	6.67×10^1	1×10^1
Pallas..........	2×10^{20}	2.4×10^5	5.5×10^4	3×10^2

An energy-level diagram similar to that shown in Fig. 2-9 can be drawn to schematically describe the typical missions in this class.   The example shown is for the earth, but the same thing may be done for any object.   Figure 2-11 illustrates the energy-level concept for launching missions.

Levels for satellite orbits may be included on Fig. 2-11 by adding the kinetic energy of rotation to the potential energy.   The satellite velocity V_s is derived from the equality of gravitational and centrifugal forces in a satellite orbit:

$$\frac{M V_s^2}{r} = \frac{\gamma M M_p}{r^2}$$

$$V_s = \sqrt{\frac{\gamma M_p}{r}} \qquad (2\text{-}26)$$

The total energy is then:

$$E_t = \frac{\gamma M M_p}{2r} - \frac{\gamma M M_p}{r} = -\frac{\gamma M M_p}{2r} \qquad (2\text{-}27)$$

Energy increments for surface missions are calculated as follows:
For escape,

$$\Delta E_M = \left| 0 + \frac{\gamma M M_p}{R} \right|$$

For satellite launching,

$$\Delta E_M = \left| - \frac{\gamma M M_p}{2r} + \frac{\gamma M M_p}{R} \right|$$

These increments are shown on the diagram of Fig. 2-11. Of course, some reduction in ΔE_M is possible by launching so as to take advantage of the earth's rotational velocity. To emphasize the meaning of ΔE_M,

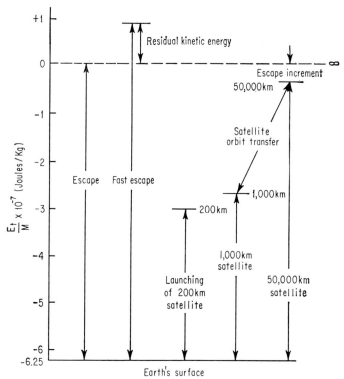

FIG. 2-11. Energy-level diagram for planetary surface missions. The satellite levels include the kinetic energy of rotation.

it is the minimum energy increment. If there are dissipative effects or intentional, additional accelerations, ΔE_V will be larger than ΔE_M.

The energy relationships that have been given are not designed for practical calculations. Instead, they are intended to serve only as guides in the design of propulsion systems. More accurate methods exist for the practical launching calculations. Many of these are referred to in the Bibliography. An attempt will be made, however, to list a few of the most important equations pertinent to each mission class. For example, the following equation is frequently used in approximate planetary-surface-mission calculations:

$$\Delta V = g_0 I_{sp} \left[\left(1 - \frac{D}{F} \right) \ln \frac{M_0}{M_{bo}} - \frac{W}{F} \left(1 - \frac{M_{bo}}{M_0} \right) \sin \alpha \right] \quad (2\text{-}28)$$

where M_{bo} = vehicle mass at burnout

D = drag forces

α = angle with the horizontal

Here some of the mission parameters used in previous analysis are again evident.   The first term inside the brackets gives the velocity change

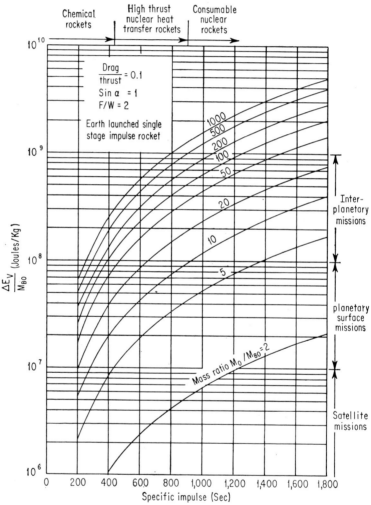

FIG. 2-12. Mass ratios for various specific impulses and vehicle energy increments. For single-staged impulse vehicles only.

due to the expulsion of propellant.   Drag retardation is included.   The second term introduces the effects of gravitation.   This equation is used in plotting Fig. 2-12 for single-stage earth launchings.   Multistage rockets can be calculated by repeated use of Eq. (2-28).

The planetary surface mission is state of the art today.   Chemical rockets can now boost payloads in the ton class into satellite orbits. Table 2-3 indicates the current launching capabilities of multistaged rocket vehicles.   Figure 2-13 extends Table 2-3 to the even larger rockets

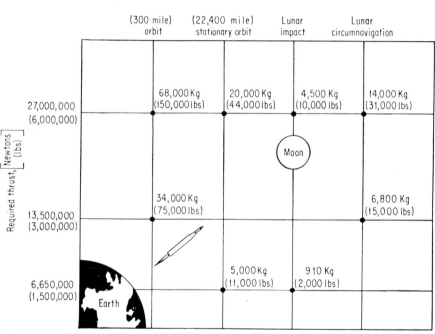

FIG. 2-13. Capabilities of advanced, high-thrust chemical rockets.   Approximate payloads are indicated at the intersections of the thrust and mission lines.   (*Adapted from a chart provided by the Rocketdyne Division of North American Aviation, Inc.*)

now under consideration.   Nuclear rockets are well along in development and will launch higher payloads into orbit.   In a sense, launching is the key mission in space flight.   Large quantities of men and material must be placed into orbits or escape trajectories if space travel is to advance rapidly.   Barring the possibility of being able to manufacture propellant and generate power from interplanetary matter and radiation flux, the launching mission may well be the controlling factor in the speed with which space flight is developed.   Certainly, the great bulk of the commercial business in space technology will be in the production of fuels, propellants, and rockets for the planetary surface missions.

TABLE 2-3. SUMMARY OF CURRENT AND EXPECTED PAYLOAD CAPABILITIES*

	Van-guard	Jupiter-C	Thor, Jupiter	Atlas, Titan	Saturn-class rockets†
Gross mass:					
Kilograms............	10,000	22,700	45,400	90,800	
Pounds..............	22,000	50,000	100,000	200,000	
Thrust:					
Newtons.............	125,000	335,000	670,000	1,330,000	6,700,000
Pounds..............	28,000	75,000	150,000	300,000	1,500,000
Mission:					
480-km orbit:					
Kilograms.........	9	14	910	3,600	17,000
Pounds............	20	30	2,000	8,000	37,000
Moon impact:					
Kilograms.........	....	....	360	1,400	5,000
Pounds............	....	....	800	3,000	11,000
Moon satellite:					
Kilograms.........	....	....	220	680	2,700
Pounds............	....	....	500	1,500	6,000
Moon soft landing:					
Kilograms.........	....	....	140	450	1,800
Pounds............	....	....	300	1,000	4,000
Mars or Venus probe:					
Kilograms.........	....	....	270	1,100	5,500
Pounds............	....	....	600	2,500	12,000
Jupiter probe:					
Kilograms.........	....	....	180	680	1,100
Pounds............	....	....	400	1,500	2,500

* Adapted from Ref. 2-29.
† Nova class rockets would multiply these figures by approxmately a factor of 4.

2-14. Satellite Missions. If we lived on a much smaller planet, where escape would be easy, the satellite concept might well be superfluous. To the inhabitants of any planet with deep potential well, the satellite is an essential ingredient in the conquest of outer space. It is necessary to place not only equipment in orbit to obtain vital measurements but also satellite staging platforms to serve as the first rungs in the ladder leading to interplanetary travel. Presumably, a being living on a much smaller planet would find it so easy to explore space that satellites might seem unimportant. However, artificial moons are essential to us, and a discussion of satellite propulsion is appropriate at this time.

Contemporary satellites do not yet possess the refinement of a propulsion system. As instrumentation becomes more sophisticated and projects more ambitious, there will be requirements for attitude control, mobility within the satellite orbits themselves, and the many other possible maneuvers listed in Table 2-1. In addition, the satellites may serve as test beds for the interplanetary engines of the future. The complexity of some of the future satellites is typified by Fig. 2-15 where a five-man space station is illustrated.

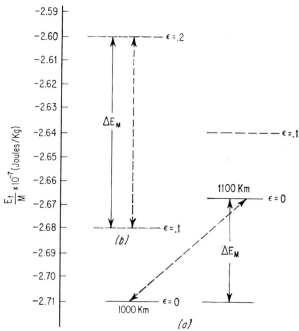

Fig. 2-14. Energy-level diagram for earth satellite maneuvers. (a) Orbit transfer maneuver; (b) orbit-trimming maneuver for orbits with the same perigee but different eccentricities.

The energy concept is again employed to portray the energy increments involved in satellite propulsion. In Fig. 2-14 the satellite energy levels, which were indicated in Fig. 2-11, are broken down into more finely divided levels representing different altitudes and eccentricities. The total energy for the circular orbit as a function of radius is given by Eq. (2-27). In general, satellite orbits will not be circular, although we may wish to use propulsion to make them that way after launching. To incorporate the elliptical cases within the energy-level framework, the following equation is used:

$$E_t = \frac{\gamma^2 M M_p{}^2(\epsilon^2 - 1)}{2V^2r^2} \tag{2-29}$$

where V and r are evaluated at apogee or perigee and ϵ equals the eccen-

tricity.   Using this equation, Fig. 2-14 might be filled in its entirety
with energy levels representing different eccentricities.   For a given value
of total energy there will be an infinite number of different satellite orbits
possessing this energy.   As the eccentricity ϵ increases from zero to one
in Eq. (2-29), the total energy approaches zero.   At precisely $\epsilon = 1$, when
E_t also equals zero, conditions are then such that a parabolic trajectory
results.   This is the orbit that would be followed by an object which has

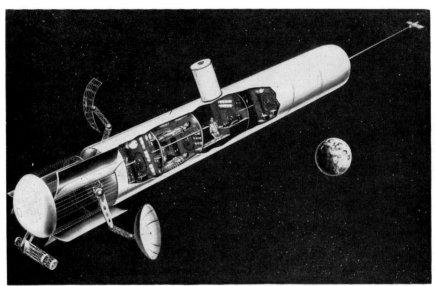

FIG. 2-15. Five-man space station.   The dimensions of this conceptual design are
7 ft in diameter and 35 ft in length,   With a 6,000,000-lb-thrust rocket, the station's
total weight of 65,000 lb could be placed in a 24-hr orbit.   (*Rocketdyne Division of
North American Aviation, Inc.*)

been given the escape velocity by an impulse rocket.   Once E_t exceeds
zero, hyperbolic orbits are obtained.   These relationships are indicated
on Figs. 2-9 and 2-11.

The equation for the velocity of a satellite in a circular orbit has already
been derived, Eq. (2-26).   The escape-velocity concept has also been
mentioned.   The equation for this quantity is derived from the fact
that the depth of the potential well is equal to the kinetic energy associated with the escape velocity V_e.

$$\frac{M V_e{}^2}{2} = \frac{\gamma M M_p}{r}$$

$$V_e = \sqrt{\frac{2\gamma M_p}{r}} \tag{2-30}$$

The period of a satellite, again for a circular orbit, is found by dividing the orbit circumference by the velocity obtained in Eq. (2-26).

$$t_s = \frac{2\pi r}{V_s} = \frac{2\pi r^{3/2}}{R \sqrt{g_0}} \tag{2-31}$$

For convenience these variables have been plotted in Fig. 2-16.

Referring to the list of satellite maneuvers on page 24, it is seen that a number of these are amenable to a generalized treatment. In particular, orbit-transfer and orbit-trimming maneuvers have definite values of

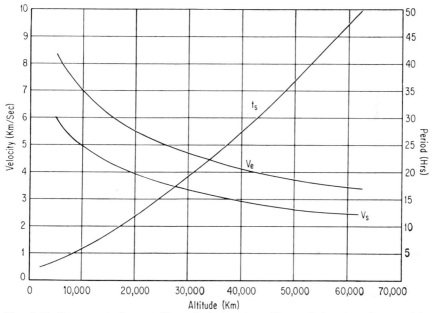

FIG. 2-16. Escape velocity, satellite velocity, and satellite period as functions of altitude above the earth's surface.

ΔE_M, as shown in Fig. 2-14. The other maneuvers, such as attitude control, must have the specifics of the vehicle (dimensions, cross section, moments of inertia) determined before calculations can begin. Many satellite maneuvers are *holding actions* where parasitic or perturbing forces must be canceled out. No net work is done upon the vehicle in these instances, but ΔE_{PS} will not be zero even though $\Delta E_M = 0$. Some useful equations describing the various satellite maneuvers are given below.

In the case of orbit transfer, the objective is to move from one satellite altitude to another. This is equivalent to moving up or down the energy-level ladder in Fig. 2-14. There are numerous ways in which this feat can be accomplished. A small tangential or circumferential thrust may be applied to the vehicle, and it will spiral slowly out to its destination. Or an impulse propulsion system may be used. In this case, the vehicle will enter a transfer orbit, one of the conic sections, which intersects the target orbit. Upon arriving at the desired radius, another impulse is applied, and the mission is complete.

An approximate equation for the case of tangential thrust is derived by considering the energy given the satellite by the applied thrust. Strangely enough, when a very small thrust is directed parallel to and in the direction of the velocity, it will cause the satellite to slow down. In this case, potential rather than kinetic energy is being given to the satellite and the satellite is advanced to a higher, more energetic orbit, although it has less tangential velocity. By equating the work done by the thrust $Fr \times d\theta$ to the increase in total energy dE_t/dr, see Eq. (2-27), we can derive an equation for the increase in orbit radius due to small perturbations by a propulsion system:

$$dr = \frac{2FR}{W}\left(\frac{r}{R}\right)^3 d\theta \tag{2-32}$$

where the relationship $g_0 = M_p/R^2$ has been used to convert $g_0 M = W$, and θ = the angle along the orbit. Time may be introduced $V_s = r\, d\theta/dt$.

$$dt = \left(\frac{R}{g_0}\right)^{1/2}\left(\frac{r}{R}\right)^{3/2} d\theta$$

Combining the two equations, we find that small orbit changes produced by low thrust-to-weight propulsion systems may be described by

$$t = \frac{WR}{F\sqrt{g_0}}\left(\frac{1}{\sqrt{r_0}} - \frac{1}{\sqrt{r}}\right) \tag{2-33}$$

where r_0 = initial orbit radius
      r = orbit radius attained after a time t
The propulsion-system parameter F/W is involved in Eq. (2-33) just as it was in Eq. (2-28) describing the launching mission. The thrust-to-weight ratio appears whenever the acceleration of space vehicles is involved. It does not appear, by contrast, in any of the mathematical relations descriptive of satellite compensating torques.

The long-term effects of tangential or radial thrusts applied to satellite vehicles must be treated with more refined methods. Digital computers are frequently used to advantage where accurate calculations, including the effects of the lunar and solar gravitational fields, are desired. The results of long-term tangential thrust on a satellite vehicle are shown in Fig. 2-17, where a spiral escape trajectory from the earth has been affected with a low-thrust propulsion system.

The ballistic or impulse method of orbit transfer is also applicable to satellite maneuvers. The techniques are identical with those used in interplanetary orbit transfer and will be discussed in the next section.

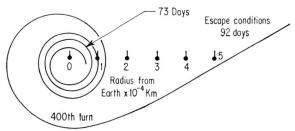

FIG. 2-17. Spiral escape trajectory taken by a low thrust-to-weight ratio (10^{-4}) vehicle. The spiral begins at a 500-km satellite orbit and requires 92 days' continuous thrust for escape. Tangential thrust is used.

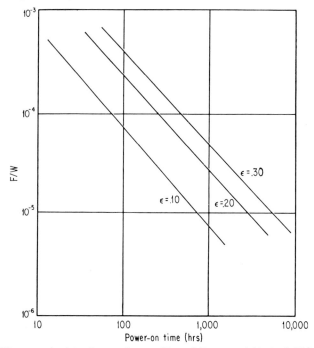

FIG. 2-18. Time required to change the satellite orbit eccentricity to 0.05 from various initial eccentricities. Tangential thrust is applied over the perigee portion of the orbit.

If the satellite is not launched at the proper altitude, the foregoing transfer methods can be used. If the initial orbit is too eccentric, a periodic tangential thrust may be applied to decelerate the vehicle in the region of orbit perigee. This maneuver is analogous to the reduction of orbit eccentricity by atmospheric contact by passive satellites. Figure

2-18 shows how this change in eccentricity in time is related to the propulsion parameters.

Two other important satellite maneuvers are drag make-up and the provision of torques for attitude control. The drag make-up thrusts become important drains on the propulsion system only below 200 km altitude. Thrust-to-weight ratios less than 10^{-6} are usually adequate

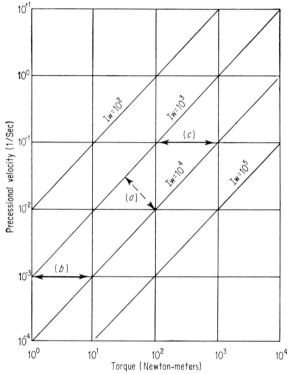

FIG. 2-19. Propulsion-system torques needed to maintain precessional velocities in the presence of internal angular momenta. (a) Range of angular momenta typical of 1 Mw electrical power supplies; (b) 100 min rotation; (c) 1 min rotation.

above this altitude. Satellite attitude control, in contrast, may require high performance from the propulsion system.

The large satellites of the future (Table 2-3) will carry large power supplies for propulsion and the provision of energy for the maintenance of life and mission implementation. For the next several years, at least, rotating machinery will generate this power (Chap. 4). Rotating machinery generates internal angular momenta and therefore the possibility of gyroscopic torques during maneuvers. These torques may be important even during the slow controlled rotation of satellite vehicles. Figure 2-19 plots the satellite torques expected for a wide range of internal

angular momenta and precessional velocities.   An advanced satellite like
that shown in Fig. 2-15 would necessitate propulsion-system torques to
maintain proper attitude or spin in the presence of external perturbations
and gyroscopic effects.

There is little question that propulsion systems of some sort will be
mandatory on advanced earth satellites.   The addition of mobility and
attitude control will be a decided asset in the successful completion of
many of the ambitious applications that have been proposed for satellites.

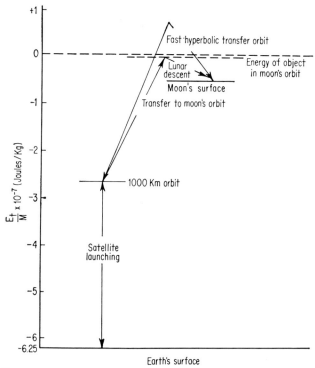

Fig. 2-20. Energy-level diagram for the lunar trip.   Note the small energy difference
between the escape energy and the energy of an object in the moon's orbit.

Before treating interplanetary flight, a few words must be added about
lunar flight.   The moon is a satellite of the earth just as the Explorers
and Sputniks are.   There is, however, a major difference.   The moon is a
massive body with a deep potential well (Table 2-2).   It is necessary
to consider the gravitational effects of the moon and powered descent to
its surface.   In this sense, the lunar trip is similar to interplanetary
voyages even though it is a satellite of the earth.   Figure 2-20 illustrates
the energetics of lunar flight for the case of transfer from a satellite orbit.
First, there is the energy increment from the initial satellite orbit to

the moon's orbit. Then, there is an additional increment for the powered descent to the moon's surface. The possibility of aerodynamic braking during atmospheric reentry does not exist on the moon. The first trips to the moon will probably be ballistic and will originate from the earth's surface instead of from a satellite orbit. For accuracy, lunar missions

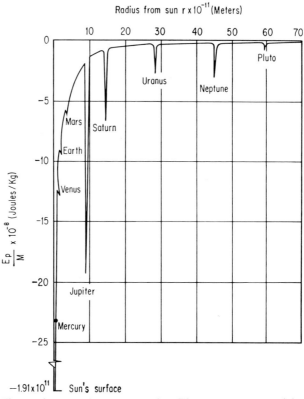

Fig. 2-21. The sun's potential-energy well. The separate potential wells of the planets are superimposed.

must be first calculated on automatic computers to account for the perturbations of the earth, moon, and sun. The minimum energy increment ΔE_M, however, can be extracted from Fig. 2-17.

2-15. Interplanetary Missions. In this class, we have the first true space expeditions. These are the multimillion-kilometer trips across the immense gaps between the planets. In this unexplored void, we have the *deep space* of the science-fiction writers. Eventual navigation in this void is the major goal of our present limited forays into nearby space.

Once we have mastered the art of escaping from the earth, we have hurdled the major barrier. The minimum energy requirements for travel to Mars and Venus are not much larger than the energy needed to escape the earth's gravitational field. The desirable fast trips will be more expensive in energy, but, as indicated in previous sections, a technology reaching the space-travel phase must already be rich in energy.

A potential-energy diagram of the solar system is shown in Fig. 2-21. The true depth of the sun's potential well cannot be conveniently shown on the diagram. Most of the planets are well up on the flared-out sides

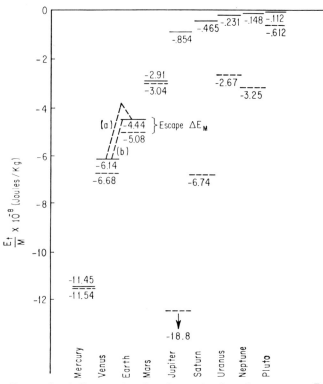

FIG. 2-22. Energy-level diagram for the planets in the solar system. Dotted lines represent the planet surfaces; solid levels, the energies of objects in the planetary orbits. (a) and (b) show fast and slow trips.

of the well. Jupiter is the most massive of all the planets, a fact that might well deter any Jovians from progressing very rapidly towards space travel. An energy-level diagram, including the kinetic energy of the planets, can be drawn to facilitate the calculation of the minimum energy increments needed for the various interplanetary trips (Fig. 2-22). The key importance of satellite staging platforms for interplanetary ventures is obvious from the small energy changes needed once stations in orbit have been established. Table 2-4 provides easy access to the values of ΔE_M, the mission duration, and other pertinent information for ballistic transfer between coplanar, circular planetary orbits.

TABLE 2-4. DATA FOR ONE-WAY, ORBIT-TO-ORBIT, INTERPLANETARY
MISSIONS ORIGINATING AT THE EARTH*

Target planet	n	u	ϵ	$\Delta E_M \times 10^{-8}$ joule/kg	t, yr
Mercury............	0.387	0.694	0.441	7.01	0.289
Venus..............	0.723	0.862	0.161	1.70	0.400
Mars...............	1.524	1.262	0.208	1.53	0.709
Jupiter............	5.20	3.102	0.678	3.59	2.732
Saturn.............	9.54	5.27	0.810	3.98	6.05
Uranus............	19.19	10.10	0.901	4.21	16.12
Neptune...........	30.07	15.54	0.936	4.29	30.6
Pluto..............	39.5	20.2	0.950	4.33	45.5

* Ref. 2-26.   For Hohmann-type transfer orbits between coplanar, circular planetary orbits,

n = ratio of final to initial orbit radii
u = ratio of the semimajor axis of the transfer orbit to the initial planet radius

The planets are solar satellites, and the techniques developed in Sec.
2-14 for earth satellites will also suffice here.   There are an infinite number of ways for traveling from one planet to another.   The classical

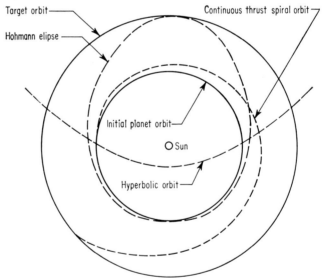

FIG. 2-23. Possible transfer orbits between planetary orbits.   All are conic sections.

method of interplanetary orbit transfer is the minimum energy ellipse,
the so-called "Hohmann transfer orbit."   In Fig. 2-23, the Hohmann
transfer ellipse is seen to be cotangential with the initial and target orbits.
It is initiated by an impulse from the vehicle's engine which injects the

spaceship into the Hohmann ellipse. Exit from the transfer orbit, when tangency with the target orbit is achieved, is again accomplished by an impulse from the propulsion system.

It can be shown that this method of orbit transfer requires less energy than any other trajectory.

The Hohmann orbits, despite their economy of energy, will seldom be used in space travel. The time periods required are much too long for humans, whose life spans are comparable to many one-way Hohmann trajectories (Table 2-4). Figure 2-23 also shows other elliptical transfer orbits as well as hyperbolic trajectories. Vertregt and Moeckel have made studies of these faster, more energetic, and more interesting orbits (Refs. 2-15 and 2-26). *Isoerg* diagrams, like the one shown in Fig. 2-24, can be drawn for all interplanetary trips. The corresponding *isochrone* plot shown in Fig. 2-24 indicates lines of equal time. A comparison of the two graphs clearly points out the price to be paid in energy units for a saving in time. The reduction in travel time with small increases in energy is significant. Figure 2-25 illustrates this fact in a generalized fashion.

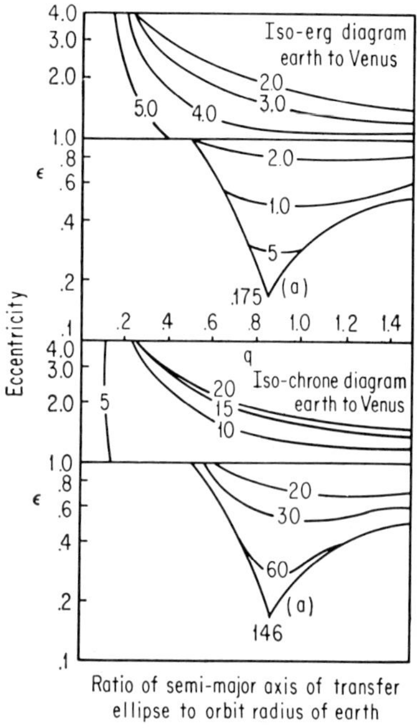

The velocity increments for twin impulse orbit transfers between coplanar and circular orbits take the following form for Hohmann ellipses (Ref. 2-17):

Ratio of semi-major axis of transfer ellipse to orbit radius of earth

FIG. 2-24. Isoerg and isochrone (equal-time) diagrams for the earth-to-Venus trip. The energies are measured, in Vertregt's notation, as multiples of the earth's orbital velocity. Isochrones are measured in days. (*a*) The minimum energy trip. Only orbit-to-orbit transfers are considered. (Adapted from Figs. 8 and 9, *M. Vertregt, Interplanetary Orbits, J. Brit. Interplanetary Soc.*)

$$\Delta V = V_0 \left[\frac{1}{\sqrt{n}} + (n-1)\sqrt{\frac{2}{n(n+1)}} - 1 \right] \qquad (2\text{-}34)$$

where V_0 = orbital velocity of the spaceship before the transfer begins

n = ratio of the planetary radii

Equation (2-34) may be easily transformed into an energy form by squaring both sides and dividing by 2. Note that Eq. (2-34) may also be applied to ballistic, earth satellite missions as well as the twin impulse interplanetary trips.

Interplanetary orbit transfer may also be accomplished using continuous thrust in a fashion identical to that described for satellite orbit transfer.

Continuous-thrust operation is advantageous in interplanetary travel since constant orbit correction is possible. In addition, the low thrusts

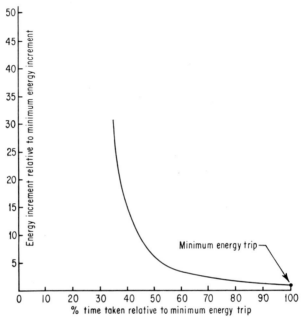

FIG. 2-25. Generalized chart showing time savings as a function of multiples of the minimum energy increment for the earth-to-Mars trip.

that can be used in such continuously powered missions can be generated by high-specific-impulse propulsion systems leading to high payload-to-gross-mass ratios. Along with these advantages, the use of continuous thrust in the presence of a gravitational field requires more energy than the impulse method. This is true because the gravitational force will continually be opposing the thrust during the entire mission. An equation analogous to Eq. (2-34) may be written for small, continuous, tangential thrust:

$$\Delta V = V_0 \left(1 - \frac{1}{\sqrt{n}} \right) \qquad (2\text{-}35)$$

In the limit, as $n \to \infty$, $\Delta V \to V_0$. This applies to escape from any gravitating mass. Examining Eq. (2-26) and Eq. (2-30), it is evident that

$V_e = \sqrt{2}\, V_0$ for the escape maneuver using impulse techniques. In terms of the velocity and energy increments involved, the continuous and impulse methods may be compared for the case of escape from a satellite orbit by the following equations,

$$\frac{\Delta V(\text{continuous})}{\Delta V(\text{impulse})} = \frac{1}{\sqrt{2} - 1}$$

$$\frac{\Delta E_M(\text{continuous})}{\Delta E_M(\text{impulse})} = \frac{1}{3 - 2\sqrt{2}} = 5.8 \qquad (2\text{-}36)$$

The implications of the foregoing analysis are that continuous-thrust propulsion systems will need considerably more energy than the impulse or ballistic types not only for the escape mission but also for satellite and interplanetary orbit transfers, since the ratio in Eq. (2-36) will be greater than one even when n does not approach infinity. Only for small changes in orbit radius can continuous-thrust engines compete with impulse systems on an energy basis.

Irving (Ref. 2-10) has shown that the extra energy burden borne by the continuous-thrust systems may be overcome through the use of a carefully calculated, variable-thrust and specific-impulse program. The consequence of this fact is that the propulsion-system designer should take pains to make the performance of his continuous-thrust engines flexible enough to take advantage of modulated thrusts and specific impulses.

To indicate the present state of the art for space propulsion, we quote the Rand "Space Handbook" (Ref. 2-29). It states that modifications of present ICBM equipment should be capable of achieving the following feats:

1. Orbit satellite payloads of 4,500 kg at 480 km
2. Orbit satellite payloads of 1,100 kg in a 24-hr orbit
3. Impact 1,350 kg of instruments on the moon
4. Land, intact, 500 kg of instruments on Venus or Mars
5. Probe the atmosphere of Jupiter with 500 kg of instruments
6. Place a man in a satellite orbit around the earth and recover him after a few days of flight

The energy-level tables and diagrams in the preceding sections provide a summary of the energy requirements for various space missions. Although the minimum energy interplanetary orbit transfers are somewhat more demanding of energy than most escape missions, fast interplanetary trips will require energy increments much larger than that assigned to the earth-escape mission. In the interplanetary missions, we are approaching the situation where the potential-energy differences between the origin and terminus of the trip are small in comparison with the high vehicle kinetic energies that are desirable for fast interplanetary trips. In the next class of space missions, the interstellar trips, this trend becomes more pronounced.

2-16. Interstellar Missions. Travel to the stars and the planets that are expected to be associated with them is a distant goal of astronautics. While the objectives of interplanetary travel and satellite operations do not seem to ask the impossible, the interstellar trips require energies and durations which are orders of magnitude higher. No doubt the spaceships will eventually reach the stars, but they are far beyond our present capabilities.

Some rough estimates of the difficulties to be encountered can be made from simple considerations of the distances involved. Alpha Centauri is 4.3 light-years away. Since a light-year is equal to 9.45×10^{15} m, the propulsion system of an Alpha Centauri ship must transport the vehicle across about 4.1×10^{16} m of space. Fortunately, the gravitational potential hills along the way are not very high. The major portion of the energy increment ΔE_V will originate in the kinetic energy of the spaceship. In an interstellar trip, the spaceship would probably accelerate as rapidly as possible to a fixed speed close to that of light. It would retain this velocity until it must decelerate preparatory to entering the target star's gravitational field of influence. The time the ship takes to build up its velocity depends upon the maximum allowable acceleration, which, in turn, is fixed by the propulsion system or structural limitations of the vehicle. The theoretical maximum velocity is that of light. In practice, this might be approached but never equalled due to the infinite energy requirements. A great deal has been written about relativistic effects. While it is generally agreed that a spaceship's mass will apparently increase and its clocks run more slowly compared with standards on an external reference frame, say on the earth, there is no widespread accord on the subject of time dilatation and its implications with reference to space flight. The effects of acceleration to relativistic velocities upon time dilatation are not understood. It may indeed be possible to tour the universe within one's lifetime, but clear proofs cannot yet be given by either side in this controversy (Chap. 9). For these reasons, the maximum velocity allowed the spaceship in our calculations will be $0.9c$. Figure 2-26 illustrates several possible flight conditions for the Alpha Centauri trip. The immense energies required are quite evident.

When more distant interstellar trips are contemplated, it is apparent that the limitations on velocity will seriously impair the exploration of our galaxy. If time dilatation does not permit spaceship crews to make extensive trips within their lifetimes, the obvious solution to galactic exploration requires the launching of spaceships containing whole communities. Many generations would have to live and die before the distant stars are reached. These implications have engendered many fanciful creations: faster-than-light drives, travel in other dimensions, teleportation, and so on. While we cannot close our minds to anything at this stage of space technology, such ideas are beyond the confines of the present discussion.

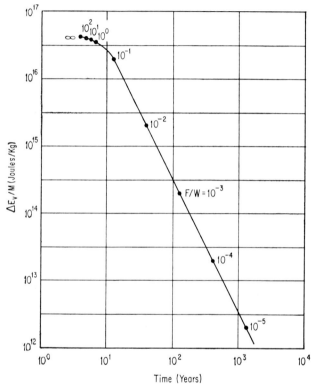

Fig. 2-26. Time-energy relationship for trips to Alpha Centauri. Thrust-to-weight ratios are indicated along the curve.

2-17. The Energetics of Space Travel.   In the four different classes of space missions that have been treated, there has been one unifying concept: that of energy. To gain a clear picture of the relative-energy requirements of the different classes, Fig. 2-27 has been constructed. Clearly, the satellite missions are the least demanding. Planetary surface missions are usually significantly less energetic than the minimum energy interplanetary trips. Interstellar travel requires more energy than any of the other three classes.

Once the energetics of the mission have been fixed, it is possible to optimize the propulsion-system parameters through the use of some figure of merit related to the mission. The mission parameters, especially the energy increments, can be linked to the propulsion-system parameters through some of the equations developed in the preceding sections. Ideally, it is possible to translate ΔE_M and ΔE_V into thrust-to-weight ratios and specific impulses, but the techniques for doing this are not available in a generalized form.

It is not the intention here to provide detailed mission data but rather to present an evaluation of the gross mission requirements and how these

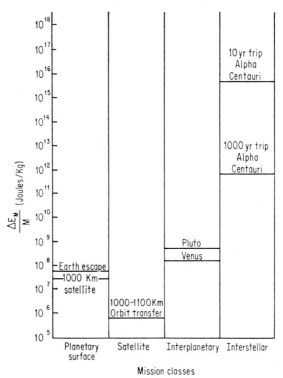

FIG. 2-27. Typical values of $\Delta E_M/M$ for the different mission classes.

may be related to the space engines. The selection of the propulsion system, once the mission is fixed, is controlled by the figures of merit adopted. The optimization of a system for a minimum gross mass may lead to the choice of an entirely different set of engine parameters than optimization for maximum reliability.

Other quantities might have been chosen to provide unity to this book, but energy has a simple physical meaning and is readily understood by most people. More important it focuses attention upon the most critical commodity in space technology: energy itself. It is a frequent assertion of this book that the success of space flight depends upon the ultimate development of better power-generating equipment, better fuels, and better energy storage devices. Space conquest is synonomous with the large-scale harnessing of energy.

PROPULSION-SYSTEM SELECTION

2-18. The Process of Selection. The foregoing analysis of performance and mission requirements is wanting in two respects. No handy rules of thumb are given in regard to propulsion-system selection. Equations and energy-level diagrams are adequate but do not give the immediate answers that many people desire. Second, some examples of how the material that has been presented might be used would be helpful.

To begin, let us take an example. Suppose a mobile satellite were badly launched into an orbit with an altitude of 1,000 km instead of the target orbit at 1,100 km. If it is desired to reach the target orbit in 10 hrs through the use of a small propulsion system, probably one designed specifically for satellite attitude and orbit control, it is a simple matter to calculate the propulsion-system parameters. First, Eq. (2-33) may be used for such small perturbations. It is found that

$$\frac{F}{W} = 5.09 \times \frac{10^0}{t} = 1.4 \times 10^{-4}$$

Let us assume that the initial vehicle mass is 10,000 kg. Then the propulsion-system thrust must be 13.8 newtons. Equation (2-23) permits the computation of the optimum I_{sp} for minimum gross mass. Taking a power-plant specific mass of 5 kg/kw, it is found to be 387 sec. The corresponding power supply and propellant masses are 131 kg each. It would be expected that a larger allowance for the propulsion system and propellant would be made since additional maneuvers would be anticipated in any practical mission. With the thrust-to-weight ratio and specific impulse calculated, it is possible to select among the propulsion systems available for space missions. In fact, the best over-all indicators of the propulsion-system capabilities are F/W and I_{sp}. Chapters 5 through 9 are devoted to establishing the probable values of these two parameters for various propulsion systems and nominal values of payloads. Since M_0 does include the payload and structure masses, there is some indefiniteness in this procedure. It is not serious for gross calculations. One other interesting fact emerges from the above example. The very small masses required for the propellant and power supply point to the possibility of using specific impulses other than the optimum one. Indeed, if a large enough allowance in mass is made for these items, a wide range of propulsion systems may be made applicable to such missions.

When a broad view of the problem of matching mission requirements with propulsion-system capabilities is desired, it is convenient to reduce the multitude of possible parameters to just two F/W and I_{sp}. Both the missions requirements and engine capabilities can be roughly spelled out with just these two factors. As will be shown in the following chapters,

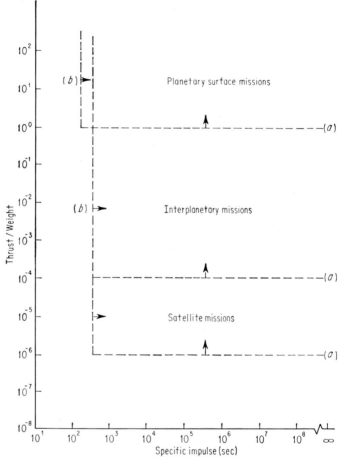

Fig. 2-28. Approximate performance limits for the different mission classes in the F/W-I_{sp} plane. (a) Minimum thrust-to-weight ratios for successful completion of the mission; (b) minimum specific impulse consistent with reasonable performance of the mission.

the specific impulse offers an excellent way of fixing the ranges of applicability of the many different space propulsion systems. The example given in this section illustrates how the mission requirements can bracket a range of specific impulses when upper and lower limits are placed on the combined power supply and propellant mass. In a similar fashion, a minimum thrust-to-weight ratio is needed to accomplish a mission successfully in a given time period.   In some cases an upper limit to this ratio also may be set from human and structural considerations.   Usually, however, the accelerations which cause vehicle damage are orders of magnitude above the range of interest.   While the thrust-to-weight ratio must include vehicle masses in addition to those of the propulsion system, the ratio of the thrust to the weight of the propulsion system alone is frequently very close to the thrust-to-weight ratio of the entire system for many space vehicles.   Keeping in mind the approximate nature of this procedure, a simple system for selecting propulsion systems can be set up.

Each class of missions can be crudely represented by lower limits on the $F/W-I_{sp}$ plane.   Figure 2-28 illustrates how this can be done.   Each propulsion-system type can also be approximately represented on the same plane by the upper limits of its performance.   By superimposing the missions graph (Fig. 2-28) over the performance charts to be determined in the later chapters, a mechanism is created whereby engine types may be assigned to mission classes.   As clarification and more accurate specification of the different space missions become available, the regions thus delineated on the $F/W-I_{sp}$ plane will become better defined.   Similarly, the boundaries of the regions assigned to the different types of propulsion systems will become better determined as technology progresses.   One of the important objectives of this book is the specification of the performance of each variety of space engine in terms of the thrust-to-weight ratio and specific impulse.   Knowledge of this kind is necessary to the sound selection of space propulsion systems to perform the various classes of space missions.

CHAPTER 3

THE ENVIRONMENT OF SPACE

3-1. Elements of the Void. The regions between the planets and the stellar systems are popularly referred to as *voids* or, collectively, *deep space*. If these terms were completely accurate and space a true vacuum, space travel would be a great deal simpler. Outer space, however, is not as empty as it is purported to be. In many respects it is more complex than the familiar atmosphere of our own planet. The earth's atmosphere, in fact, serves as a shield against the diverse and sometimes dangerous fluxes of particles, radiations, and force fields that are dominant a few hundred kilometers from the surface. This chapter describes this rather hostile environment of space and its probable effect upon the propulsion systems that will be expected to operate within it.

In this discussion of space environment, the topics of space medicine and the self-inflicted biological effects due to nuclear-power sources will be omitted. The treatment will be limited to the ways in which the environment will compromise the engines of space craft.

Specifically, there are three major components of the environment:

1. The particulate mass
2. Electromagnetic energy
3. Action-at-a-distance forces

The data to be presented here are far from complete and want a great deal more accuracy. This lack of knowledge stems from the near inaccessibility of outer space at the present time. The measurements that are available come from the sparse observations made from rockets, balloons, and satellites. Through the use of astrophysical and cosmological theories, many inferences may be made from the data. In this fashion, a model of outer space may be created. Our confidence in these models wanes as the distance from the earth increases. It must be admitted that we cannot be certain that the physical laws based upon terrestrial science can be extrapolated into space. Naturally, we can only assume that earth laws will also be space laws at the present time, for we have no better information. It is to be expected that many cracks will appear in the physical theories as the exploration and mapping of space proceeds.

54

A complete description of the particulate mass, photons, and force fields that populate space would consist of an accurate prognosis of the following quantities for each point in space as functions of time:

1. Particulate matter: particle masses, fluxes, velocities, densities, angular distributions, compositions, and electric charges

2. Electromagnetic radiation: fluxes, wavelengths, and angular distributions

3. Force fields: strengths, directions, and character

For all three classes of phenomena, we need to know the potential interactions with the materials, components, and instruments that comprise the propulsion system.

We hardly begin to have such information available today. The gaps in the picture that follows will be filled in as time progresses. Of the many discoveries of scientific importance awaiting on the paths to the planets, many will be in this area of environment study.

PARTICULATE MASS

3-2. The Mass Spectrum. In Fig. 3-1, the immense range of the mass spectrum of the universe is shown. At the upper end of the spectrum, there are the largest known masses, the stars themselves. At the lower end, the particles with the smallest masses are the neutrinos. The velocities of these particles may be anything from zero to nearly the speed of light, depending, of course, upon the reference frame in which they are measured. The effects upon the propulsion system include surface erosion, surface penetration, and even complete vehicle demolition upon collision with large asteroids. It is interesting to note that all of the effects just mentioned are inimical. Space is a harsh environment. It must be sealed out and attenuated, if man and his equipment are to survive for the long periods of time necessary for interplanetary travel. The optimist, however, can point to the possibilities of gathering this material, which occupies interplanetary and interstellar space, for use as propellant or as a source of energy.

3-3. Stars to Asteroids. The predominant effects of the larger astronomical objects, the stars, planets, and moons, will be through their gravitational fields. To fill in the upper end of the mass spectrum, we note that the largest stars are approximately one hundred times the mass of the sun, while the smallest are about one-tenth of this value. This is not a very wide range when the whole mass spectrum is considered. There are physical reasons for believing that stars must fall within a certain range of masses to be stable. These reasons stem from the delicate balance of gravitational, magnetohydrodynamic, and radiation forces existing in a star. Densities, on the other hand, exhibit extreme variations.

The star Antares has a mean density only 1/2,000 that of air. White dwarf stars may have specific gravities approaching one million (Ref. 3-2).* Stellar velocities within our galaxy are of the same order as those of the planets. The orbital velocity of the earth, for example, is 29.8 km/sec.

We know the planets of the solar system well, but we have only suspicions concerning those of other stars. The planets, like the stars, are

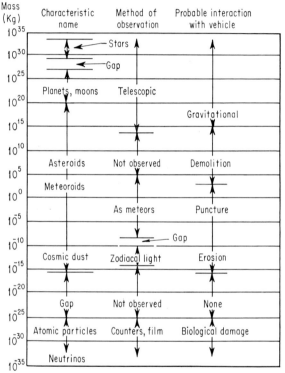

Fig. 3-1. The mass spectrum of the universe. Methods of observation and the probable effects on the spaceship are indicated in the parallel columns.

well charted and may be approached or avoided at will if a competent propulsion system is available. The planetary masses have been given in Table 2-2. Apparently, they grade fairly smoothly into the stellar masses with only a two-decade gap. Comparing Mercury and Jupiter in Table 2-2, planets occupy four decades in the spectrum. Planetary velocities and densities are comparable with those of the earth.

Over 30 moons have been discovered in the solar system. Their portion of the mass spectrum runs from 10^{23} down to 10^{19} kg. The positions of these objects are well known. Instead of being hazardous to space

* References are listed in the Bibliography at the back of the book.

travel, they will probably perform valuable services as staging platforms and intermediate space-vehicle bases. The shallow potential wells of many of them (Table 2-2) make them ideal for such purposes.

There are over 1,500 asteroids whose orbits have been determined (Ref. 1-2). It has also been estimated that there are over 100,000 asteroids with visual magnitudes smaller than 20. Many more have smaller sizes. By virtue of their great numbers, they constitute a distinct threat to space vehicles. They are so numerous and usually so small that their orbits have never all been charted. A spaceship traveling between Mars and Jupiter, where they are concentrated, might well fall under severe bombardment. Although many asteroids have orbits which intersect that of the earth, their contribution to the meteorites that strike the earth's atmosphere is supposed to be small (Ref. 3-23).

The total mass of all the asteroids is about 2×10^{21} kg. Ceres (Table 2-2) makes up much of this amount. It is believed that the asteroids originated when a small planet between Mars and Jupiter disintegrated. The asteroidal masses fit into the mass spectrum with no discontinuities. Velocities and densities are similar to those of the planets. Like the planets, they also tend to be concentrated in the plane of the ecliptic but exhibit much higher angles and eccentricities.

Except for the small asteroids, which overlap the mass spectrum of the meteorites, all other astronomical objects described in this section are so large that their positions and characteristics are well known. The stars, planets, moons, and larger asteroids will be targets for future exploration. Some asteroids will be menaces to navigation, but the larger ones, as well as major streams of smaller objects, will certainly be indicated on the space charts. There is little question, however, that there is a great deal of asteroidal material occurring in sizes too small to be easily detected and yet large enough to demolish a spaceship upon impact. In many respects, the objects ranging from stars to asteroids resemble the continents, reefs, and islands in the earth's oceans. Once a map is prepared, they can be landed upon, bypassed, or even used for raw materials as the situation demands. As the next sections will show, the real danger is from the fluxes and storms of smaller asteroids and meteoroids.

3-4. Meteoroids, Micrometeoroids, and Cosmic Dust. Each day the earth is bombarded by many thousands of kilograms of meteoric material. These particles may puncture and erode the components of the propulsion system. Pressurized fluids may be liberated. Optical and specially prepared surfaces may be degraded. It is essential to have sound estimates of the physical characteristics of this material and how it might interact with space-engine components.

A word of caution must be inserted here. The data and observations discussed in this section are open to many criticisms. Data on meteoroids and cosmic dust are notoriously hard to obtain. For example, meteoroid penetration probabilities may be wrong by a factor of 100 to 1,000 in either direction. The picture will be clarified only when dependable satellite data appears.

In order to emphasize the difficulty in getting information of this type, a portion of Fig. 3-1 is expanded in Table 3-1 so that the various methods of observation can be shown. Between the basic observations and the refined figures presented in Table 3-2, there are numerous assumptions and inferences of debatable nature.

TABLE 3-1. ORIGINS OF METEORIC DATA

Meteoroid masses, kg	Methods of observation
10^3 to 10^{-8}	Photographic and radio techniques. The larger meteoroids in this range may reach the surface of the earth. Photographic data is good enough to make one confident of most of the frequency data in this range.
10^{-8} to 10^{-10}	No information available. Satellite experiments should fill in this gap.
10^{-10} to 10^{-14}	This region is observed through the Zodiacal Light and the meteoroid-like particles found in the deep sea oozes.
10^{-14} and below	These particles are supposedly removed from the solar system by interaction with sunlight.

With the combined efforts of telescope, radio, and physical theory, the following generalizations have been made concerning meteoric material. Most of this information is derived from the Harvard Photographic Meteor Program and represents some substantial changes in thinking from previous generalizations (Ref. 3-23).

1. Meteoroids are nearly all of cometary origin. There is a very small asteroidal component. Most meteoroids are members of the solar system. The meteoroid flux falls off with distance from the earth. There may be some concentration of this material in the plane of the ecliptic, but this is not a strong effect.

2. The velocities of meteoroids at the earth's orbit vary between 11 and 72 km/sec (solar-system escape velocity minus and plus the orbital velocity of the earth). The most probable velocity of the visual meteoroids is about 28 km/sec. For space vehicles within a few hundred kilometers of the earth, the meteoroid penetration probabilities will be decreased by a factor of 2 due to the shielding effect of the earth.

3. Most meteoric material is stony in composition. Iron-containing types probably make up less than 10 per cent of the total (Ref. 1-2). The densities of meteoroids appears to be as low as 0.05 g/cc, indicating a high porosity (Ref. 3-23). This is consistent with their postulated cometary origin.

4. Theoretically, meteoroid masses have no upper limit, however, masses greater than 1,000 kg are extremely rare. It has been estimated that the smallest meteoroids are about 1 μ in diameter. Any smaller particles spiral into the sun by virtue of their relativistic interaction with sunlight. The corresponding cut-off mass indicated on the mass spectrum is in the neighborhood of 10^{-14} kg.

Perhaps the most critical of the assumptions to be used in meteoroid studies are those involved in specifying the frequency spectrum. Whipple's data have been used here (Ref. 3-23). The information of interest to the propulsion-system designer is given in Table 3-2. These data are in good agreement with the sparse information coming from the satellites. Table 3-2 incorporates an interesting assumption. It has been postulated that the meteoroid mass decreases by a factor of 2.512 for each step in visual magnitude. Note also that frequency figures are cumulative; each entry includes those preceeding it in the frequency column.

Once the meteoroid mass and frequency table has been set up, the other half of the environment problem can be considered. What effects can be expected when a meteoroid collides with a propulsion-system component? Here again there are as many estimates as there are investigators. Fortunately, experiments can be carried out in the laboratory on high velocity impact. The velocities obtainable today, experimentally, are less than 5 km/sec, or about one-fifth those of the meteoroids themselves. Consequently, laboratory data must be extrapolated almost an order of magnitude.

Experimental data indicate that the following equations describe the impact phenomenon at laboratory velocities (Ref. 3-8). It will be assumed that they also apply to meteoroids.

$$\frac{UK}{E} = 17.5 \left(\frac{K}{K_0}\right)^{0.26} \tag{3-1}$$

$$x = 2 \left(\frac{E}{K}\right)^{0.33} \left(\frac{K}{K_0}\right)^{0.09} \tag{3-2}$$

where K = modulus of elasticity of the target material
$K_0 = 7 \times 10^4$ kg/cm^2 (10^6 psi)
E = particle energy
U = volume of the crater
x = depth of the penetration*

The combined use of Eq. (3-2) and Table 3-2 results in the construction of penetration-frequency charts such as that shown in Fig. 3-2. This graph gives the frequency of penetration as a function of the thickness of the material. Figure 3-2 will be used in Chap. 4 when the vulnerability of power-supply radiators to meteoroids will be evaluated.

* See Table of Symbols at the back of the book.

TABLE 3-2. METEORIC FREQUENCY DATA*

Visual magnitude	Mass, kg	Radius, μ	K.E., joules	Penetration in steel, cm	Frequency, 1/m²-hr†
0	2.5×10^{-2}	49,000	1.0×10^7	9.9	
1	1.0×10^{-2}	36,000	4.0×10^6	7.3	
2	4.0×10^{-3}	27,000	1.6×10^6	5.3	
3	1.6×10^{-3}	20,000	6.3×10^5	3.9	
4	6.3×10^{-4}	14,000	2.5×10^5	2.9	
5	2.5×10^{-4}	11,000	1.0×10^5	2.1	3.3×10^{-8}
6	1.0×10^{-4}	7,800	4.0×10^4	1.6	9.5×10^{-8}
7	4.0×10^{-5}	5,700	1.6×10^4	1.2	2.4×10^{-7}
8	1.6×10^{-5}	4,200	5.9×10^3	0.83	6.0×10^{-7}
9	6.3×10^{-6}	3,100	2.2×10^3	0.60	1.5×10^{-6}
10	2.5×10^{-6}	2,300	8.0×10^2	0.43	3.8×10^{-6}
11	1.0×10^{-6}	1,700	2.9×10^2	0.31	9.5×10^{-6}
12	4.0×10^{-7}	1,200	1.1×10^2	0.24	2.4×10^{-5}
13	1.6×10^{-7}	910	3.9×10^1	0.16	6.0×10^{-5}
14	6.3×10^{-8}	670	1.4×10^1	0.11	1.5×10^{-4}
15	2.5×10^{-8}	490	5.1×10^0	0.079	3.8×10^{-4}
16	1.0×10^{-8}	360	1.8×10^0	0.056	9.5×10^{-4}
17	4.0×10^{-9}	270	6.6×10^{-1}	0.040	2.4×10^{-3}
18	1.6×10^{-9}	200	2.3×10^{-1}	0.028	6.0×10^{-3}
19	6.3×10^{-10}	140	8.2×10^{-2}	0.020	1.5×10^{-2}
20	2.5×10^{-10}	110	2.9×10^{-2}	0.014	3.8×10^{-2}
21	1.0×10^{-10}	78	1.1×10^{-2}	0.011	9.5×10^{-2}
22	4.0×10^{-11}	57	4.6×10^{-3}	0.0076	2.4×10^{-1}
23	1.6×10^{-11}	40	1.8×10^{-3}	0.0056	6.0×10^{-1}
24	6.3×10^{-12}	25	7.2×10^{-4}	0.0041	1.5×10^0
25	2.5×10^{-12}	16	2.9×10^{-4}	0.0030	3.8×10^0
26	1.0×10^{-12}	10	1.1×10^{-4}	0.0022	9.5×10^0
27	4.0×10^{-13}	6	4.6×10^{-5}	0.0016	2.4×10^1
28	1.6×10^{-13}	4	1.8×10^{-5}	0.0012	6.0×10^1
29	6.3×10^{-14}	3	7.2×10^{-7}	0.00089	1.5×10^2
30	2.5×10^{-14}	2	2.9×10^{-7}	0.00065	3.8×10^2
31	1.0×10^{-14}	1	1.1×10^{-7}	0.00022	9.5×10^2

* Reference 3-23 for columns 1, 2, 3, 4, and 6.   Column 5 is based on Ref. 3-8.

† Figures in the Frequency column are cumulative.   A factor of ½ multiplies the figures in the Frequency column to take earth shielding into account.

Some of the surfaces to be examined will have highly polished surfaces for reflecting sunlight. Some will use solar cells with special silicon layers on the order of 1 μ thick. Radiator surfaces may be coated with oxides or paints to enhance heat rejection. All specially prepared surfaces of this nature will be subjected to the eroding effects of *cosmic dust* (micrometeoroids*). The estimates of the probable erosion rate

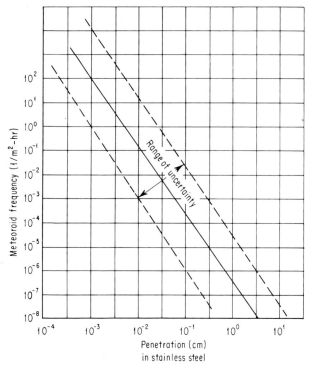

FIG. 3-2. Meteoroid flux versus penetration distance in stainless steel. The wide range of uncertainty emphasizes the character of the data presently available.

in space vary widely, from 2×10^{-4} to 10^{-6} cm/yr (Refs. 3-8 and 3-15). The probable eroding mechanisms include sputtering, sublimation, and chipping. Since many of the special surfaces mentioned above become seriously compromised when layers from 10^{-4} to 10^{-5} cm are removed, it may prove impossible to use some otherwise attractive devices (solar cells, for example) in space without protective equipment.

Although the damage expected from meteoroids appears imposing, there are several positive actions to be taken in solving the problem. Meteoroid bumpers are one example. This concept involves placing thin protective sheets of metal or plastic over the sensitive area. The

* See Glossary of Terms at the back of the book.

additional layer, about one-tenth the thickness of the layer protected, is supposed to fragment the incoming meteoroids into pieces too small to be harmful. A great deal of experimental work must be done to prove out this idea.

Since most space vehicles will be mobile, there is always the possibility of reducing meteoric effects by moving out of zones of concentrated meteoric activity. Meteoroid frequencies are estimated to drop off as the distance from the earth to the $-\frac{3}{2}$ power (Ref. 3-5). In a similar vein, there is a chance that orbits perpendicular to the plane of the ecliptic may be safer than the usual, coplanar orbits calculated for interplanetary travel.

3-5. Atoms and Atomic Particles. At the low end of the mass spectrum, we have the basic particles of nature, the atoms, molecules, and subatomic species. The action of sunlight creates a gap in the spectrum between 10^{-14} and 10^{-24} kg. Below this there will be *natural* gaps arising from the noncontinuous mass distribution of atoms and their components. Included in the present category are the particles emitted from the sun, interplanetary gas, primary cosmic rays, and the particles emitted by nuclear reactions.

The primary cosmic rays have been exhaustively studied. Experiments with rockets, balloons, and high-altitude aircraft have stimulated work in this interesting phase of physics. The primary cosmic rays are composed of atomic nuclei traveling with kinetic energies up to 10^{+17} ev or 1.6×10^{-2} joule (compare this with the meteoroid energies, Table 3-2). Protons make up about 79 per cent of the primary flux; alpha particles, 20 per cent; and heavier nuclei like iron, about 1 per cent (Ref. 3-3). Investigations show that if these particles were not deviated by the earth's magnetic field, their flux would be nearly isotropic. The magnitude of the primary-cosmic-ray flux is about 0.6 particles/cm²-sec outside the earth's influence. The real origin of these particles and the precise nature of the processes which accelerate them are in doubt. It does seem probable that some cosmic-ray showers owe their origin to solar phenomena. The energy flux associated with cosmic rays is only about 7×10^{-6} watt/m². This is miniscule compared with the energy available in sunlight. Fortunately for the propulsion system, the primary cosmic rays are of such a low intensity and are so penetrating that negligible damage to inorganic components will be incurred even during long exposures. The same conclusion cannot be made regarding their effects on the human body, since the rays are highly ionizing and thus constitute a distinct biological hazard. The magnitude of this danger is unevaluated at present.

The sun is also the source of intense streams of protons with kilovolt energies (10^{-16} joule). Fluxes are on the order of 3×10^{14} protons/m²-sec. Their high velocities may cause surface sputtering in the amount of 10^{-3} to 10^{-4} cm/yr. This effect added to the meteoroid erosion accentuates the improbability of successfully using coating, reflecting surfaces, and solar cells over extended periods of time.

The high incidence of radiation encountered by earth satellites (Refs. 3-20 and 3-25) is difficult to assess at the present time. This radiation begins at about 400 km. Figure 3-3 illustrates the present locations,

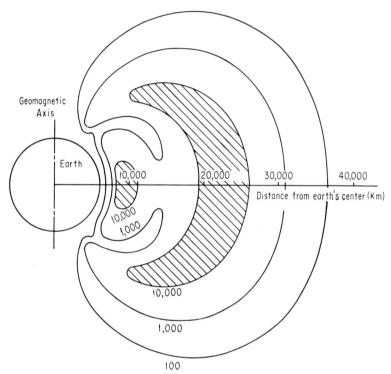

FIG. 3-3. The Van Allen radiation belts. The contours are labeled in counts per sec. Since the precise character of the radiation is unknown, the conversion to biological dosage (rem per hr) cannot be made.

intensities, and dimensions of the so-called "radiation belts." Presumably, the belts are composed of either protons or electrons that are trapped in the earth's magnetic field. The consequences of the radiation belts will be serious for manned spacecraft, especially those with low-acceleration propulsion systems. Propulsion-system components would be unaffected by this radiation as long as organic materials and semiconductor instrumentation are not used. This fact does not make the impact of this radiation upon space flight any less severe. True space flight will be with manned vehicles. Men must be protected from environmental radiation as well as that emanating from any nuclear-power sources aboard the space vehicle.   The high intensity of the radiation belts will probably preclude long-term operation within the belts.   Escape from the earth will be best accomplished with high thrust-to-weight ratio propulsion systems to minimize the time spent in the regions of dangerous radiation.   Polar launchings will further reduce the hazard.   The slow, spiral escape trajectories of low thrust-to-weight ratio propulsion systems (Fig. 2-17) will put these space engines at a serious disadvantage for this maneuver.

3-6. Planetary Atmospheres.   In addition to the fluxes of particles originating external to the earth, the atmosphere itself extends thousands of kilometers into space.   Spaceships and satellites will encounter drag and heating effects when passing through this gas.   Other planets and even some of their natural satellites have atmospheres (Ref. 3-9), but the discussion here will be confined to the earth.

The primary consequence of the atmosphere to space vehicles is that of frictional drag.   For the earth satellites it is not serious above 200 km. Heating of the space vehicle during reentry is important; however, the role of the propulsion system is relatively minor during this maneuver. On the other hand, when powered descent is used, the effects of the atmosphere are not a dominating factor.

The properties of the earth's atmosphere according to some recent measurements are given in Fig. 3-4.   These data include observations made on the Soviet satellites (Ref. 2-28).

3-7. Utilization of the Mass Spectrum.   In Sec. 2-5, the concept of using momentum exchange with massive astronomical objects as an aid to space flight was discussed.   Now this approach can be carried further. Is it feasible to extract either propellant or energy from the various components of the mass spectrum?

The latter question is easy to answer.   Meteoroids, cosmic rays, and the other particulate fluxes may carry high amounts of energy per particle, but the average over-all energy flux is only about 10^{-5} watt/m^2 compared with the 1,400 watts/m^2 for sunlight at the earth's orbit (Ref. 3-15).   This ratio of eight decades in energy makes the particles an unlikely source of energy in comparison to sunlight.   In the upper atmosphere of the earth, the situation is somewhat improved because of the dissociation of diatomic atmospheric molecules into "free radicals." The so-called "recombination ram jet" will be studied in Chap. 5.   This engine is an example of an environmental propulsion system.   It uses the potential energy stored in the dissociated atmospheric oxygen and nitrogen to obtain power.   It is just one example of several ideas which circumvent the problem of carrying fuel and propellant on space trips. The conventional ram jet scoops propellant out of the atmosphere as it moves along. This engine itself is not a space propulsion system, but its principle can be applied in outer space. It has been estimated that density of meteoric dust in nearby space is about 10^{-14} to 10^{-15} particle/cm³. The associated mass density is about 10^{-24} g/cm³, or 10^{-23} kg/m³ (Ref. 1-2). Close to the earth these values are increased

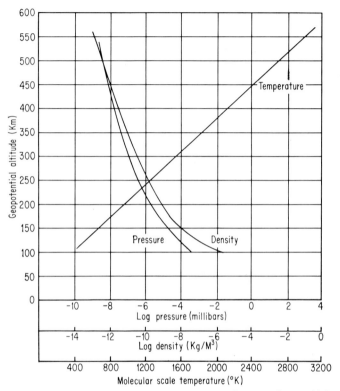

FIG. 3-4. Properties of the earth's upper atmosphere above 10 km. (*Adapted from Smithsonian Contributions to Astrophysics, Orbital Data and Preliminary Analyses of Satellites 1957α and 1957β.*)

by a factor of 100. The density of interstellar matter is calculated to be 1 proton per cubic centimeter, or 10^{-20} kg/m³, in the vicinity of the sun. The usefulness of such matter depends on the propellant consumption of the spaceship. The pertinent equation is

$$\dot{m} = \rho A_c V \tag{3-3}$$

where $\dot{m}$ = rate at which mass is collected
ρ = density of the matter being collected
A_c = effective area of the collector
V = spaceship velocity

Consideration of the low densities available leads to unwieldy collecting devices; however, if a great deal of power is available so that relativistic vehicle velocities could be obtained, it is conceivable that enough material could be scooped up at velocities near that of light to supply an extremely high specific impulse propulsion system. For example, at $0.9c$ the amount of interstellar gas collected is 2.7×10^{-12} kg/m²-sec. A large scoop, made of some structural material or possibly a shaped magnetic field, would be needed to make this small amount of interest. There is also the question of whether the material that is brought aboard is suitable for propellant. The answer depends upon the kind of propulsion system being employed. If it is a thermal machine (nuclear rocket), then the low-atomic-weight debris present as interstellar gas is desirable. On the other hand, ion propulsion systems operate well on the high-atomic-weight propellant available in meteoric substance. No final answer can be given here, but it is expected that space ram jets will be marginal because of the very low density of interplanetary and interstellar matter.

In the same train of thought, large asteroids might be mined for propellant and fuel without severe energy penalties because of their shallow potential-energy wells. There is little question that the ultimate space technology will be developed in the direction of self-sufficiency in propellant and energy in space. It is reassuring to note that the composition of the asteroids seems to be much like that of the earth, and that there is a tremendous source of energy in sunlight. All the important ingredients are present in space for the development of a self-sustaining complex of space vehicles, orbital hydroponic farms, mines, and power collectors.

ELECTROMAGNETIC RADIATION

3-8. The Electromagnetic Spectrum. The great bulk of the electromagnetic energy intercepted by a space vehicle located in the vicinity of the earth will come from the sun. The quantity of energy is measured by the solar constant, equal to about 1,400 watts/m² at the earth's distance from the sun. The value, of course, varies inversely with the square of the distance from the sun. Starlight contributes a negligible fraction of this energy flux.

The electromagnetic spectrum peaks at about 5500A. A graph of the sun's spectrum is presented in Fig. 3-5. The radiation is continuous in character, although the spectrum is interrupted by numerous Fraunhofer lines caused by absorption processes in the cooler layers of the sun's atmosphere. While most of the radiation is typical of a black body at 5800°K, different portions of the spectrum actually have different temperatures. When the ultraviolet region is examined, the sun's temperature is only about 5000°K. At radio wavelengths, the sun's corona has an apparent temperature in the millions of degrees. Radio energy, however, constitutes only a minute fraction of the total emitted. There are also small energy contributions in the X-ray and gamma-ray regions of the spectrum.

Moving away from the sun, interstellar space has a black-body temperature of only 3.5°K. The radiation density there is about 10^{-13} joule/m³ (Ref. 1-2).

3-9. Effects of Electromagnetic Radiation. Ignoring again the human factors, the effects of solar-emitted quanta upon the propulsion system will be of three types.

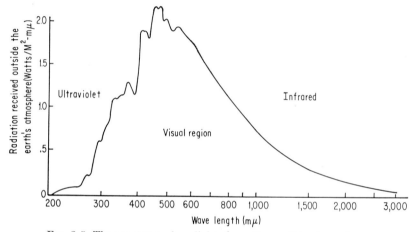

FIG. 3-5. The spectrum of sunlight above the earth's atmosphere.

The first is the adverse interaction with paints and other specially prepared surfaces. Ultraviolet light is known to deteriorate many such surfaces. Paint and oxide coatings will suffer with the changes in temperature encountered as a space vehicle alters its attitude in space. The magnitudes of these effects cannot be accurately determined until actual experiments are carried out in space.

Most spaceships will have power supplies of one sort or another. With closed-cycle systems, it will be necessary to radiate the rejected heat to the environment. The size of the radiating surface will be affected by the effective temperature of the environment. In the preceding section, the black-body temperature of interstellar space was quoted as 3.5°K. This low value will certainly not seriously concern the radiator designer; however, in the neighborhood of stars and planets, the radiation sink temperatures will be much higher and correspondingly more important. This will be particularly true when the lowest temperature in the cycle is close to the sink temperature.

The effective sink temperature of space may be calculated by employing the Stefan-Boltzmann law

$$W_r = e\sigma A_r(T^4 - T_0^4) \tag{3-4}$$

where W_r = radiant emittance
A_r = radiating area
e = surface emissivity
σ = Stefan-Boltzmann constant
T = radiating temperature
T_0 = effective temperature of space

For an object close to a planet, the effective temperature is

$$T_0 = \left(\frac{\omega_s}{4\pi} T_s^4 + \frac{\omega_p}{4\pi} T_p^4\right)^{1\!/4} \tag{3-5}$$

where ω_s = solid angle subtended by the sun
T_s = temperature of the sun's surface
ω_p = solid angle subtended by the planet
T_p = temperature of the planet's surface

For a 80.5-km earth satellite,

$$T_0 = 303°\text{K}$$

where T_s = 5720°K
T_p = 289°K
e = 1.0

The third effect of electromagnetic radiation is that of pressure. Using Eq. (2-8), we obtain the following relationship for a surface at the earth's orbit

$$p = \frac{F}{A_v} = 4.67 \times 10^{-6} \text{ newton/m}^2$$

where p = radiation pressure
F = force
A_v = area normal to the sun

If complete reflection is assumed, the value calculated above is doubled. Although this pressure may be used to advantage in the solar sail (Chap. 8), it may also exert important torques and thrusts on large, low-density low-thrust spaceships and energy collectors.

At the present time, it is impossible to tell whether or not sunlight will be an unmitigated blessing to space travel. There is no question that it does represent a sizable, attractive energy source, if large light-weight collectors can be constructed. Direct thrust through pressure is also possible. However, in its effects on materials, radiator sizes, and—

even through unwanted—vehicle forces, sunlight may not be wholly beneficial to the propulsion picture.

FORCE FIELDS IN SPACE

3-10. Action-at-a-distance Fields. The most important force field in space is, of course, that of gravity. The effect on the propulsion system was discussed in the preceding chapter where the problems of overcoming gravitational potential wells were treated. For the purposes of the propulsion-system designer, Newton's law of gravitation is adequate in all cases except where irregularities in the field may cause considerable perturbation of orbits. An example is the influence of the earth's bulge upon satellite orbits.

The earth's magnetic field and also the magnetic fields of the other stars are important through their possible influence on cosmic-ray trajectories and the streams of charged particles emitted during solar eruptions. The sun's surface magnetic field has been measured as 5×10^{-4} weber/m² or 5 gauss. The interstellar magnetic field is estimated to be about 10^{-9} weber/m² (Ref. 1-2). The various magnetic fields are not expected to exert any appreciable forces on space vehicles. As Chap. 4 will explain, there are some remote possibilities of using the earth's magnetic field for the generation of thrust and power.

The geomagnetic field can be represented approximately by the field of a short magnet or dipole placed at the center of the earth. The dipole would be oriented along a straight line intersecting the surface of the earth at latitude 78.6°N, longitude 70.1°W. The vertical field at the geomagnetic poles is about 6.3×10^{-5} weber/m². At the geomagnetic equator, the strength of the horizontal field is approximately 3.1×10^{-5} weber/m². Both fall off with the inverse cube of the distance from the earth. These values vary with time as do the positions of the magnetic poles.

Electrostatic fields in space seem unlikely because of the high electrical conductivity created by the protons existing in interstellar space (Ref. 3-1).

Apparently the only action-at-a-distance force field of any real importance in space travel is that of gravitation. In this discussion, we have omitted the fascinating problem of whether or not space is curved. Space structure is manifestly part of environmental studies. However, the curvature of space, like time dilation, is a highly debatable subject. Happily, both effects are likely to be very small for our limited forays into space, and we may proceed with confidence using Euclidian geometry and nonrelativistic equations for most space propulsion work.

3-11. Control of the Space Environment. Survival in space is a matter of energy control. The mass devoted to the protection of the vehicle against radiation and hazardous particles compromises the mission. High radiation sink temperatures increase radiator sizes. Atmospheres cause parasitic drag. Even the maintenance of the human environment necessitates an energy drain on the power supply. Control of the space environment is only an extension of our continual attempts to control our environment on earth. To be philosophical, the nuclear-heat source in the spaceship is analogous to the fire at the mouth of a cave a million years ago.

CHAPTER 4

POWER GENERATION IN SPACE

4-1. Power Requirements in Outer Space. Satellites and the many other space vehicles that have been proposed are outposts of the earth itself. If man is to survive in these vehicles and complete his extraterrestrial expeditions successfully, immense quantities of energy must be provided for propulsion, simulation of the earth's environment, and for the vehicle's instrumentation. This kind of problem, involving human activity in remote, inhospitable environments, has been met successfully before. Aircraft, ships, and Arctic bases all present the same fundamental problem of remote-power generation. Space power, in principle, is perhaps most similar to aircraft auxiliary power. Weight is extremely critical in both instances. In outer space, however, the penalty of excessive weight is doubly important. Each extra pound makes both vehicle launching and the subsequent vehicle maneuvers in space more difficult. In this chapter, the various ways of generating power in outer space, converting it from one form to another, and rejecting the unused portion to the environment will be discussed in some detail. In a sense, this is the central chapter of any book on space propulsion. The ultimate success of all space engines is dependent upon the ability of an energy source to produce large quantities of power over long periods of time with a minimum investment in mass.

There are five important questions to be answered in connection with power production in outer space:

1. What type of power is required—electrical, thermal, or kinetic?
2. What power level is desired?
3. How long must this power level be maintained?
4. What is the state of the art* applicable to the mission, vehicle, and power supply?
5. What constraints does the environment place on the power supply? The answers to these questions are ultimately reflected in the mass of the power plant. For example, high-grade electrical energy demands heavy conversion equipment. Each kilowatt of power capacity requires so many kilograms of power-supply mass. Each hour that power is pro-

---

* See Glossary of Terms at the back of the book.

vided is reflected in the fuel mass and the design life of the machinery. In a realistic design, the power-source specifications must be consistent with the state of the art being considered for the rest of the system. As a case in point, a thermonuclear power plant would not make sense in a 1965 satellite design because the basic problems in fusion technology have not been solved. Finally, protecting the power plant from meteoroids and other effects of the space environment will add mass to the final system design.

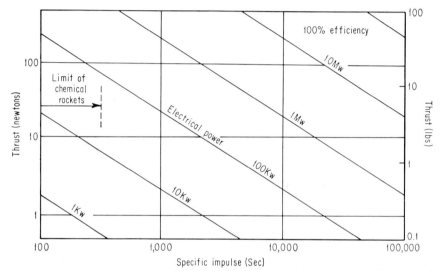

FIG. 4-1. Power requirements of electrical space propulsion systems. Even small thrusts necessitate high power levels at high specific impulses.

Looking ahead from the contemporary, 1-watt satellite power supplies, we can expect a rapid growth in the demand for space power as space vehicles grow in size and complexity. Reconnaissance satellites and exploratory probes of the near future will consume perhaps kilowatts of power. It is not an unrealistic extrapolation to contemplate the existence of megawatt space power plants before 1970, particularly for use with electrical propulsion systems (Fig. 4-1). There is much truth in the statement that power requirements always outstrip the power-producing capacity. The existence of realistically designed lightweight megawatt power sources would certainly stimulate ambitious space projects.

A new order of reliability must be built into space power plants, for they must be able to operate for long periods in the inhospitable environment of outer space. Since repairs will be difficult and perhaps impossible in space, much equipment will be designed for unattended operation, a difficult design feat even on the surface of the earth.

4-2. The Power-plant Spectrum. A schematic diagram of the space propulsion system was given in Fig. 1-1. Three of the four components shown there belonged to the power supply proper. In Table 4-1, these components are further subdivided into the specific methods for producing, converting, and rejecting power. The splitting of the energy sources into transportable and environmental types is very significant in space technology. In this division lies the opportunity to circumvent the launching into space of massive nuclear reactors and large quantities of chemical fuels. Likewise, the separation of direct conversion from mechanical-electrical conversion equipment emphasizes the possibility of eliminating rotating machinery from space vehicles. From the lists in Table 4-1, many combinations of the three basic power-plant components may be selected. It is impossible to cover all of these in one chapter. Consequently, attention will be focused on only the more likely candidates for extraterrestrial operations.

TABLE 4-1. POWER-PLANT COMPONENTS

Transportable-energy sources	*Environmental-energy sources*
Chemicals	Solar power
Radioisotopes	Wireless power
Fission and fusion	Ion recombination
Mechanical	Magnetic fields
Electromagnetic	

Electromechanical conversion	*Direct electrical conversion*
Turbomachinery	Thermionic converters
Piston engines	Thermocouples
Electrical generators	Fuel cells
Nozzles	Batteries
	Solar cells

Waste-heat rejection
Radiators
Particle emission
Portable sinks

4-3. A General Approach. For each specific mission there will usually be several combinations of power-plant components that will satisfy the power level, lifetime, vulnerability-to-the-environment, and state-of-the-art requirements. What criterion can be used to choose between them?

Recalling the discussion of propulsion-system performance in Chap. 2, it is evident that the power-plant specific mass M_{sp} plays an important role in determining the performance of any space propulsion system. In fact, in many space vehicles, the ratio of the thrust to power-plant weight is only slightly greater than the over-all thrust-to-weight ratio for the entire spaceship. The specific mass will be used in this book as a measure of the excellence of the power supply. Accurate comparisons, of course, can be made on this basis only if all other factors are equal.

As inferred above,

$$M_{sp} = f(eP, t, \text{vulnerability, state of the art})$$

where eP is the amount of power delivered to the propulsion system, which in turn converts a faction e' into the directed kinetic energy of the propulsive jet, and t is the mission duration.*

Each component of the power supply can be treated separately in most space power systems. Consequently, M_{sp} can be broken down into its three constituent parts:

$$ePM_{sp} = PM_{sp}(S) + ePM_{sp}(C) + (P - ee'P)M_{sp}(R) \qquad (4\text{-}1)$$

The letters in the parentheses refer to the different components of the power supply: (S)ource, (C)onversion equipment, and (R)adiator. The specific mass of each component is defined in terms of the power it delivers. A nuclear-heat source would be rated in kilograms per kilowatt of heat delivered to the conversion equipment. Turbomachinery would be rated in terms of the amount of shaft power it produces and so on. In this way, the component specific masses are independent of the rest of the power supply. Once the specific masses of the power-supply components and their efficiencies are known, any compatible combination of components can be synthesized into a complete power supply (see Fig. 2-6).

TRANSPORTABLE ENERGY SOURCES

4-4. Chemical Sources of Power. Chemicals represent one transportable source of energy. All chemical energy originates in the energy of the chemical bond. The inherent weakness of this bond, in comparison with nuclear binding energies, is a basic limitation on the use of chemical energy in outer space. Still, with the exception of the nuclear submarines, chemicals presently provide all earth-bound vehicles, as well as most of the stationary power-generating plants, with energy.

At their best, chemical bonds are measured as a few electron volts (ev) of energy. Contrasted with nuclear reactions, where changes in the nuclear rather than the electronic structure of the atom are made, chemical reactions provide many million times less energy per reaction. For example, the ionization of hydrogen takes 13.6 ev while the fission of U-235 releases 200 million ev (200 Mev). On a per atom basis, chemicals look very poor indeed; however, once nuclear fuel has been diluted in

* See Table of Symbols at the back of the book.

fuel elements and surrounded with biological shielding, it can be shown that chemicals can easily compete successfully, on a specific mass basis, for short periods of time.

The number of potential chemical fuels is very large. A few possibilities are listed with their specific energy contents in Table 4-2. Some attempt to list them in order of their state of the art has been made. The first chemicals in the list are operational today, while free radicals may never reach practicality. Metastable atoms (atoms with an outer electron in a high-energy long-lived state), like free radicals, are the subject of much theoretical and experimental work. No satisfactory way of stabilizing either in useful concentrations has yet been found.

TABLE 4-2. CHEMICAL ENERGIES

Chemicals	Energy, kilojoules/kg
Hydrogen peroxide	4,050
Gasoline and air	10,000
Lithium and hydrogen	11,300
Hydrogen and fluorine	13,400
Boron and fluorine	16,400
Lithium and fluorine	23,500
Atomic hydrogen, recombination	216,000
Metastable helium	468,000

Most chemical fuels are burned in air, although other oxidizers like fluorine are now getting more attention because of their better performance. Typical conversion equipment used with chemical power sources are piston engines, gas turbines, rocket nozzles, fuel cells, and batteries. Their function is to take the energy produced by the power source and convert it into shaft, jet, or electrical power. The mass of the conversion equipment is properly chargeable only to that component. Except for burners, storage tanks, valves, and piping, chemical power supplies involve little mass over and above that of the fuel itself. This is shown in the invariance of $M_{sp}(S)$ with power over the upper end of the range in Fig. 4-2.

The strong effect of time on the specific mass of chemical power sources is also shown in Fig. 4-2. The sheer mass of chemicals needed for time periods over one day eliminate them from consideration for many space missions. This situation should be contrasted with the same curves for radioisotopes and fission reactors (Figs. 4-5 and 4-9).

There is little doubt that chemicals will continue to be the most important energy source in space propulsion for many years to come. They, as yet, have no equals in planetary surface missions where the short period of engine operation permits the use of low energy density fuels. During the 1960s, space propulsion and chemical rockets will be practically synonomous. In addition, there are also the short-time specific mass advantages of chemicals for the production of shaft power and electricity shown in Fig. 4-2.

4-5. Radioisotopes.   A few natural and many of the artificial isotopes are unstable in time.   When they decay, high-velocity subatomic particles and gamma rays are emitted.   If the energy possessed by these radiations can be stopped and converted into heat, a useful power source will be created.   It is also conceivable that the nuclear fragments from radioisotope decay might be absorbed nonuniformly in order to produce thrust directly.   The *fission product sail* is an example of this type of

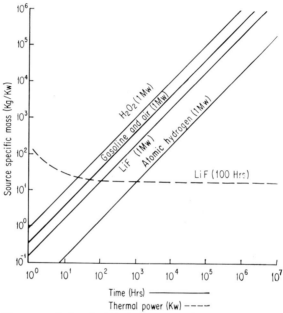

FIG. 4-2. Specific mass of chemical fuels as a function of time and power.   At low power levels, the mass of the combustion chamber is included.

propulsion system (Chap. 7).   As heat sources or thrust generators, radioisotopes represent highly interesting power sources for several space applications.

In terms of the amount of energy available per atom, radioisotopes fall between nuclear fission (200 Mev) and chemical reactions (under 20 ev).   Radioisotope decay energies generally range from 0.01 Mev to 10 Mev (see Fig. 4-3).   From this standpoint, they should be heavier than fission reactors at a given power level.   Radioisotopes, however, have special advantages over fission reactors.   At low thermal power levels (under 10 Mw), nuclear fission reactors become size-limited because of the critical mass and volume restrictions on the nuclear core.   Radioisotopes do not have this limitation and may have lower specific masses than fission power sources at the lower end of the power spectrum. Four important disadvantages of radioisotope power sources are as follows:

1. Radioisotope heat production cannot be controlled. There is no method for power modulation other than the rejection of the unwanted portion to the environment. Failure of a coolant pump, for example, will cause a melt down if the radioisotope cannot be jettisoned.

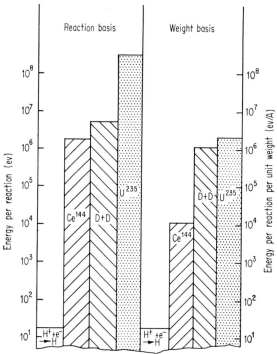

Fig. 4-3. Energy available in chemical reactions, radioisotope disintegrations, fusion, and fission.

2. The power level of the source will drop with time according to the equation $P(t) = P_0 \exp(-\lambda t)$
where $\lambda = 0.693/T_{1/2}$

λ = radioactive decay constant
$T_{1/2}$ = half-life

3. It is necessary to shield equipment and humans from the radiations that are emitted.

4. Radioisotopes are very expensive and difficult to obtain in the quantities needed for space power supplies.

Most radioisotopes suitable for power production emit alpha or beta particles. Fortunately, both of these can be shielded very easily, a fraction of a centimeter of metal usually being sufficient. Frequently, gamma rays are also emitted along with the other radiations. These may require several centimeters of lead to attenuate them to the desired level. Neutrons are not emitted directly by any of the sources contemplated for space power; however, alpha particles do react with oxygen nuclei to produce secondary neutrons. When radioisotope oxides are employed, this effect must be taken into account. The quantity of shielding needed depends upon the type of radiation, power level of the source, the dose level desired, and the distance of the object being shielded. All specific masses quoted in this chapter are calculated without shielding since shielding specific masses cannot be easily generalized.

The costs of radioisotopes are highly artificial. They are set rather arbitrarily by the Atomic Energy Commission. Current prices are reduced to dollars per watt of initial power produced in Table 4-3. A watt of power may cost anywhere from a million to ten dollars at current prices. The more expensive isotopes are created artificially in nuclear piles. Others are produced by bombardment of nuclei in cyclotrons or other particle accelerators. The cheapest radioisotopes for space power use are those separated from the radioactive wastes produced by nuclear-power generating stations. Currently, most of these wastes are stored, buried, or dumped at sea. Abundant though these waste products are, the costs of separating, purifying, and handling the radioisotope fuels make them so expensive that radioisotopes will probably be applicable only to power levels below 10 kw electrical.

TABLE 4-3. PROPERTIES OF PROMISING RADIOISOTOPES*

Isotope	Po-210	Pu-238	Ce-144	Sr-90
Particle emitted..................	Alpha	Alpha	Beta	Beta
Particle energy, Mev..............	5.30	5.46	1.25	1.10
Half-life, years...................	0.378	86.8	0.781	28
Gamma energy (Mev)†...........	0.80	0.045	0.134	1.73
Photons/decay....................	10^{-5}	weak	0.25	0.0002
Curies/watt......................	31.9	30.9	135	154
Grams/watt, pure................	0.0071	0.58	0.041	0.76
Cost, dollars per watt............	320	?	9.20	770
Fission yield (per cent)...........	......	......	6.0	5.8
Density, g/cm³...................	9.2	19	6.7	2.5
Melting point, °K................	523	......	913	1073

* Adapted from Ref. 4-28.

† The gamma energy shown is the most common one; others are emitted less frequently. The next row gives the total number of gammas of all energies.

There is a bewildering array of isotopes to choose from. Considerations of cost, half-life, and energy of decay rapidly narrows the list down to a half dozen or so. Table 4-3 summarizes some important data for four of the more interesting species. The most likely candidates for space power are Po-210 and Ce-144, the former because it can ultimately be produced in quantity by transmutation of bismuth in bismuth-cooled power reactors, and the latter because it is an abundant fission product.

Once the isotope is selected, one must attend to the problem of removing heat from a highly concentrated, uncontrollable energy source. As Table 4-3 points out, the power densities are much higher than those usually encountered in chemical-heat sources. If this heat is to be removed, the isotope must first be fabricated into fuel elements, perhaps like the one shown in Fig. 4-4. Generally, the isotope will be alloyed

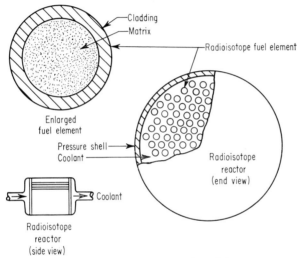

FIG. 4-4. A possible configuration of a fluid-cooled radioisotope heat source. Conduction- and radiation-cooled radioisotope elements are also important.

or used in compound form to raise the melting point and dilute the high specific power fuel. The stainless-steel fuel-element cladding shown in Fig. 4-4 also serves to stop the subatomic particles before they leave the element. The fluid-cooled radioisotope heat source would comprise many such elements within a pressure shell. A gas or liquid metal would pass over them to carry off the heat and deliver it to the conversion equipment. The radioisotope-generated heat may also be conveyed to direct conversion elements by means of thermal radiation and conduction.

The maximum temperatures obtainable from radioisotope sources are fixed by the structural materials. Nuclear heat is so concentrated that tens of thousands of degrees could be easily produced, if a container and coolant could be found. The maximum temperatures, therefore, are functions of the state of the art, the coolant, and the isotope itself. The identical situation exists in nuclear fission reactors.

When a realistic design has been established, values of $M_{sp}(S)$ may be calculated and plotted. Fig. 4-5 shows some examples. Note that $M_{sp}(S)$ is not a strong function of time as it was in the case of chemical energy, although it does increase as the radioisotope supply diminishes because of radioactive decay.

Radioisotopes may be linked to turbomachinery through a variety of working fluids. The heat may also be transferred to direct-conversion

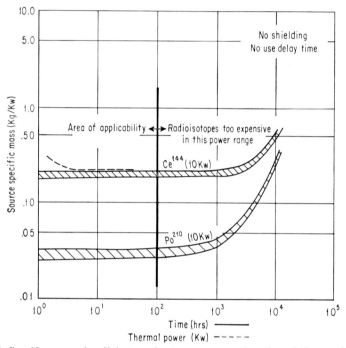

FIG. 4-5. Specific mass of radioisotope heat sources as a function of time and power. Isotope decay causes a rise in specific mass with time. The radioisotope reactor is assumed to be 4 times the mass of the pure isotope.

devices. One can even employ particles radiated during the disintegration to create dissociated atoms for use in fuel cells (Sec. 4-20).

Attractive as radioisotopes may be from the standpoint of low specific mass, there still remain the disadvantages of high costs, lack of power modulation capability, and shielding weight. No kilowatt-size radioisotope heat sources have yet been manufactured, although very small nuclear batteries have produced fractions of a watt. The Atomic Energy Commission is sponsoring the SNAP-I program at The Martin Company, where Ce-144 is to be the fuel (Ref. 4-43).* Presumably, this power

* References are listed in the Bibliography at the back of the book.

supply will produce hundreds of watts.   If the problems of cooling the heat source during the launching phase and power modulation can be solved, radioisotopes will serve as excellent sources of heat power for small space auxiliary power plants and possibly for very small electrical propulsion systems.

4-6. Nuclear Fission and Fusion.   The very large power supplies for use in outer space will undoubtedly be designed around the nuclear-fission reactor.   For power levels over 10 kw and operating times greater than one month, they are superior to other power sources for most applications.

The primary advantage of fission reactors is their low specific mass and long life at high power levels.   While the heat obtained from chemicals and radioisotopes is always proportional to the amount of fuel used, a fission reactor can produce any desired power level that is consistent with the cooling system.   Like a radioisotope source, the nuclear reactor can also capitalize on the excellent properties of inert gases and liquid metals for heat removal.

When the minimum size of the fission reactor is determined by the capability of the coolant to remove heat, its size is *heat-transfer-limited*. Since fission reactors also need to have a critical size and mass, which depend upon the materials of construction and the physical geometry, they may be *criticality-limited* at low power levels.   The latter condition is usually undesirable, leading to very high specific masses.   The thermal power level at which nuclear reactors become heat-transfer-limited varies with the type of coolant and allowable temperature difference across the reactor but usually lies between 1 Mw and 10 Mw (Fig. 4-9).

A fission reactor comprises a mass of fissionable fuel usually surrounded by a neutron-reflecting material.   The reflector is not absolutely necessary, but its presence permits much smaller cores and lower critical masses.   Figure 4-6 illustrates the basic nuclear reactor design (Refs. 4-10 and 4-33).   The nuclear fuel may be U-233, U-235, or Pu-239.   For the high temperatures desirable in space power supplies, compounds and mixtures like UC, UO_2, and UO_2-stainless steel are employed for the actual fuel material.   U-235, the most common nuclear fuel, may be dispersed in graphite, put into solutions, or incorporated in slurries and mixtures of liquid metals.   A typical reactor fuel element is shown in Fig. 4-6.   The cladding surrounding the fuel-bearing material protects it from coolant corrosion and prohibits the leakage of radioactive fission products from the reactor.   Neutron reflectors are made from light atomic-weight materials like Be, BeO, H_2O, and graphite.   Reactors can be classified in many ways.   If the fuel is in liquid or slurry form, the term *homogeneous* is applicable.   When the fuel is in the form of fuel elements, the reactor is *heterogeneous*.   With this very brief introduction to a complex technology, we shall now discuss nuclear reactors as they are specialized for space applications.

The size of the reactor will be strongly affected by the cooling mechanism. Gas-cooled plants must have high-core free-flow areas and large fuel element surface areas. Liquid metals will permit smaller reactors for the same power level, with correspondingly lower biological shield masses. This seeming advantage is partially offset by the lower temperatures possible with liquid metals due to corrosion and mass transfer effects. Sodium, lithium, lead, NaK are all difficult to handle and use at high temperatures. Figure 4-7 shows the probable maximum effluent temperatures from gas- and liquid-metal-cooled reactors (and radioisotope

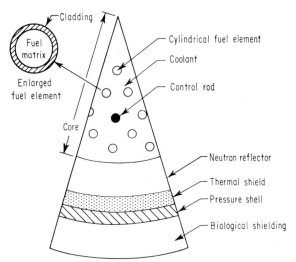

FIG. 4-6. Section of a heterogeneous fission reactor.

sources) as functions of the state of the art. The maximum temperatures indicated are those which are consistent with the practical design of a nuclear reactor with a 10,000-hr lifetime. Later in the chapter, it will be demonstrated that reactor temperatures are only one part of the story. The sizes of the shielding, the conversion and heat-rejection equipment are also highly influential in fixing the over-all specific mass and in determining which coolant is preferable.

Not only can electricity and shaft power be created from the heat produced by nuclear fission, but direct-thrust generation is also appealing. The nuclear rocket is an example of this approach. It will be examined in detail in Chap. 5.

Figure 4-8 illustrates the three types of fission reactors most applicable to space propulsion, the gas-cooled, the liquid-metal-cooled, and the radiation-cooled. Next, Fig. 4-9 shows the approximate specific masses

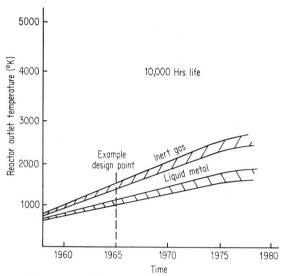

Fig. 4-7. Estimated reactor outlet temperatures for inert gas and liquid metals as functions of the state of the art.

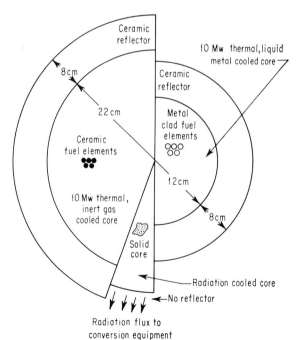

Fig. 4-8. Three reactor core sections showing the relative sizes of gas-cooled, liquid-metal-cooled, and radiation-cooled reactors. All are sized for approximately 10 Mw of thermal power.

for the first two types.   Design data on radiation-cooled reactors, where the heat is conveyed to the conversion equipment by radiation alone, are very scarce.   Unlike the chemically and radioisotope-fueled systems, the specific mass of nuclear fission reactors is almost constant in time.   Reactor designs are highly variable and a spread in specific masses is shown rather than a sharp line.   One point of interest is the sharp rise in specific mass when the reactor becomes criticality-limited at low power levels.

On a specific mass basis, for thermal-power levels over 10 mw, gas-cooled and liquid-metal-cooled reactors are comparable from the data

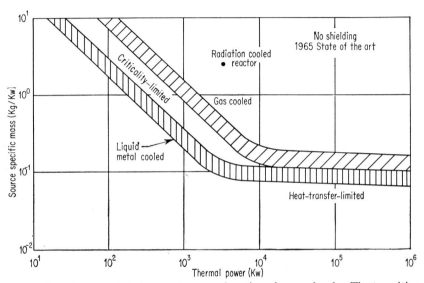

Fig. 4-9. Specific mass of fission reactors as a function of power level.   The transition from criticality-limited to heat-transfer-limited cores occurs between 1 and 10 Mw thermal power.

shown.   The reactor specific mass, however, is not the sole determinant of power-plant performance.   For example, the maximum temperature available in the cycle will have a strong effect on the radiator size and specific mass.   The lower temperatures for the liquid metals, predicted as a function of the state of the art in Fig. 4-7, will also affect the comparisons of the two basic types of nuclear-space power supplies.

Fuel for fission reactors is expensive.   Prices, like those for the radioisotopes, are set by the Atomic Energy Commission.   U-235 presently sells for about $20 per gram in the highly enriched form (90 per cent) necessary to high performance reactors.   Considering that a reactor for space applications will have anywhere from 5 to 200 kilograms of U-235 in its core, nuclear fuel will represent a large capital expenditure.   Even worse is the fact that this fuel cannot be completely utilized.   The lifetime of the reactor is set, not by the amount of fuel present but by the accumulation of neutron-absorbing fission byproducts and the weakening of the fuel elements caused by high temperatures and the accumulation of fission product gases. In most cases, less than 20 per cent of the contained uranium can be successfully burned. Many space missions using large quantities of power may be time-limited by reactor fuel burnup.

The power level of nuclear-fission reactors is controlled by the addition and withdrawal of neutron absorbers from the core and by the variation in the fraction of neutrons escaping through the reflector. The latter effect is accomplished by changing the properties of the reflector. Once criticality is attained, however, any power level can be realized providing the heat can be properly removed by the coolant.

Operating fission reactors emit copious quantities of gamma rays and fast neutrons. Both are harmful to humans and structural materials.

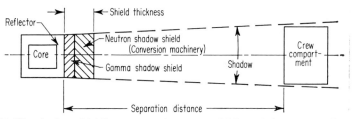

FIG. 4-10. The shadow-shielding concept for space vehicles. Power-conversion equipment might make up part of the shadow shield.

Humans require the most shielding. Semiconductors and organic materials can tolerate fluxes of radiation four orders of magnitude higher. Finally, metals are fairly resistant to radiation damage. Since the flux of these nuclear radiations decreases with the inverse square of the distance from the reactor, many space power-plant designs rely partially upon the physical separation of the reactor and crew compartments as a shielding technique. Cables or long booms are commonly used to isolate the reactor from the main part of the spaceship. This approach is helpful as long as the maneuvering and packaging problems incurred are not worse than the deterioration of performance resulting from the shielding masses that would otherwise be employed. At some critical distance, the mass of additional lengths of cable or boom becomes larger than the mass of equivalent shielding layers. This critical distance is in the neighborhood of 1 kilometer for electrical cables connecting a 1-Mw electrical power source with a crew capsule. Some compromise between distance and material shielding always results in the minimum specific mass. Figure 4-10 schematically shows the principle of shadow shielding. This concept is applied very satisfactorily in outer space where there is no air to scatter radiation around the shields. Care must be taken that portions of the space vehicle (the radiators, for example) do not scatter neutrons and gamma rays around the shields.

The design of reactor shields, like the design of the reactor itself, is a difficult art (Ref. 4-30). Gamma rays are best attenuated by high density substances like lead, tungsten, and steel. Fast neutron shields are usually made from hydrogenous materials like water, some of the hydrides, and organics. Since shielding masses are highly dependent on the mission duration, vehicle configuration, and power level, they are not included in the specific mass graphs.

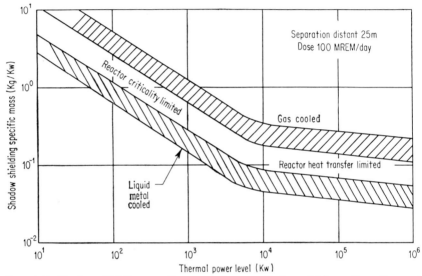

FIG. 4-11. Shadow-shielding specific masses for a particular vehicle configuration and dose rate as a function of power level.

Figure 4-11 gives the shielding specific mass as a function of reactor power level for a particular space-vehicle design. Note how the specific mass of shadow shielding drops rapidly with increasing power. Part of this rapid decrease occurs because the radiation flux is directly proportional to the reactor power level while the shield-attenuation capabilities are an exponential function of the shield thickness. The most important cause of high specific mass at low power levels is the minimum critical size of the reactor core. The core and thus the shield diameter are constant below the point where the reactor becomes criticality-limited. Another interesting observation from Fig. 4-11 is that gas-cooled reactors occupy considerably more volume than the equivalent liquid-metal-cooled varieties. Gas-cooled reactors have much larger coolant channels and are generally made from lower density materials. The larger physical sizes of the gas-cooled reactors lead to the larger shield specific masses shown in Fig. 4-11.

Comparing Figs. 4-2, 4-5, and 4-9, it is apparent that nuclear-fission heat sources hold supremacy at high power levels for long-lived space missions.

Two space power reactor development programs have been announced. These are designated as SNAP-II and SNAP-VIII by the Atomic Energy Commission. The electrical power levels of the complete power plants will be 3 kw and 30 kw respectively. Atomics International, a division of North American Aviation, is responsible for the reactor portions of these programs.

What are the prospects of thermonuclear fusion power in outer space? Although a propulsion system will be described (Chap. 5) which employs thermonuclear reactions, we cannot expect to have operational thermonuclear power supplies for at least 20 years. The development of this new source of energy is being vigorously pushed at the Livermore, Oak Ridge, Los Alamos, and Princeton laboratories by the Atomic Energy Commission as part of the Sherwood Project. Even with the traditional optimism of the spaceship designer, one cannot contemplate the presently projected fusion machines, some of which are hundreds of feet in length, as components of the first generation of space vehicles. The unproven status of thermonuclear power supplies permits us to bypass them and proceed on to the more readily available power plants.

4-7. Mechanical and Electrical Energy Storage. Of the transportable energy sources, chemical and nuclear fuels are the most common. They do not, however, exhaust the possibilities. It is possible to store energy in mechanical and electrical devices in quantities large enough to be practical for short-time applications. Some specific examples are listed in Table 4-4. Like chemicals, these energy sources have specific masses which vary linearly with time, because the amount of storable energy is directly proportional to their mass. Table 4-4 is, in principle, the same

TABLE 4-4. ELECTROMECHANICAL ENERGY STORAGE*

Type of device	Energy storage, kilojoules/kg
Pyranol condenser	0.045
Large inductance	0.075
Steel spring	0.45
Rubber bands	7.5
Flywheel	108
NaCl and container	198
LiH and container	476
Silver cell	440
Gasoline and air	10,000

* Adapted from Ref. 4-3.

as Table 4-2.   Specific masses as functions of time and power may be
scaled directly from Fig. 4-2 by ratioing the energy storage capabilities.
Gasoline plus air are again listed in Table 4-4 to provide a bench mark.
The silver cell is also given for the purposes of comparison, although it
produces electricity directly while the other sources require some sort of
conversion equipment if electrical energy is desired.   Chemical batteries
are discussed further in Sec. 4-21.

Even in comparison with the chemical sources of energy (gasoline plus
air) these mechanical and electrical storage schemes seem poor.   On the
other hand, their specific masses do not increase rapidly at the very low
power levels.   At power levels of just a few watts, the mass of chemical
burners and pumps and the critical masses of nuclear-fission heat sources
force their specific masses to extremely high values.   Consequently, for
a few watts of power, for a few minutes of time, the energy storage devices
in Table 4-4 may well be the best sources.   They are occasionally used
in missiles for this very reason.

ENVIRONMENTAL ENERGY SOURCES

4-8. Basis of Environmental Energy Sources.   In contrast with the
transportable energy sources, the possibility exists of extracting power
directly from the space environment itself.   In the discussion of the
space environment (Chap. 3), it was pointed out that both the particle
and photon fluxes existing in outer space carry energy which might be
tapped by space vehicles.   On the basis of the approximate measurements
available today, it is evident that cosmic rays, solar protons, starlight,
and the meteoroids all possess energy fluxes which are several orders of
magnitude below that of sunlight at the earth's orbit.   The sun, at least
for the first forays into space, will be a prime source of environmental
energy.   It is available in large quantities and we know how to use it
from earth-bound experimentation.

When space vehicles operate near the earth, additional environmental
energy sources are available.   The utilization of the free radicals created
in the upper atmosphere by the action of sunlight should be considered.
Similarly, the generation of electrical energy through the interaction of
the space vehicle with the earth's magnetic field is a possibility.   The
century-old dream of wireless transmission of power should be reexamined
to see if it has any practicality in space operations.

The central problems of environmental power sources are those of
collecting and concentrating the low density energy which exists in space
whatever its form.   In the case of material particles, the funnel-shaped
scoop of Fig. 4-12a would be typical.   This collector shape might be used
in the recombination ram jet discussed in Chap. 5.   In principle, an

interstellar spaceship might use a self-generated magnetic field to sweep
in the charged particles existing between the stars for use as propellant.
Electromagnetic energy, solar or radio, can be collected and focused by
rigid or balloon-mounted mirror surfaces (Figs. 4-12b and 4-12c). If the
pressurized balloons prove excessively vulnerable to meteoroids or vehicle

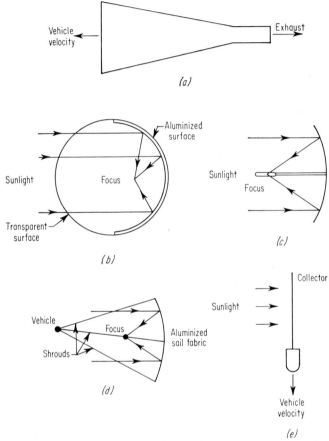

FIG. 4-12. Collector structures for gathering environmental energy. (a) Funnel for
collecting atmospheric free radicals; (b) balloon-type mirror; (c) rigid parabolic mirror;
(d) sail-type mirror; (e) flexible collector extended by acceleration forces.

accelerations, unpressurized extended surfaces may be created through
the use of light pressure or inertial forces as illustrated in Figs. 4-12d
and 4-12e. Every scheme for the collection of energy should have a low
specific mass, be invulnerable to meteoroids and cosmic dust, readily
packageable, and easily assembled in outer space. Representative
specific masses for some of these collectors will be given in the following
paragraphs.

When the energy being collected is not isotropic in distribution, an additional restriction is placed on the operation of the environmental engine. It is that of orientation. Solar power provides an obvious example. For maximum effectiveness, the collector must be kept oriented towards the sun.

Environmental energy sources are not completely *free*. Though the energy occurs naturally and is there for the taking, the collector and orienting mechanism must still be provided. Whatever the origin of the energy, the power per unit area of collector will be very small in comparison with the quantities needed aboard any manned space vehicle. Thus, the collectors needed to sweep usable amounts of power out of space will be extensive and heavy. Their mass must be charged to the power supply in lieu of the mass of the chemicals or nuclear reactor that they replaced. Conversion equipment to generate the kind of power desired from that collected will raise the specific mass of the power supply still further. Environmental power will be important only if it can be shown that, even with *free* energy, the specific masses of the complete environmental power supply are lower than those of the transportable energy sources.

4-9. Solar Power Sources. The environmental energy source with the greatest potential application to space propulsion is sunlight. This power source pervades all nearby space. Its intensity decreases with the distance from the sun according to the inverse square law. At the earth's orbit, the power available is about 1,400 watts/m². The efficient utilization of solar power has been a dream of mankind for centuries. A great deal of effort and money has already been expended in this direction (Refs. 4-7 and 4-42). Already sunlight is used on the earth to heat homes, drive steam engines, melt refractory materials, power telephone lines, and distill fresh water from sea water. This *free* source of energy will have many applications in space. Solar cells already power the instrumentation in some of the first satellites. This section will discuss the characteristics of the solar energy source and some of the problems which must be solved before large-scale use of sun power is possible.

The first decision that must be made in the design of any solar collector is whether or not it is to be kept oriented toward the sun. Obviously, the more sunlight intercepted per unit collector area, the smaller the power-supply specific mass. Some of the collector types illustrated in Fig. 4-12 can be kept positioned through the action of light pressure. The slight attenuation of light pressure with distance over the dimensions of the collector will generate a very small torque which will tend to keep the collector normal to the sun's rays. If other forces are present, those due to gravitation or the propulsion system, proper orientation of the collector will probably have to be maintained through the use of flywheels or a propulsion system. An omnidirectional collector, which presents a constant area of interception to all space, is a possibility, but only one-fourth of its area will be effective at a given instant. In selecting the type of collector to be employed, one must balance the extra weight of the omnidirectional collector against the supplementary propulsion required by the directional collector. Usually the orientation equipment will have a mass less than one-tenth that of the collector, thus making orientation desirable.

One of the simplest types of solar collectors is that diagrammed in Fig. 4-13. It is the rigid flat-plate type. Although it is too heavy and unwieldy for space use, it serves to illustrate some important points, the first of which is the concept of trapping solar radiation. Sunlight enters the collector through a glass plate, penetrates an insulating air film, and

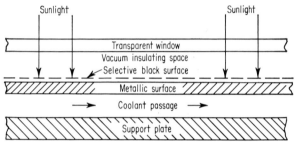

FIG. 4-13. Flat-plate type of solar collector. Not applicable to space power supplies.

impinges on what is termed a *selective black* surface. These are metallic surfaces coated with a thin layer of carbon or similar material. The surface appears black to solar radiation and will absorb up to 90 per cent of it, but the polished metal surface underneath has a low emissivity for the wavelengths characteristic of its black-body temperature. Consequently light is trapped by selective absorption. This stratagem is the reverse of the frequently suggested technique of painting space radiators with a thin white coating. The effect of either a black or white paint is striking. The selective black surface boosts the temperature that would be obtained by a nonselective surface by the following factor:

$$\left(\frac{\text{Absorptivity for solar wavelengths}}{\text{Emissivity for emitted wavelengths}}\right)^{1/4}$$

This factor can be made to approach 2. Ordinary flat-plate collectors can produce effluent temperatures of 370°K. With selective black surfaces, 740°K may eventually be obtained. Even with the best techniques, flat-plate collectors alone have specific masses of about 2 kg/kw exclusive of all conversion and rejection equipment. This value is very high for heat sources and rules out this variety of collector for space use. In addition, the low attainable temperatures lead to low conversion efficiencies. The units are also fragile and difficult to handle. Other solar power units are much more attractive for space operations.

The focusing type of solar-heat source is lighter than the flat-plate variety and may achieve much higher temperatures through concentration of the sunlight. The parabolic mirror is currently used on the earth's surface to obtain very high temperatures for experimentation. In the limit, it can produce temperatures close to the surface temperature of the sun (5800°K). Unfortunately, parabolic surfaces are difficult to obtain in space without resorting to clumsy, heavy, rigid structures. The specific mass of such a rigid collector is estimated to be about 0.15 kg/kw, including the metallic surface and supplementary structure but not the conversion equipment. Although this specific mass is comparable with those obtained for fission reactors, the areas needed for substantial power levels (700 m^2/Mw of thermal power) make the collectors unmanageable and immensely difficult to package and assemble in space.

A more promising approach substitutes a spherical mirror for the parabolic one. Spherical surfaces can easily be made from such flexible materials as sections of balloons, umbrellas, and sails. A very low gas pressure (0.01 to 0.001 atm) is adequate to keep a large balloon inflated in space in the absence of accelerations. Thin sheet plastic (Mylar) is the basic material in such proposals. Mylar can be made as thin as 0.001 cm. It is lightweight and easily packaged. It can be aluminized and made either transparent or opaque. Specific masses vary directly with the film thickness. For a 0.001-cm layer, the specific mass is 0.01 kg/kw of thermal power at the earth's orbit. A potential disadvantage of plastic film is its sublimation in the vacuum of outer space.

The spherical mirror will focus the sun's energy into a small volume located halfway between the center of curvature and the mirror surface. Spherical aberration and physical distortion of the mirror surface will spread the sun's image over the target to be cooled by the heat transfer fluid (Fig. 4-14). The temperature realizable in the target is limited by the materials available. By using a tungsten target, one might hope to obtain a coolant temperature of 1600°K. The heat absorbed by the coolant can be used to vaporize a working fluid which drives turbomachinery, or direct-conversion devices may be heated to produce electricity statically. Another temperature limitation in the power source may be set by the properties of the materials used in the conversion equipment. Generally, 1300°K would be considered to be an upper limit despite the higher values obtainable from concentrated sunlight. Figure 4-7 should be applied in this instance as well as for nuclear systems. Both the fission reactor and focusing solar collector can produce temperatures in excess of those that can be handled by present technology.

Just as earth-based solar collectors are useless at night, solar-powered satellites will be without power for an appreciable fraction of the time. It is, of course, possible to launch a satellite whose orbit is perpendicular to a radius vector from the sun; however, as the earth moves around the sun, the satellite will soon be in the earth's shadow part of the time. Orbits so far from the earth that the fraction of the satellite's period

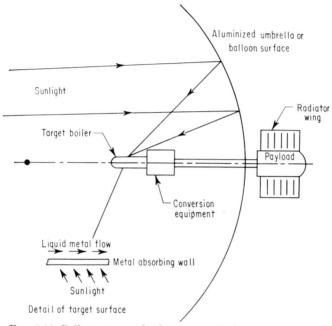

FIG. 4-14. Balloon-mounted mirror type of solar power supply.

spent in the shadow is small are possible, but it is difficult to imagine important missions for such satellites. A propulsion system might be used to keep the satellite continually in the sun, although this would be costly in propellant and diverted power. The solution used on the earth is that of storing the electrical power that is produced in batteries. As Table 4-4 shows, battery specific masses are very high and, consequently, unappealing for large space power supplies. Power storage requirements usually increase the specific mass of the whole solar power plant by a factor between 4 and 8 for earth satellites. For these reasons, the larger earth satellites will probably not use solar power, but the sun's energy will be an ideal source of power for small, unmanned, instrumented satellites and probes.

The meteoroid problem is especially critical for solar power sources. If a gas is employed to create structural rigidity, as in a balloon, meteoroid punctures will cause a loss of mass from the system and distortion of the collecting surface.   If Fig. 3-2 is a good representation of the actual frequency of meteoroids, a 0.001-cm Mylar film will receive over 100 punctures/m²-hr.   Even though the gas will leak out very slowly through the small holes, the effectiveness of the balloon type of support will be impaired over long periods of operation.   Figure 4-15 is included to permit estimates of gas leakage from punctured containers.

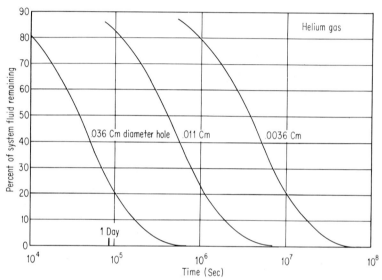

FIG. 4-15. Estimated loss of gaseous working fluid due to meteoroid punctures of pressurized systems.   The effects of smaller-sized holes may be found by area scaling.

Another obstacle to the use of solar power in outer space arises through the effects of cosmic dust.   Referring back to Sec. 3-4, meteoroid erosion may be as great as 2×10^{-4} cm/yr.   Solar protons (Sec. 3-5) may add another 10^{-3} to 10^{-4} cm/yr to the total erosion rate.   It seems likely that highly polished mirror surfaces and transparent balloon surfaces will soon be degraded by this dust and rendered ineffectual.   Probably the upper limit of acceptable performance of solar mirrors will be about one year.

All of the collecting and concentrating devices so far described may feed their output directly into a heat engine.   Direct-conversion elements may also be used in conjunction with the solar energy source.   Subsequent sections of this chapter will treat the conversion equipment and the integrated power supply.   Section 4-22 describes the solar cell, while Sec. 4-27 integrates and summarizes the various combinations of sources, converters, and heat rejectors.

The state of the art is nonexistent for space-located solar power supplies of the mirror type. Most questions concerning their utility involve the environment. The only acceptable answers can be found through actual experimentation in space. Until such facilities are available to test the performance of these power supplies in the actual environment, final decisions concerning their use in space travel must wait.

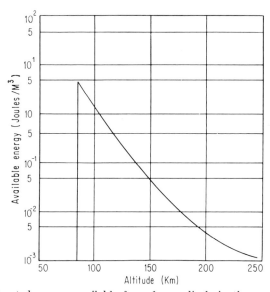

FIG. 4-16. Estimated energy available from free radicals in the upper atmosphere.

The only generalization that can safely be made is that solar power supplies, including solar cells, seem most applicable at electrical power levels under 10 kw because of the immense collector sizes and the magnified environmental problems associated with the larger power supplies. The reader should refer to the summary sections of this chapter (Secs. 4-27 and 4-28) for comparisons of solar power with the other methods of producing power in space.

4-10. Free Radical Energy from the Atmosphere. One other source of free energy exists high in the atmosphere in the form of dissociated oxygen and nitrogen. The data that are available indicate that, in the region from 80 km and upwards, the concentration of free radicals created by the action of sunlight is sufficient to sustain orbital vehicles in the presence of atmospheric drag losses. The amount of energy available is given in Fig. 4-16. The scoop and equipment necessary to collect and make this energy usable are a function of the type of vehicle, its velocity, and the operating altitude. It is impractical to give any generalized specific masses for the collector at this point. Instead the reader is referred to Chap. 5 where a specific recombination propulsion system is discussed.

4-11. Utilization of the Earth's Magnetic Field. The ring-shaped satellite shown in Fig. 4-17 is designed to generate electrical energy by cutting the earth's magnetic lines of force during its passage around the earth. If the satellite is in an orbit containing the geomagnetic poles,

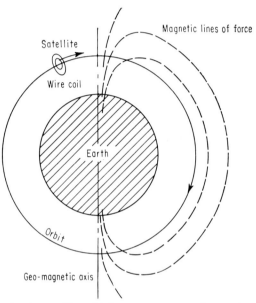

Fig. 4-17. Schematic of a satellite which generates power by cutting the earth's magnetic lines of force.

the flux cutting the plane of the coil, which is kept perpendicular to the direction of satellite motion, will go through one complete cycle for each satellite revolution. The electromotive force generated is given by

$$\mathcal{E} = \frac{d(BA)}{dt} \tag{4-2}$$

where B = magnetic intensity

A = area of the coil

$\mathcal{E}$ = electromotive force

The maximum value of the magnetic intensity is 3.1×10^{-5} weber/m². Considering one turn of wire encompassing an area of 1 m², substitution in Eq. (4-2) yields $\mathcal{E} = 2 \times 10^{-8}$ volt/m²-turn. The power extracted from such a satellite generator would depend upon the external load and the internal resistance of the source. The above calculation is sufficient to show that even with loads of just a few ohms, the maximum power obtainable will be measured in microwatts per turn. Rough specific masses for such a conception are on the order of 10^{18} kg/kw. The weakness of the earth's magnetic field is an important contributor to this poor performance. The final *coup-de-grâce* to such systems arises in the fact that the generation of electrical energy in the above manner must, from the law of conservation of energy, slow the satellite down. The satellite in reality is only a means of storing mechanical energy and afterwards extracting it in the form of electrical energy. This method of generating energy is instructive, but has no practical applications.

4-12. Wireless Transmission of Power. The transmission of practical quantities of electrical power through space by means of radio waves has always been another favorite objective of engineers. Tesla made some serious studies of the subject many years ago, but, because of the many losses and inefficiencies, the concept has received little further attention. Now that a new area of power application is opening up, the concept should be reexamined for feasibility in outer space.

Two possible applications are considered here. One is the case where ground-generated power is transmitted in a tight beam to a satellite. The second involves intersatellite transmission, say from a specialized power-generating satellite to accompanying satellites with other missions. These applications are indicated schematically in Fig. 4-18.

The crucial question, as with all environmental energy sources, asks whether the low efficiencies of generation, transmission, and reception of power are more than balanced by the mass savings arising from the elimination of the power source from the space vehicle.

Although the efficiencies vary with the frequency of the radiated energy, a rough estimate of the over-all efficiency of a wireless power transmission system can be made with a few, fairly realistic assumptions. There are four places where energy is unavoidably lost:

1. In the conversion of heat to electricity at the transmitting station (30 per cent efficiency)

2. In the conversion of electrical energy into electromagnetic energy at the transmitter (25 per cent)

3. Transmission losses due to absorption, scattering, and unavoidable $1/r^2$ attenuation (1 per cent)

4. Conversion of electromagnetic energy into useful electrical energy at the vehicle (25 per cent)

Items 1, 2, and 4 are estimated from experience with radar transmission and reception. Item 3 assumes that the cross-sectional area of the transmitting antenna is 40,000 m² and that of the receiving antenna is 1 m². Spherical wavefront transmission between points 50 km apart is used. The over-all efficiency, from these assumptions, turns out to be only 0.02 per cent, from the thermal energy produced on the ground to the vehicle's electric busbars.

It is interesting to note that only the power source is affected by using wireless transmission of power. Conversion equipment and a radiator to reject the waste heat are still necessary. The source specific mass must be compounded from the receiving antenna mass and the aiming and control system masses. Needless to say, these vehicle-located source

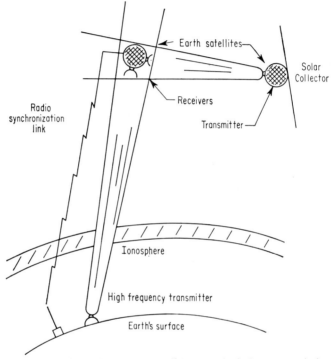

FIG. 4-18. Operation schematics of two possible uses of wireless transmission of power in outer space.

components will not be small. Estimates put their specific masses as high as 10 kg/kw.

We may conclude that wireless transmission of power is a very wasteful process. It does not eliminate the source specific mass aboard the vehicle. It is not competitive with other power sources for applications in outer space.

THERMAL MECHANICAL-ELECTRICAL ENERGY CONVERSION

4-13. Heat to Electricity. The ultimate objective of any space propulsion system is the conversion of the energy stored in the power source into the kinetic or potential energy of the vehicle. At present, space engines are typified by the chemical rocket. In this engine, the input thermal energy is changed into the kinetic energy of the jet by a convergent-divergent nozzle. In thermodynamic language, the working fluid (fuel and propellant) goes through a thermodynamic cycle and is made to do mechanical work on the rocket vehicle. The temperature limitations imposed by the materials making up the engine have forced the propulsion engineers to look for radically new types of engines for use in outer space. Many of the space propulsion systems which successfully bypass the temperature problem consume large quantities of electricity. Ion drives, plasma jets, and magnetohydrodynamic propulsion systems have all, in one way or another, circumvented the temperature limitations imposed on the pure thermal engines. Since so many of the advanced space engines rely on electrical energy, a number of sections in this chapter will be devoted to the different methods of generating electricity in space. Many of the conclusions reached concerning electric power for propulsion will also be applicable to the generation of auxiliary power aboard space vehicles.

In the parlance of power engineers, electricity is *high-grade* energy. The inference is that electricity is more expensive and difficult to obtain than *low-grade* thermal energy. These things are true, and, in space, the distinction of energy quality is far more important than it is on the earth. The majority of the power sources that were described in the first part of this chapter were heat sources. Heavy conversion equipment is needed to turn their heat into the electric current needed by the advanced space propulsion systems treated in Chap. 6. With this fact in mind, we would expect to find a discontinuity between the thrust-to-weight ratios of the thermal and electrical space propulsion systems. The graphs which summarize propulsion-system performance at the end of Chap. 10 show this fact very plainly.

We now take the various heat engines that show promise for space use and ally them with rotating electrical generators. The two potentially useful heat engines which use conventional working fluids are the gas turbine and the gas piston engine. Each may be coupled mechanically to electromagnetic or electrostatic generators to produce the desired electrical energy from the thermal energy extracted from the heat source. Later, this approach will be contrasted with the direct conversion of heat to electricity. In spite of the supposed advantages in eliminating rotating machinery from space vehicles, it will be shown that there are many technical and state-of-the-art superiorities incorporated in rotating equipment. There are also strong doubts whether direct-conversion devices will be more reliable than the more conventional rotating machinery in practice.

4-14. Thermodynamic Cycles (Ref. 4-40).   The two unique features of electrical power production in outer space through the use of a thermodynamic cycle utilizing working fluids are:

1. The necessity for conserving the working fluid, since its loss would lower the effective specific impulse of the propulsion system

2. The fact that all waste heat eventually must be rejected by radiation These fundamental observations have a profound effect on the nature of the space power equipment.   First, closed-cycle systems are a necessity for all except the shortest missions (probably under a few hours).   Second, the mass of the waste-heat radiator will dominate the entire power-supply mass at electrical power levels over approximately 100 kw.

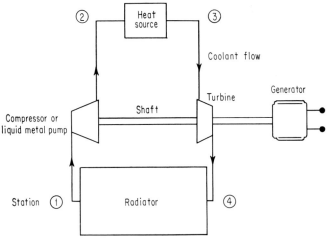

Fig. 4-19. Schematic diagrams of the gas- and vapor-cycle power supplies.   The circled numbers correspond to those on the *T-S* diagrams in Fig. 4-20.

Both the Brayton cycle (gas turbines) and the Rankine cycle (vapor engines) assume importance in space power.   Figure 4-19 shows the schematic diagram for both of these basic power supplies.   Next, the *T-S* diagrams for each type are presented in Fig. 4-20.   These two illustrations highlight a number of important differences and characteristics which are summarized in Table 4-5.   Much of the information given in Table 4-5 evolves only after extensive studies of the two cycles, but the opposing characteristics all stem from the basic differences between the gas and vapor cycles.

Gas cycles are not especially attractive theoretically from the standpoint of high efficiency, for heat is not added at the highest cycle temperature nor is it all rejected at the lowest cycle temperature.   To some extent, the potentialities for obtaining higher cycle temperatures through the use of an inert gas coolant mitigate this disadvantage.

In designing a closed-gas cycle for use in space, the compressor-pressure ratio is usually selected so that maximum mechanical work is obtained. The turbine-inlet (reactor outlet) temperature will be fixed by the state of the art of either the reactor or turbine materials. Usually, the reactor will set the maximum operating temperature in the cycle. The compressor-inlet temperature is fixed by minimizing the radiator surface area for a given power output. The high vulnerability of the power-plant radiator to meteoroid damage makes this approach desirable. The only major system parameter left undetermined is the absolute gas pressure. This is generally chosen from considerations of ducting masses and turbo-machinery design. Gas pressures in space power packs usually do not exceed 20 atm.

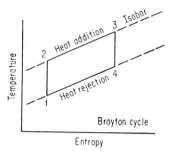

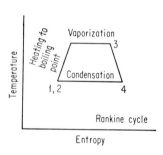

To give a better feeling for the effects of different cycle temperatures on the radiator area, Fig. 4-21 is included. Here, one sees how the radiator area may be minimized for a given value of turbine-inlet temperature. The importance of a high-turbine-inlet temperature is also obvious.

Turning now to the two-phase or vapor cycle, Table 4-5 has indicated that this cycle is desirable because of the low pumping powers and high effective radiator temperatures. In addition, higher theoretical cycle efficiencies are possible with the vapor cycle because it more nearly approaches the ideal Carnot cycle (Fig. 4-20). In practice, however, this difference in efficiencies is small or nonexistent. Figure 4-21 also shows the radiator areas needed by the vapor cycle at various efficiencies and condensing temperatures. Apparently the operating point of the vapor cycle de-

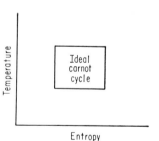

Fig. 4-20. Temperature-entropy diagrams for the Brayton, Rankine, and Carnot cycles. Note that the Rankine cycle more nearly simulates the ideal Carnot cycle.

pends strongly upon the physical properties of the working fluid. Table 4-6 lists some of the important properties of several of the possible working fluids for the Rankine cycle. Water has an excessively high vapor pressure at even low temperatures. Since high radiator temperatures are a necessity for small radiator areas, steam cycles are usually

TABLE 4-5. COMPARISON OF GAS AND VAPOR-CYCLE CHARACTERISTICS

Gas Cycle	Vapor Cycle
Many gases have excellent nuclear properties.	Water and most of the liquid metals have good nuclear properties for thermal reactors. Almost any fluid can be used in a fast reactor from the standpoint of the nuclear physics.
The gases are not severely activated in the reactor.	Most fluids will be activated, possibly necessitating extra shielding.
The inert gases are noncorrosive.	Liquid metals are corrosive, especially at high temperatures. Cold traps and corrosion inhibitors are usually used.
Gases have fair heat-transfer properties.	Water and the liquid metals are outstanding as heat-transfer fluids.
Nuclear closed gas cycles have been developed in England.	Water-vapor systems are well developed. Some mercury-vapor experience is available, but the other liquid metals are not developed for use in vapor cycles.
Large reactors and consequently, high-shield masses.	Small reactors and shield masses.
Relatively high state-of-the-art temperatures (see Fig. 4-7).	Relatively low state-of-the-art temperatures (see Fig. 4-7).
High pumping powers.	Low pumping powers.
Mass of fluid inventory is negligible.	The fluid inventory may substantially add to the system specific mass.
Gas-lubricated bearings are possible but not well developed.	Hydrodynamic and liquid-metal bearings are not well-developed for high-power systems.
Generator may be cooled with radiator discharge.	A separate subcooling loop is needed to cool the generator.
The closed gas cycle may be completely sealed.	Shaft seals to the generator compartment are needed.
Relatively low cycle efficiency theoretically.	High-theoretical-cycle efficiency.
Very large radiators result from low effective radiator temperatures (see Table 4-8).	Small radiators due to condensation at relatively high temperatures (see Table 4-8).
No phase separation or condensation problems.	Phase separation and condensation techniques may compromise the performance.
No freezing problem.	Fluid may freeze in the radiator under several conditions.

not considered for space systems because, at temperatures high enough to reject heat effectively, the masses of the ducting and pressure shells become unattractively high. The same reasoning may be applied to mercury, but the effect is less severe.

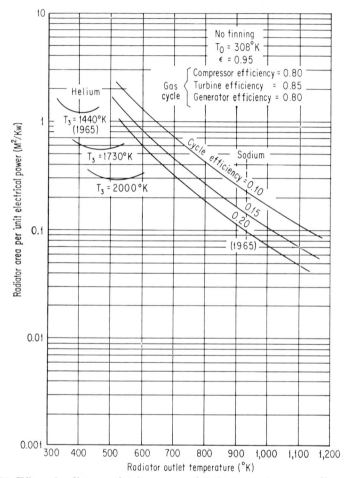

Fig. 4-21. Effect of radiator outlet (compressor inlet) temperatures on radiator specific area for different turbine inlet temperatures. In the gas cycle, the lowered cycle efficiency as the radiator temperature approaches the heat source temperature increases the radiator area despite the higher radiant emittance. The radiator specific areas are plotted for different, fixed cycle efficiencies in the case of the vapor cycle and these minima do not occur. 1965 state of the art is indicated.

The only vapor cycle power plants that have been built beyond the well-proven steam turbines have been the stationary mercury power plants. Some of these have been running successfully for 10 to 20 years. A good indication of the reliability of this type of rotating equipment may

TABLE 4-6. PROPERTIES OF SELECTED LIQUID METALS

Metal	Melting point, °C	Boiling* point, °C	Density,† g/cm³	Specific heat,† cal/g
Bismuth..............	271	1560	10.2 (271)	0.029 (297)
Cesium...............	28.5	670	1.87 (20)	0.058 (50)
Lead.................	327	1620	10.6 (360)	0.038 (360)
Lithium..............	186	1336	0.534 (20)	1.37 (190)
Mercury.............	−38.9	357	13.5 (20)	0.033 (100)
Potassium...........	62.3	760	0.83 (62)	0.200 (90)
Rubidium............	38.5	700	1.53 (20)	0.091 (50)
Sodium..............	97.5	880	0.93 (100)	0.32 (100)
Sulfur...............	113	445	1.81	0.220 (115)
Zinc.................	419	907	6.48	0.096 (100)

* At 1 atm.
† The temperatures at which the measurements were made are indicated in the parentheses.

be found in the analysis of these plants. Steam turbines may run year in year out without maintenance. Even the less well developed mercury turbines run without trouble for thousands of hours.

The advantages of the metallic vapor cycle have been recognized for many years. These merits carry over into space applications. The problems of liquid-metal corrosion and mass transfer at the high temperatures and many thousand hours of operating life expected from space power plants lead to challenging development problems which have not been completely solved. In Table 4-7, the various characteristics of the liquid metals are listed. Historically, we have progressed down the list to ever-higher temperature materials. The first space Rankine cycles will probably use mercury or possibly potassium. As development proceeds, the higher temperature fluids like sodium will be used as working fluids. Once the high-temperature vapor machinery has been developed, the basic performance advantages of the Rankine cycle (Table 4-5) will make them preferable to the gas cycle.

From the standpoint of the cycle alone, the Rankine cycle is superior; however, this is far from a complete picture. Table 4-5 supplies ample evidence that the Rankine cycle is a much more difficult and complex engine to develop. The over-all performance of the power supply is a synthesis of the cycle efficiency, the specific mass of the components, and the host of qualitative factors summarized in Table 4-5. The final choice between the gas and vapor cycle is not completely clear. A glance at the summary performance charts at the end of the chapter (Fig. 4-41) shows a clear victory for the vapor cycle on the basis of specific mass. This particular chart is based on the cycle data shown in Table 4-8, which

TABLE 4-7. COMPARISON OF WORKING FLUIDS

Fluid	Nuclear properties	Corrosion	Heat transfer	Cost	State of the art	Remarks
Helium	G*	G	F	P	P	Requires many stages of turbomachinery
Neon	G	G	F	F	P	
Argon	G	G	F	G	P	
Nitrogen	G	G	F	G	F	Nitriding of materials
CO_2	G	G	F	G	F	
Water	F	F	G	G	G ⎫	High pressures needed at
Mercury	P	F	G	G	G ⎭	the radiator temperatures desired
NaK	F	P	G	G	G ⎫	Corrosion and mass trans-
Rubidium	F	P	G	F	P ⎪	fer necessitate much de-
Potassium	F	P	G	G	F ⎪	velopment for use at high
Sodium	F	P	G	G	F ⎭	temperatures
Lead	F	P	G	G	P	
Sulfur	F	F	F	G	P	
NaOH	F	P	F	G	P	

* G = good, F = fair, and P = poor.

TABLE 4-8. GAS AND VAPOR CYCLES COMPARED

Parameter	Gas cycle	Vapor cycle
Fluid	Helium	Sodium
Shaft power, Mw	1.25	1.25
State of the art	1965	1965
Compressor/pump inlet pressure, atm	5.64	.086
Compressor/pump inlet temperature, °K	325	933
Reactor inlet pressure, atm	20.4	.660
Reactor inlet temperature, °K	687	933
Turbine inlet pressure, atm	19.6	.660
Turbine inlet temperature, °K	1444	1110
Radiator inlet pressure, atm	6.53	.086
Radiator inlet temperature, °K	1010	933
Turbine efficiency	.85	.75
Compressor efficiency	.80	
Vapor quality	....	.802
Cycle efficiency	.163	.179
Fluid flow rate, kg/sec	1.95	1.83
Radiator area, m^2*	1560	139

* No finning.

is an extrapolation of present technology to 1965. In other words, if the temperatures and operating conditions shown for the sodium vapor cycle in Table 4-8 can really be achieved by reliable, long-lived reactors, turbines, and radiators, then the vapor cycle will be superior to the gas cycle for outer space applications. Today, there is every indication that the operating conditions shown for inert gas and metallic vapor in Table 4-8 will be achieved by 1965 and that the Rankine cycle is the best choice for space power plants.

4-15. Heat to Mechanical Energy. Once thermal power has been created in the source, it is conveyed to the heat engine by radiation, conduction, or a heat-transfer fluid. With rotating machinery, one of the working fluids from Table 4-7 can be used. Although reliable gas piston engines have been manufactured (the Stirling engine), the gas or vapor

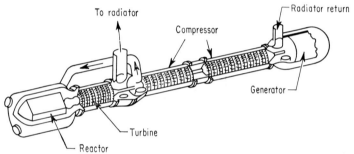

Fig. 4-22. One possible configuration of the components in a closed-gas-cycle power pack. The radiators could be winglike structures extending radially.

turbine has the advantages of fewer lubrication problems, simplicity, and vibrationless operation. In the case of the gas cycle, the turbomachinery will consist of the turbine, compressor, and an electrical generator all located on a single shaft. Figure 4-22 shows one common arrangement of the components. It should be mentioned that gearing between the generator and the rest of the system is not usually feasible because of the difficulty of providing long-life gear lubricants under nuclear irradiation. In the vapor cycle, the arrangement of the turbomachinery is quite similar. The compressor of the gas cycle is replaced by a much smaller and lighter liquid-metal pump. A typical arrangement of vapor turbomachinery is shown in Fig. 4-23.

The states of the art for both the gas and vapor turbomachinery are closely related to their allowable operating temperatures. A projection in time of these temperatures, similar to those projected for nuclear reactors, is given in Fig. 4-24. Comparing Figs. 4-7 and 4-24, it is again apparent that the maximum cycle temperatures will be controlled by the advances in reactor technology. The technical growth to higher temperatures will probably involve a transition from metallic to ceramic materials. While ceramic materials have been experimented with for gas reactors and turbines, little has been done with ceramic-liquid metal systems. There is a possibility that the maximum allowable temperatures may continue to rise with the gas cycle, while liquid-metal Rankine cycles may eventually hit an upper limit in materials development.

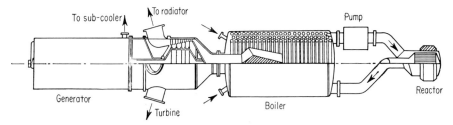

Working fluid: sodium

FIG. 4-23. One configuration of a vapor-cycle space power plant. Phase separation is accomplished by rotation of the entire power pack.

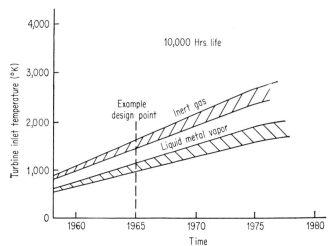

FIG. 4-24. Projected state-of-the-art turbine inlet temperatures for the gas and vapor cycles. These are somewhat higher than the corresponding temperatures for the reactor outlet temperatures (Fig. 4-7).

Recalling that nuclear reactors are size-limited by criticality conditions, it is reasonable to ask whether the specific masses of turbomachinery may not vary as a function of power level. It is found that the mechanical efficiency of turbines and compressors drops significantly as the blade dimensions get very small. Blade lengths of half a centimeter are close to the lower limit. As the shaft power falls below 10 kw, it is necessary to decrease the system pressure to maintain reasonable volume flows through the turbomachinery or accept the lower efficiencies. It is not uncommon to find turbine efficiencies falling below 50 per cent when the shaft power drops under 5 kw because of losses due to miniaturization. Thus, at very low power levels, an increase in the specific mass of the turbomachinery is expected. Figure 4-25 gives some representative values of turbomachinery specific mass as a function of shaft power level. The graph clearly shows the rise in $M_{sp}(C)$ at very low power levels.

One of the major differences between the design of space power supplies and comparable earth-bound power plants results from the lack of force fields when the space vehicle is in orbit or far from a gravitating planet. Phase separation and condensation will be seriously affected unless artificial forces are created to replace gravity. One technique employs

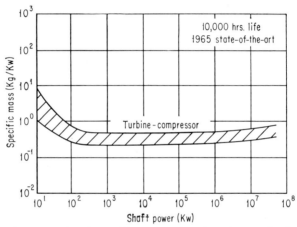

FIG. 4-25. Specific mass of turbomachinery as a function of power level. Efficiencies fall rapidly at low power levels.

cyclone separators to produce centrifugal forces through the rotation of the fluid itself. Helical coils and separators generally add pressure drop to the cycle and reduce the over-all performance. The alternative is to rotate the entire power supply. This is undesirable from the standpoints of the crew and the successful accomplishment of the mission. The vapor-cycle power plant shown in Fig. 4-23 employs system rotation to effect phase separation and condensation in the boilers and radiators.

4-16. Electrical Generators. Once a portion of the heat extracted from the power source has been converted into shaft power, the next step is that of transforming mechanical power into electrical power. Two fundamentally different kinds of electrical generators are available for use in outer space. The more familiar type is the electromagnetic a-c or d-c generator. In this type of machine, an electromotive force is generated when an electrical conductor is caused to cut magnetic lines of force.

In the electrostatic generator, a current is created when conducting surfaces pass through electrostatic fields. The appropriate equations are

$$\mathcal{E} = \frac{d(\mathbf{B} \times \mathbf{A})}{dt} = \frac{d\Phi}{dt} \qquad \mathbf{I} = \frac{d(\mathbf{E} \times \mathbf{A})}{dt} = \frac{dQ}{dt}$$

where $\mathcal{E}$ = electromotive force
$\mathbf{B}$ = magnetic field intensity
$\mathbf{A}$ = area
Φ = magnetic flux
$\mathbf{E}$ = electric field intensity
$\mathbf{I}$ = current
Q = charge

Each type of machine has its own particular advantages and disadvantages in outer space.

The predominant earth-bound electrical generator is the electromagnetic type. Both a-c and d-c versions are available over a wide range of power. The specific mass is a function of shaft speed, electrical frequency, and the operating temperature of the equipment.

The generators in space power supplies will usually be coupled directly to the turbines. High shaft speeds, in the neighborhood of 20,000 rpm and higher, will be necessary. Generator specific masses drop slowly with increased speed of rotation. Both the generator and turbine will be limited by the maximum tip speeds of the rotating parts, which is generally about 300 m/sec.

Another critical problem is that of generator cooling. The shaft power which is not converted into electricity must be removed from the generator and rejected by radiation. This waste energy, measured by the generator inefficiencies due to frictional and ohmic losses, ranges between 5 per cent and 20 per cent of the total shaft power. Except for the smallest generators, where radiation cooling may be sufficient, the generators must be cooled by some heat-transfer fluid. In the gas cycle, the gas itself can perform the task providing the compressor inlet (radiator discharge) temperature is less than 500°C. In the vapor cycle, the liquid metal from the coolest portion of the cycle, or possibly subcooled fluid from a separate radiator section, may be circulated directly through the stator of the generator. Provision of coolant to the generator will lower the final system specific mass, since the added mass of the subcooling loop will be more than offset by the increase in generator efficiency with adequate cooling. These effects are included in the summary graphs at the end of this chapter.

A-c machines are generally lighter than equivalent d-c equipment by 20 per cent or so. Another advantage of the a-c generator is that it may be built with slip rings rather than with the comparatively short-lived brushes needed by d-c machines. Alternating current may be conveniently stepped up or down by transformers. The transmission of a-c over cables between the power plant and crew compartment is also more efficient than the transmission of direct current. The specific mass of the alternator is also a function of the electrical frequency. A minimum is usually reached in the neighborhood of 1,000 cps. Beyond this value the generator efficiency begins to drop rapidly. Below 1,000 cps, the amount of iron in the generator causes high specific masses.

For applications where alternating current is satisfactory, the a-c generator is obviously superior. If direct current is essential, say in an

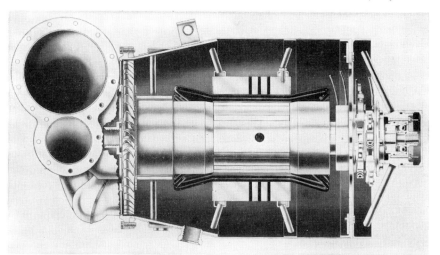

Fig. 4-26. The Turbonator, an example of 1957 state of the art in electromagnetic generator design. This machine develops 40 kva at 24,000 rpm. Including the bleed air turbine, it weighs 96 lb, yielding a specific mass of 1.1 kg/kw. (*General Electric Co.*)

electrical propulsion system, the d-c generator is competitive with the a-c generator plus the requisite rectifiers. The specific masses of both the a-c and d-c generators are fairly constant with power level. Alternators are operating today with specific masses between 0.4 and 1.0 kg/kw (Ref. 4-27). An example of the state of the art is the generator shown in Fig. 4-26. Its specific mass is just over 1 kg/kw including the small gas turbine attached to its shaft. None of today's generators is specifically designed for space operation. It is expected that a development program would reduce the specific masses quoted above by perhaps 30 per cent.

In comparison with the electromagnetic generators, little serious design work has been done on electrostatic machines. The Wimshurst machine and the many electrostatic generators of the Van de Graaff variety are of little use as power generators. These machines were built primarily for high-voltage sources in physics experiments. Still, their characteristics are similar to a practical power generator. Electrostatic generators are primarily high-voltage low-current machines. In general, their minimum voltages are higher than 10,000 volts. Such voltages, however, may have important applications in the design of high specific-impulse ion drives (Chap. 6).

Since electrostatic generators depend upon electrostatic rather than magnetic fields, they will not need heavy windings and magnetic cores. Low specific masses may therefore be expected. A. J. Gale has reported the design of one electrostatic generator with a specific mass of 0.2 kg/kw

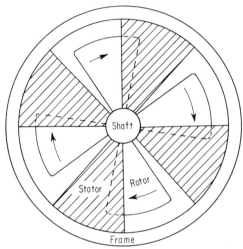

FIG. 4-27. Diagram of an electrostatic generator. Note the similarity to a variable condenser.

at a power level of 100 kw (Ref. 4-9). The machine described runs at 10,000 rpm and has an efficiency of 90 per cent. The specific mass of 0.2 kg/kw may be used over the entire power range.

The most popular configuration for the high-power electrostatic generator is similar to the familiar variable condenser. Figure 4-27 illustrates this type of geometry.

Space propulsion is particularly weak in the design and development of electrostatic power generators. There is little reason to change from electromagnetic to electrostatic generators on the earth's surface; however, the low specific masses of the electrostatic generator will doubtless stimulate its rapid development for use in space.

DIRECT CONVERSION

4-17. Direct Conversion of Heat to Electricity. The possibility of converting heat directly into electrical energy without the employment of rotating machinery is another goal of the engineer. This goal has already been attained many times in many ways, but the efficiencies so far achieved have always been far below those available with conventional rotating machinery. A number of direct-conversion schemes of importance to space flight will be discussed below. There is no typical direct-conversion system; they operate on several diverse principles. In spite of their disappointing past, developments in direct conversion under way today threaten the electrical technology built around the rotating alternator. In special applications, like small satellite power supplies, they are already competitive with rotating machinery, primarily because turbomachinery is very inefficient in the very low power range. See Fig. 4-25. The simplicity and reliability that are expected from these devices promises to make them ideal for use in outer space.

One fact often overlooked in connection with direct-conversion devices is that they eliminate the need for moving parts only in the very small power supplies. Thermal power must still be conveyed from the source to the converter. The waste heat must then be transported to the radiator. Unless this energy can be transferred by radiation or conduction (and this appears possible only for electrical power levels less than 100 kw), the only moving part eliminated from the power supply will be the electrical generator. The heat sources, pumps, compressors, radiators, and control equipment are still needed. The real question is whether the direct-conversion power plants are actually more reliable than conventional power plants, and, for the same state of the art, have lower specific masses. It is a fact that conventional electromechanical conversion equipment is already efficient, reliable, and fairly lightweight. Conventional equipment should not be indiscriminantly replaced by direct-conversion equipment unless true superiorities in specific mass and reliability, under comparable conditions, can be proved. These potential superiorities of direct conversion have not yet been demonstrated.

The great bulk of the direct-conversion systems are limited in the maximum voltage generated per unit. Top voltages are usually less than 1 volt. The weakness of the electronic bonds is the source of the low-voltage characteristic. Consequently, many direct-conversion units must be connected in series to create the voltages needed by space propulsion systems. In the case of ion drives, where upwards of 10,000 volts may be needed, strings of many thousands of units must be arranged in series, with the attendant increases in vulnerability and decreases in reliability.

In the descriptions of the devices that follow, it should be remembered that some of the developments are quite new. Adequate experimental data do not exist in many instances. The specific masses that are given here are approximate and perhaps conservative.

4-18. The Thermionic Converter. The fundamental ideas behind thermionic converters have been known for many years. Yet, it is only recently that serious attempts have been made to employ this concept for the direct conversion of heat into electricity. Substantial programs now exist at the General Electric Company (Refs. 4-39 and 4-41), the Massachusetts Institute of Technology (Ref. 4-13), and the Radio Corporation of America (Ref. 4-15).

In its simplest form, the thermionic converter consists of two metal plates separated by either a vapor or a vacuum. It is shown schematically in Fig. 4-28. Heat is added to one electrode, the cathode, and, if the temperatures are sufficiently high, large numbers of electrons

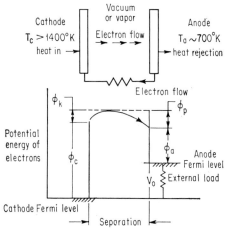

FIG. 4-28. Schematic and potential-energy diagram for the thermionic converter.

will be given sufficient energy to escape from the metal surface. This process is called *thermionic emission*. The emitted electrons would flow to the anode with little hindrance if the electrons themselves did not set up a counteracting space charge between the electrodes. Even the retarding space charge, however, will be overcome by the more energetic electrons. The saturation current of the cathode is given by the Richardson equation,

$$J_c = A T_c^2 \, exp \left(- \frac{\phi_c}{k T_c} \right) \tag{4-3}$$

where J_A = current density

T_c = cathode temperature

ϕ_c = cathode work function

A = constant

k = Boltzmann constant

If the anode is kept much cooler than the cathode, the reverse current will be negligible. A voltage across an external load can be generated by this device if there is a difference in the magnitudes of the cathode and anode work functions. The potential-energy diagram (Fig. 4-28) shows the relationships between the work functions, output voltage, and space charge potential. The highest voltage will be generated when the electrons passing through the space charge impinge on the anode with zero kinetic energy. The maximum voltage, neglecting the initial velocities of the electrons, is just the difference in the work functions. In general,

$$V_0 = \phi_c + \phi_k - \phi_p - \phi_a$$

where V_0 = output voltage

ϕ_k = kinetic energy of the electrons

ϕ_p = plasma drop

ϕ_a = anode work function

The efficiency is given by the ratio of the electrical energy produced to the thermal energy supplied:

$$\text{Efficiency} = \frac{V_0 J_c}{L + R + K + Z + J_c(V_c + 2kT_c/q)} \qquad (4\text{-}4)$$

where L = lead losses

R = radiation losses

K = conduction losses

Z = ionization losses

$2kT_c/q$ = average kinetic energy carried by the electrons emitted from the cathode

Thermodynamically speaking, the thermionic converter is a kind of heat engine. The electrons make up the working fluid. They are boiled off the cathode and condensed on the anode. Heat is added to the electrons at the cathode to boost them over the potential-energy hill shown in Fig. 4-28. When they fall into the anode and pass through the load, useful work is extracted.

One difficulty that must be overcome in the converter is the build-up of space charge between the electrodes. To reduce the effect, we may employ external electric or magnetic fields, an ionized gas between the electrodes, or the electrodes themselves can be moved closer together. The two types of converters receiving the most development effort today are classified by the manner in which they overcome the space-charge problem.

The vacuum type of thermionic converter requires that the electrodes be placed 10 μ or less apart for effective operation. Space-charge effects are greatly reduced and the efficiencies improved by such close spacing. From a mechanical design standpoint, the maintenance of a 10-μ clearance between surfaces imposes an almost intolerable burden on the structures engineer. The small spacing must be retained through vehicle maneuvers and thermal cycling. Figure 4-29 pictures a vacuum-type thermionic converter constructed at the General Electric Research Laboratory.

The second type of thermionic converter uses an easily ionized gas like cesium between the electrodes. The positively charged ions located in the gap between the electrodes counteract the electron space charge. Larger spacings (0.1 cm) are possible here, but cesium corrosion is a problem and cesium ionization losses may be high.

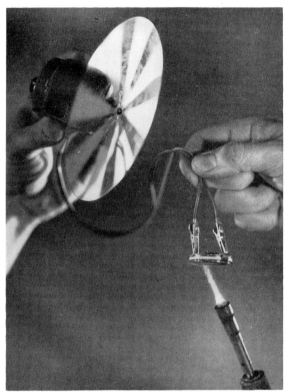

Fig. 4-29. Photograph of a vacuum type of thermionic converter. (*General Electric Co.*)

Figure 4-30 illustrates how thermionic converters may be incorporated in a power supply. They may be used directly in a nuclear reactor, in contact with radioisotope fuel, or any of the heat sources mentioned earlier. The heat sink may be space itself, through radiation, or a heat-transfer fluid. Figure 4-30 shows the thermionic converter used as a topping device in conjunction with a Rankine cycle.

The strong dependence of the cathode saturation current on temperature makes it desirable to operate the cathode at very high temperatures. A limit is reached only when the evaporation of the cathode material is so great that it compromises the lifetime of the element. The temperatures shown in Fig. 4-28 are typical.

While still in the laboratory stage, thermionic converters have operated at efficiencies up to 15 per cent. Output voltages are generally less than 1 volt. Power densities of 10 watts/cm² have been obtained with the cesium vapor converters. With such empircal data, specific masses of 10 kg/kw, including electrodes, structure, leads, are predicted. This

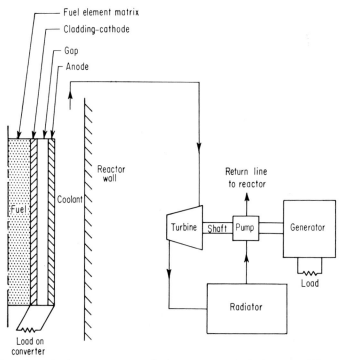

Fig. 4-30. A thermionic converter attached to a reactor fuel element. The converter is being used as a topping device in the illustration, since the fluid at its heat sink may be used to drive electromechanical conversion equipment.

specific mass would be relatively constant with power level. As time progresses, improvements in the state of the art should reduce the specific mass to about 2.0 kg/kw. Thermionic converters may eventually be competitive with conventional generators. At the present time, they have not been developed to the same state of perfection as conventional generators and have higher specific masses.

4-19. Thermoelectric Generators. The thermoelectric generator has been in common use for many years in the form of thermocouples. It has not, however, been used to produce significant quantities of electrical power. Like the thermionic converter, it has the potential for producing sizable quantities of power with a minimum of moving parts.

The thermoelectric generator depends on the Seebeck effect. When two junctions between dissimilar materials are maintained at different temperatures, an electromotive force will be set up. In the illustration (Fig. 4-31), zinc antimonide and constantan form the junctions. They are connected thermally and electrically by copper blocks. The copper pieces do not affect the thermoelectric behavior of the junctions. Semiconductor materials, like germanium and selenium, perform somewhat better than the materials shown in the diagram. The thermal efficiencies

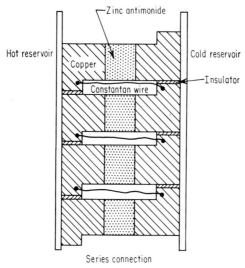

FIG. 4-31. A compact method of arranging thermoelectric elements in series.

obtained by the common metallic junctions are generally less than 1 per cent. Semiconductors may yield efficiencies approaching 6 per cent. Some of the mixed valence oxides promise even higher values. Westinghouse has reported efficiencies of 8 per cent, with 25 per cent potentially possible (Ref. 4-43).

Like most other direct-conversion devices, the voltages and currents attainable with a single thermoelectric element are very small. The voltage generated by a thermoelectric element is directly proportional to the temperature difference. This aspect of performance is measured by the thermoelectric-power coefficient, which generally varies between 10 and 1000 $\mu v/°K$. Large series-parallel arrays must be built up to produce the voltages and power levels required by space propulsion systems. The arrangement of elements shown in Fig. 4-31 shows one practical method of making the many necessary interconnections. With the recent advances in the state of the art, it is possible to build thermoelectric generators with specific masses of about 10 kg/kw for the elements alone; 2.0 kg/kw may be possible in the future.   Even with the projected improvements, the thermoelectric generator is not competitive with the rotating generator on a specific mass basis.

The greatest drawback of the thermoelectric generator is the deterioration of performance with high temperatures.   The upper temperature limit for the more promising materials (semiconductors and mixed valence oxides) is around 500°K.   The cold junction temperatures would be considerably less in a realistic power supply.   This low temperature for heat rejection will impose high radiator specific masses whether the waste heat is radiated from a separate radiator or the elements themselves.

Assuming that nuclear radiation does not adversely affect the thermoelectric generator, it seems logical to put the units directly in the heat source.   Figure 4-31 shows an arrangement suitable for placement in a reactor.   Hot fluid would bathe one side of the array and radiator discharge fluid the other.   Radioisotopes and chemicals might be used as heat sources in a similar fashion.

In addition to the temperature problems, junction bonding, thermal expansion, nuclear-radiation effects, all impose difficult development problems.   The low sink temperatures and efficiencies will probably limit the application of thermoelectric generators in outer space.

4-20. Fuel Cells.   In contrast to the thermionic converter and the thermoelectric generator, which convert heat into electricity through electronic phenomena, the fuel cell converts the energy stored in chemical fuels to electricity through oxidation and reduction reactions at electrode surfaces.   A typical fuel cell is the hydrogen-oxygen variety shown in Fig. 4-32.   Here hydrogen and oxygen, under pressures between 40 and 50 atm, are introduced into porous nickel electrodes immersed in a 180°C potassium hydroxide solution.   The following reactions take place at the electrodes:

Anode: $4OH^- + 2H_2 \rightarrow 4H_2O + 4e^-$
Cathode: $O_2 + 2H_2O + 4e^- \rightarrow 4OH^-$

The electrons flow through the external circuit, and the negative ions move through the electrolyte.   The action is thus very similar to that in an ordinary chemical battery.

A great variety of possible chemicals may be used as fuels.   One popular combination is hydrogen and iodine; another, hydrogen and fluorine.

Typical fuel cells produce about 1 volt.   With the hydrogen-oxygen cell (Bacon cell), one can expect about 0.8 volt and approximately 0.4 amp/cm² of electrode surface.   Huth (Ref. 4-16) has reported a Bacon cell that is 61 per cent efficient, and which has a specific mass of 5.4 kg/kw at a power level of 30 kw. At 1 kw, the specific mass of the same cell is increased to 9.2 kg/kw. Further development work may reduce this performance parameter to more acceptable values, but there appears to be little possibility of making the fuel cell into a competitive piece of conversion equipment for space use. Although the efficiencies of energy conversion are high, it must be remembered that fuel cells consume chemical rather than nuclear fuel. Thus, the source specific masses are also high for most missions. One novel way of surmounting the fuel problem is to recycle the chemical fuel through a nuclear reactor and permit the nuclear radiation to dissociate the burned (recombined) fuel into its original components. The HI fuel cell might be used in this

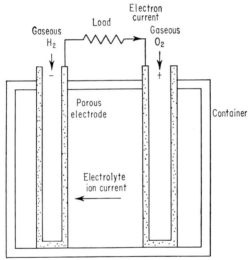

Fig. 4-32. The hydrogen-oxygen fuel cell. The hydroxyl ion carries the charge in the KOH aqueous electrolyte.

manner, although it is an inefficient way in which to use nuclear power since most of the nuclear energy appears immediately in the form of heat rather than radiation. Thermal regeneration is also possible with HI fuel cells. There are no immediate improvements on the horizon which will make the fuel cell into a conversion unit which can approach the performance of the turbogenerator for space applications.

4-21. Chemical Batteries. Chemical batteries combine the energy source and conversion equipment into a single package. The chemicals form the fuel, and the electrodes and electrolyte make up the conversion mechanism. The operation of these components is well understood and exhaustive descriptions are available in the literature.

In space operations, batteries will have important short-time applications like any other chemical system. Indeed, batteries have been used extensively on the first American and Russian satellites. For low power levels (less than 1 kw) and short periods of time (less than 100 hours), they represent a ready solution to the problem of providing electrical energy in space. Figure 4-33 summarizes the performance of two of the best battery types. The specific masses shown represent the combined source and conversion equipment.

4-22. Solar Cells. There are several ways in which the energy of sunlight may be turned into electrical energy directly. Perhaps the most familiar is the photoelectric cell. This type, however, is not a very

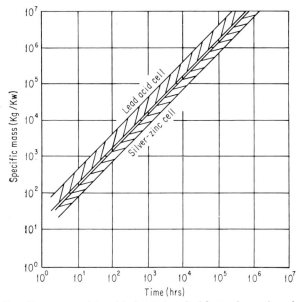

FIG. 4-33. Specific masses of two kinds of chemical batteries as functions of time.

promising space power supply component because its efficiency is usually under 1 per cent. Much more attractive for space use is the solar battery, which is an outgrowth of semiconductor development at Bell Telephone Laboratories. The present discussion will be confined to this type of conversion unit.

The basic material in the contemporary solar cell is silicon. Each silicon atom has four valence electrons. When light quanta fall on the surface of the silicon cell and are absorbed, their energies may be transferred to the valence electrons, knocking them out of their positions in the silicon crystal structure. The ejected electrons and holes left behind (which act like positive charges) are free to diffuse through the crystal. In the simple situation just described, voltages and currents would not be generated. Under a constant flux of photons, an equilibrium population of free electrons and holes would build up with no net generation of electrical power.

The key step in making a solar battery is the addition of impurities. If boron, with three valence electrons, is added to one portion of the crystal, and arsenic, with five valence electrons, is added to the remainder, conditions are created whereby electrical power may be produced through the action of sunlight. The arsenic-doped silicon forms the n layer

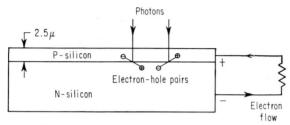

FIG. 4-34. Schematic diagram of a silicon solar cell. The photons create electron-hole pairs which diffuse across the junction under the influence of the electric field established by the n and p layers.

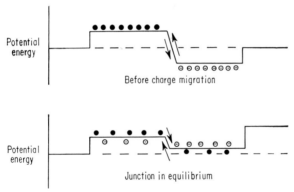

FIG. 4-35. Potential-energy diagram showing the operation of the solar cell. The solid circles represent positive charges.

(excess of negative electrons), and the boron-doped portion makes up the p layer (positive). In contact, the two regions form the p-n junction shown in Fig. 4-34.

Once in contact, the holes want to diffuse into the n region and the free electrons into the p region. Eventually, an equilibrium situation is created (Fig. 4-35), and an electrical potential difference will exist between the two regions. When photons are absorbed near the junction and generate electron-hole pairs, the positive and negative charges move under the influence of the field and cause current to flow in an external circuit.

A practical solar cell comprises a thin layer of p silicon about 2.5 μ thick overlaying a more massive piece of n silicon. The positive terminal is fixed to the p side and the negative terminal to the n side. Solar quanta are admitted to the *sandwich* through the thin p layer and penetrate to the region of the junction. Highest efficiencies are obtained when the photons are absorbed in the vicinity of the junction. This fact affects the choice of the p layer thickness. With such cells, voltages between 0.5 and 1.0 volts and power densities of 200 watts/m^2 can be obtained. The latter figure corresponds to an over-all efficiency of 14 per cent. Actually, only half of the photons in sunlight are energetic enough to create a hole-electron pair. Ohmic, recombination, and reflection losses make up the remaining inefficiencies. Theoretically, it is conceivable that 22 per cent efficiency might be obtained, but practical considerations have kept this down to between 10 and 14 per cent (Ref. 4-24).

For use in space, the p-n junction array would be mounted on some sort of collector (Sec. 4-9). A propulsion system would probably be required to keep this large surface directed toward the sun. Waste energy is rejected by radiation from both the cold and hot sides. Cell temperatures in the vicinity of the earth would be about 100°C at equilibrium. The abrasive action of meteorites and the sputtering effects of atomic particles will affect the cell in two ways. First, the reflectivity of the surface will be increased as it becomes roughened. Second, the thin p layer, 2.5 μ thick, will be abraded away. Referring to Sections 3-4 and 3-5, the erosion and sputtering rates may be high enough to remove the p layer in a year. A layer of clear plastic might be used to protect the junction surface, but its transmission properties might also be adversely affected by the space environment. With the present data, it is impossible to accurately estimate the useful life of unprotected solar cells. It is probably on the order of one year.

Specific masses for solar cells, including all wiring and supporting gridwork, run about 50 kg/kw. Of course, this integrates the source and conversion equipment masses, but the solar cell is still not competitive at high power levels. The place of the solar cell in space power production is at the low power end of the spectrum for periods up to a year. A further disadvantage of the solar cell is its high cost, $30 per watt. This fact emphasizes its relegation to the low power range.

HEAT REJECTION IN OUTER SPACE

4-23. Heat Disposal. Radiation of waste heat to space is generally the only method of heat rejection considered in the design of space power packs. For short-time applications, however, there are two other possibilities. The first is particle emission, where the energy to be rejected is expelled in the form of particle kinetic energy. In a propulsion system, part of the generated energy is normally rejected in this form and does work on the vehicle in the process. The rejection of waste heat as kinetic energy at the lowest temperature in the thermodynamic cycle would infer unacceptable specific impulses since the expulsion of all mass from the spaceship must be charged against specific impulse. Actually, such a power plant would be of the open-cycle type and inappropriate in space except for short missions. The second possibility is that of energy storage. If, at the lowest temperature in the system, it is possible to change the phase of some material, it is theoretically attractive to store the waste heat as the heat required for the phase change. Ordinary water can handle 2,200 kw-sec/kg when vaporized. Graphite is even better: 61,000 kw-sec/kg during sublimation. Here again extra mass must be carried along to absorb the waste energy and, in both methods, the performance of the power supply or propulsion unit is thus penalized. In a pulsed propulsion system, however, a significant specific mass advantage can be obtained in this fashion. Energy may also be stored in the heats of fusion or vaporization on a satellite with a solar power plant for use during the period spent in the earth's shadow.

For the great bulk of the space power supplies, waste heat will be rejected in the form of electromagnetic energy. The design of the radiator needed to perform this task is one of the central problems in all of space propulsion. Every power supply rejects heat; none is 100 per cent efficient. In some manner, the heat rejected from the thermodynamic cycle must be converted into electromagnetic radiation and emitted from the vehicle.

4-24. The Temperature Problem. If the radiator is to be of reasonable size and mass, the effective temperature of its surface must be high. The effective temperature T_{eff} is defined in the following way

$$T_{eff} = \left(\frac{\Delta Q + e \sigma A T_0{}^4}{e \sigma A} \right)^{1/4} \tag{4-5}$$

where ΔQ = amount of heat rejected
e = emissivity
σ = Stefan-Boltzmann constant
A = area
T_0 = sink temperature

When a vapor cycle is used, T_{eff} is close to the condensation temperature. In gas cycles, the large radiator areas needed to cool the gas down to the comparatively low compressor inlet temperatures force T_{eff} to low values.

Figure 4-36 shows the strong influence that the effective radiator temperature has upon the area needed to reject a given quantity of heat. An

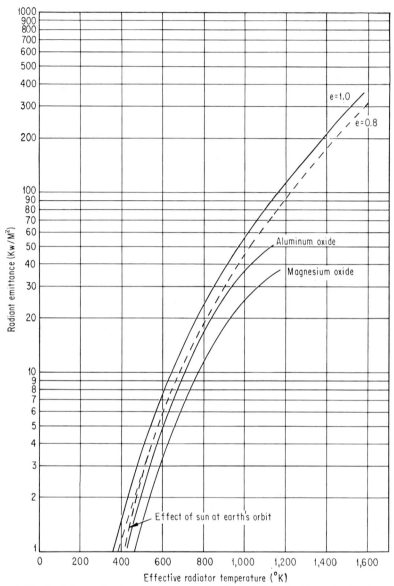

Fig. 4-36. Radiator radiant emittance as a function of the effective radiator temperature. The effects on performance of the varying emissivity of two possible radiator coatings are shown.

interesting point, also apparent from Fig. 4-36, is that T_{eff} need be only a little greater than T_0 before the effects of the sunlight and its reradiation from the earth become unimportant. The emissivity of the radiator surface will vary with temperature and, at high temperatures, may be so low that the radiator performance begins to be compromised. This effect is shown for several radiator surface coatings in Fig. 4-36.

It is often suggested that radiators can be oriented away from the sun or painted with selective white paint to reduce the effects of the environment. Both of these things can be done, but a look at Fig. 4-36 convinces one that a high-performance space power supply is going to operate at such high effective temperatures that these stratagems will probably be unnecessary. In the case of radiator orientation, the price paid in propulsion power for the orientation may be high unless sunlight itself can be used to provide the stabilizing forces. Selective white paint is always a possibility provided it is not seriously affected by cosmic-dust bombardment or ultraviolet radiation (see Sec. 4-9). All results presented in this book will ignore these two possibilities as being irrelevant to high-performance space radiators.

The actual temperature of the radiator surface will differ from the fluid temperature by the film and tube wall temperature drops. These temperature differences may be anywhere from 1 to 100°K depending upon the conditions. Even with liquid-metal vapor condensation, the heat transfer may be impeded by nonwetting fluids and vapor layers. All performance calculations in this chapter are optimistic in that they assume the radiator temperature to be the same as the fluid temperature.

4-25. Physical Construction. The radiator surface will be either a structure containing a circulating working fluid, or it will be the matrix made up of the cold junctions of direct-conversion devices. In any case, a decision must be made as to the geometric form of the surface. Is it to be flat, cylindrical, or spherical? At this point, it should be recalled that, for large power supplies, the radiator surface will have to be launched into space in pieces or in some collapsible form. While the assembly in space of a large radiator matrix may be feasible in the distant future, it does not yet seem advisable to utilize radiators employing circulating fluids which necessitate sliding or rotating joints, or assemblies requiring the making of more than a few leak-tight joints.

The flat-sheet type of radiator is probably the best configuration for space use. There is little interference between different parts of the surfaces, and maximum use is thus made of all the area. Multiple-wing types and cylindrical radiators create serious interference. In complex designs, the effective area of the radiator is just that area formed by a fictitious surface wrapped around the assembly in the fashion shown in Fig. 4-37.

For power supplies using heat-transfer fluids, the radiator will probably be composed of tube sheets. The geometry of the tubes would have to be tailored to the specific application. If the tube walls are thin enough, it may be practical to wrap the whole radiator tube sheet about a cylindrical vehicle body for the launching maneuver. Once in space, the sheets could be released to snap back into position elastically. The launching missile hull may also be used as a tube sheet.

If the radiator is a condenser for the working fluid, then an artificial force field may have to be imposed to drain the fluid condensate from the tubes. A centrifugal field created by vehicle rotation could do this. There is also some merit in the idea that the radiator tubes could be made smaller in cross section as the cold end is approached. By thus constricting the flow area, the pressure differential across the radiator would

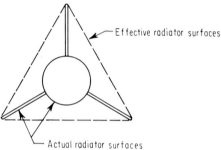

Fig. 4-37. Radiator self-interference effects may be roughly calculated by the use of a hypothetical radiator surface shown with dotted lines.

force the condensate through. An increase in pumping power would be required to accomplish this.

One last design aspect of the radiator concerns the reduction of the cross-sectional surface area which is vulnerable to meteoroid penetration. The sensitive area can be reduced by finning and increasing the webbing between tubes. In this way, the vulnerable area, containing fluid, may be augmented by metallic heat conduction. The ratio of vulnerable to total area may be made as low as 0.25. Figure 4-38 illustrates a typical finned tube sheet for a space radiator.

4-26. Meteoroid Punctures. Above 100 kw, electrical, the radiator is the heaviest component of any power supply using a working fluid (Fig. 4-42). The crux of the radiator problem is in the balancing of acceptable specific mass with allowable vulnerability. These two factors are reciprocally related: the higher the permissible vulnerability, the lower the specific mass that may be attained.

The probability of meteoroid puncture of surfaces in space was treated in Chap. 3. Figure 3-2 summarizes the best available data on the puncture probabilities for stainless steel. By combining Figs. 3-2 and 4-36 and assuming the fluid temperature to be the same as the radiator surface temperature, specific mass curves (Fig. 4-39) which are functions of temperature and meteoroid vulnerability may be generated.   In this instance, the power supply vulnerability is measured by the total number of penetrations per unit of energy rejected.   This definition is debatable, but does give a parameter which includes mission duration as well as power level.   It is evident that the rate at which working fluid is lost and the number of radiator valves employed will be proportional to the number of penetrations per kilowatthour.   Low-temperature radiators are doubly penalized by defining vulnerability in terms of total number of penetrations rather than the number per unit area, since thicker walls as well as larger areas are required for fixed vulnerability and power rejection.

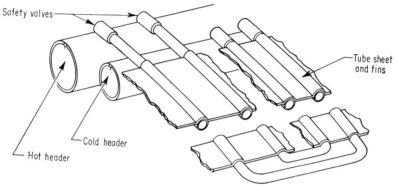

FIG. 4-38. The use of radiator finning greatly reduces the system meteoroid vulnerability for small increases in specific mass.

The specific mass implications of Fig. 4-39 leave little room for optimism in the design of lightweight space radiators for high power levels. The meteoroid problem is far from solved.   Radiator penetrations will occur regardless of the wall thicknesses used.   It is only a matter of the frequency of occurrence.   There are, however, a number of active and passive techniques which may be employed to design a space radiator to the desired vulnerability and specific mass.   A few of these possibilities follow:

1. We may accept the higher specific masses and reduced performance of the spaceship and use thicker radiator walls.

2. An attempt may be made to orient the edges of the radiator (or minimum cross section) toward the strongest meteoroid flux, assuming the flux is anisotropic.

3. In the case of earth satellites, a low-altitude orbit placing the vehicle in the wake of the earth as long as possible will reduce the penetration frequencies by almost one-half.   This effect is included in Fig. 4-39.

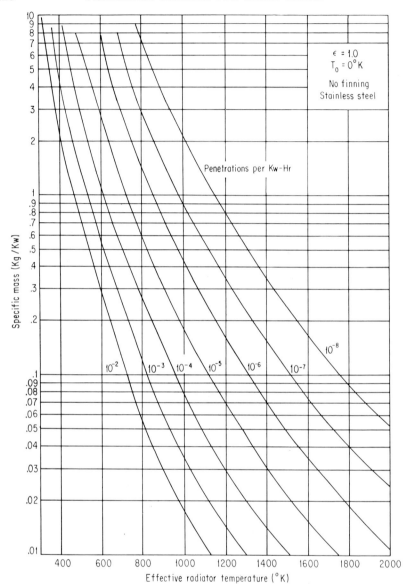

FIG. 4-39. Radiator specific mass as a function of effective radiator temperature for different numbers of penetrations per unit of energy radiated.

4. Working fluids and radiator temperatures may be varied to reduce the radiator area.   Compromises in the lifetimes of the other equipment may have to be made.

5. Meteoroid bumpers may prove valuable in certain cases.   These are thin sheets of metal or plastic which are just thick enough (about

equal to the diameter of the most frequent meteoroids) to shatter the meteoroid into ineffectual fragments. The bumpers are liable to place a high impedance in the heat-transfer system. Their value is uncertain.

6. System vulnerability can be drastically reduced by valving individual tubes or sections of tubes. Here the additional specific mass must be balanced against the lessened vulnerability.

7. Last, the inevitability of losing some of the working fluid may be admitted and a make-up supply provided.

In any real design, all the techniques mentioned above would be employed simultaneously. The design of the most effective combinations will have to wait until actual operating experience in space is available. It does appear, though, that the radiator problem is merely one of making the usual engineering compromises and is amenable to some sort of solution. The initial solutions, however, are destined to be exceedingly heavy and awkward.

The large advantage of the metallic-vapor cycle over the inert-gas systems becomes apparent in the radiator design. The condensation of vapor at a high constant temperature in conjunction with the low compressor inlet temperatures needed by the gas cycle push the gas cycle specific masses far above those of the vapor cycle at power levels over 100 kw, electrical. The summary curves, especially Fig. 4-41, show this clearly.

The direct-conversion units, using electrons as the working fluid, offer an eventual solution to the meteoroid penetration problem if their other difficulties can be overcome. If radiation or conduction can be used as the sole heat-transfer agents, then another avenue of exploration will open up. The field of space power is in its infancy; we can expect the relatively unattractive specific masses of today to be bettered significantly during the next decade.

SYNTHESIS AND EVALUATION

4-27. Intercomparison of Power Supplies. In this chapter, several different energy sources, various types of conversion equipment, and the space radiator have been examined. The objective has been to compile power-plant specific mass data as a function of power level, mission duration, vulnerability, and state of the art so that adequate estimates of performance could be made for the space propulsion systems to be described in the subsequent pages. In concluding this chapter on power generation in space, the performance of the space power supplies will be summarized. As in the previous analyses, the figure of merit used is the specific mass.

In Fig. 4-40, the capabilities of the most promising heat sources are recapitulated. 1965 state of the art has been assumed. The nuclear sources are unshielded. It is apparent from this set of graphs that nuclear reactors are the only candidates for the high power range (over 1 Mw thermal) long-term operation. For lower power levels and shorter periods of time, there are many potential sources. Batteries and chemicals have many advantages for a few hours of operation. Solar power and radioisotopes may be used to supply small amounts of heat for long missions.

The approximate performances of the many various types of conversion equipment are tabulated in Table 4-9. The ranges of specific mass

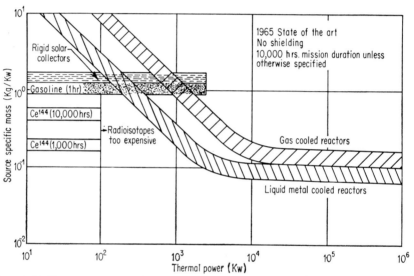

FIG. 4-40. Summary curves for source specific masses. The nuclear-fission reactor is applicable over the whole power range but is most attractive beyond 1 Mw of thermal power.

emphasize the approximate nature of the numbers shown. One striking fact emerges: all the varieties of direct-conversion equipment possess specific masses that are higher than those of the conventional rotating machinery. The final choice of conversion equipment, however, should bring in factors other than specific mass. Qualitative factors like simplicity, state of the art, and reliability must be employed to accurately evaluate the situation. Certainly, for very small power supplies (under 1 kw, electrical), direct conversion may be useful and applicable since the conversion equipment is almost negligible from a specific mass standpoint. Over 100 kw, conventional rotating machinery is almost always preferable.

TABLE 4-9. PERFORMANCE OF CONVERSION EQUIPMENT

Type of conversion equipment	Projected $M_{sp}(1965)$	Projected efficiency*	Remarks
Turbomachinery	0.3–0.5	50–85%	Efficiencies are much lower below 10 kw
Electromagnetic generator	0.4–1.0	80–95%	
Electrostatic generator	0.2–0.8	90–98%	High-voltage applications only
Thermoelectric units	5–10	1–10%	Limited by low-allowable operating temperatures
Thermionic converters	2–10	5–15%	Fabrication problems
Fuel cells	10–20	50–70%	High fuel specific mass
Solar cells	40–60	5–15%	Meteoroid effects uncertain

* Component efficiency, not overall power plant efficiency.

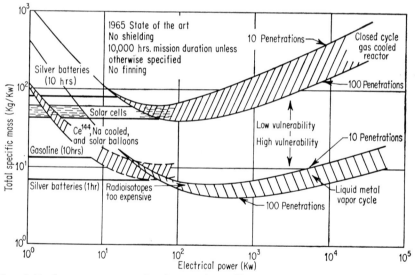

FIG. 4-41. Summary curves showing total specific masses of electrical space power supplies as functions of electrical power level. The nuclear-power sources are plotted for two different vulnerabilities. Radioisotopes are limited to 10 kw electrical and below as indicated by the dotted lines and arrow. Nuclear vapor cycles appear best beyond 100 kw electrical.

The heat sink is the final component in the power supply. Figure 4-39 summarizes the performance of heat radiators, the only type of heat sink that is practical for the overwhelming majority of space applications.

The key illustration in Chap. 4 is Fig. 4-41. It summarizes the specific masses of all space power supplies discussed as functions of the electrical power output. Components are integrated into complete systems.

Again, we see that chemicals and batteries have short-time applications. Solar cells are appropriate for electrical power levels under 10 kw. Radioisotopes are superior to nuclear-fission heat sources below 10 kw. The cost factor for the radioisotopes, which presently restricts them to small-scale power supplies, is indicated by the dotted lines beyond 10 kw. Solar collectors appear attractive below 100 kw but are heavier than nuclear power supplies above this level. Beyond 100 kw, nuclear energy is generally superior to all other power sources. Among the possible nuclear systems, the liquid-metal vapor cycle is clearly superior to the

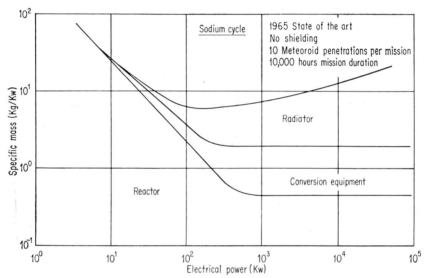

Fig. 4-42. Specific mass breakdown for the components of a sodium-vapor-cycle power plant. The reactor is dominant at low power levels, the radiator at high power levels.

closed gas cycle on a specific mass basis for the state of the art being considered in Fig. 4-41. The gas-cooled reactor is heavier at low power levels, while the gas cycle radiator is more massive than the vapor cycle counterpart at high powers. Although simplicity and reliability must enter into any choice and state-of-the-art improvements may narrow the gap, Fig. 4-41 unequivocally demonstrates that the Brayton cycle is inferior to the Rankine cycle in space power plants.

To further illustrate the differences between the gas and vapor cycles, Figs. 4-42 and 4-43 show how the total system specific masses may be differentiated into the contributions of the various components. Below 100 kw, the reactor is the most influential component; the addition of shielding would accentuate this fact as well as increase the gap between the gas and vapor cycles. Above 1 Mw, the radiator is dominant. A most important observation is that the rotating conversion equipment used in Fig. 4-41 is a relatively small contributor to the over-all specific mass at all power levels.   Direct-conversion devices, on the other hand, would dominate the system specific mass in the 100 kw range.   The vapor conversion equipment is seen to be somewhat heavier than the corresponding gas equipment due to the higher weights of fluid inventory, generator cooling loops, and seals.   The gas cycle radiators are many times heavier than the Rankine cycle condenser at a given power level for the temperature selected.

4-28. Final Evaluation.   Many of the propulsion systems treated in the following chapters depend upon electrical power for the acceleration

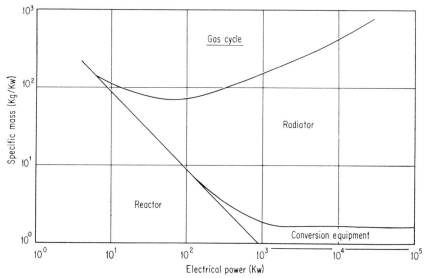

Fig. 4-43. Specific mass breakdown for the components of an inert-gas-cycle power plant.

of the working fluid.   Consequently, a great deal of space has been allocated to the subject of electrical power.   Power production, whether it be electrical or thermal, is the central problem of all space propulsion. The preceding sections describing power sources and conversion will be very useful in the forthcoming discussions of unusual modes of propulsion.

Although there are many types of useful power sources below 100 kw, space propulsion itself will generally demand power levels in the mega-watt range.   A review of mission energy increments in Chap. 2 will emphasize the necessity for high power levels.   For real space travel, only nuclear power stands out as the ultimate desirable source of energy. To be sure, chemical energy must play an important role until nuclear power is better understood, but a major conclusion derived from this chapter is that the nuclear reaction will be the ultimate source of energy for space propulsion.

CHAPTER 5

THERMAL PROPULSION SYSTEMS

5-1. Principles of Thermal Propulsion Systems. Every jet plane that streaks across the sky and each rocket that reaches toward outer space utilizes a *thermal engine*.* In some manner, the thermal engine must take the heat liberated by exothermic chemical or nuclear reactions and convert it into the kinetic and potential energies of the space vehicle. Although this book will also treat the so-called *exotic* or *nonthermal* varieties of space engines, it is clearly ordained that heat engines, which depend upon the thermal acceleration of matter, will be the prime movers in outer space for many years to come. Ion, photon, and plasma engines will be studied and built, but the chemical and nuclear thermal rockets will be the dominant propulsion systems in space during this century.

The typical thermal engine is simplicity itself. Perhaps this fact is a major reason for its continued success. The thermal space propulsion systems discussed in this chapter are all open-cycle heat engines. Heat, from chemical, nuclear, or even electrical sources, is added to a working fluid which is then expanded through a nozzle to generate vehicle thrust. Turbojets, recombination ram jets, nuclear rockets, and plasma jets are all examples of thermal engines. While the applications of the chemical rocket in satellite and probe launchings are well known, the probable uses of the other thermal engines just mentioned are not completely understood. This chapter will examine the following major types of thermal space engines and attempt to fix their positions in the space-engine spectrum: (1) air-breathing, turbojet boosters, (2) chemical rockets, (3) recombination ram jets, (4) nuclear rockets, (5) thermonuclear rockets, (6) plasma jets. Many variations of these basic types are possible. Several of these will be treated in the subsequent pages.

The critical process in the operation of a thermal engine occurs when the heat is transferred from the power source to the working fluid. If this function takes place in the presence of solid structural materials (burners, combustion chamber walls, fuel elements), then the maximum obtainable temperatures in the working fluid will be limited by the material properties of the solid structures. With such temperature limitations,

---

* See Glossary of Terms at the back of the book.

restrictions on the maximum obtainable specific impulses will also occur. The properties of materials thus place a ceiling on the propulsion-system performance when conventional-heat-transfer techniques are employed.

How may thermal energy be transferred to the working fluid without the temperature constraints imposed by solid substances? The ion drive (Chap. 6) uses electrostatic fields to suspend the beam of energetic particles and keep it isolated from the engine's solid structure, but it is not a thermal engine since it relies on electrical forces for mass acceleration. Still, a clue is inherent in this concept. If the heat-transfer process can be consummated in a region that is thermally isolated from solid materials, the way to high specific-impulse thermal engines will be open. Several intriguing methods for accomplishing this have been proposed. The basic techniques are listed in Table 5-1. Each entry in this table poses tremendous technical challenges. How well these challenges have been met and what the implications are for space flight are the subjects of this chapter.

TABLE 5-1. METHODS OF ISOLATING THE HEAT-TRANSFER PROCESS IN THERMAL SPACE ENGINES

Type of isolation	Example	Limitations
Solid materials.............	Nuclear-rocket fuel elements	Melting of solids
Fluid vortex..............	Plasma jet	Radiation to walls, nozzle erosion
Electromagnetic fields......	Plasma-core nuclear rocket	Radiation to walls, heavy electrical equipment
Distance.................	Nuclear-bomb propulsion	High accelerations, waste of nuclear fuel, spread of radioactivity
None....................	Completely consumable nuclear rockets	Waste of nuclear fuel, spread of radioactivity

Regardless of the method used in isolating the reaction zone from the solid structure, there will still be heat leaking to the structure via nuclear and thermal radiation, conduction, and convection. The impetus to find better high-temperature materials will always be pertinent to the design of space propulsion systems. Just as materials and heat-transfer technologies are basic to the design of contemporary chemical rockets, they will be also vital to the thermonuclear engines 50 years hence. Although ways have been found to partially circumvent the temperature problem in space engines, the development of new materials for use at high temperature will have great impact in the design of new propulsion systems.

Once the working fluid has been heated to the highest possible temperatures, it is customarily expanded through a nozzle, either solid or magnetic, and expelled to the environment. The nozzle is the heat engine which converts the heat power to vehicle motion. The thermal jet is its own radiator. This fact gives the thermal engine an important advantage over electrical space engines in its reduced vulnerability to meteoroids. How much thrust and what specific impulses may be expected from such a propulsion system? To answer these queries, let us first examine the thermodynamic principles underlying the operation of thermal engines and then place each of the major engine types under scrutiny to determine its place in space flight.

5-2. Thermodynamics of Thermal Engines. The common denominator of all thermal engines is the thermodynamic cycle. In the electrical propulsion systems, the propulsion unit is separated from the cycle

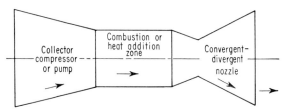

FIG. 5-1. Schematic drawing of a thermal engine.

by the electrical conversion equipment. In thermal engines, the heat source, the cycle, and the energy conversion equipment (the nozzle) are not so easily dissected. The generalized space-propulsion system (Fig. 1-1) can be specialized for thermal engines to the schematic shown in Fig. 5-1. The thermodynamic description of the working fluid as it progresses from the pump, through the heater, and out the nozzle is almost identical for all thermal engines.

During the operation of a thermal propulsion system, the working fluid is admitted to the engine from the environment or from storage tanks. It is pressurized and fed into the heat source. Heat is added at approximately constant pressure, and the hot working fluid is allowed to expand isentropically through the nozzle. Typically, the fluid velocity preceding the nozzle throat is subsonic and becomes supersonic in the divergent portion of the nozzle as shown in Fig. 5-2. The most common type of nozzle is the De Laval variety also shown in Fig. 5-2. When the gas is expanded to precisely the environmental pressure, optimum expansion is said to prevail. This ideal state of affairs rarely exists. Numerous factors like friction losses in the nozzle, nozzle divergence, and energy loss through radiation also detract from perfect performance. Texts on rockets and jet engines should be consulted for a more detailed discussion of these factors (Refs. 1-16 and 5-22).*

The basic equations describing the above processes are given below. From the law of conservation of energy

$$c_p(T_1 - T_2) = \frac{v_2{}^2 - v_1{}^2}{2}$$ (5-1)

where c_p = specific heat at constant pressure†
$\quad T$ = temperature
$\quad v$ = gas velocity

The subscripts refer to the stations shown in Fig. 5-2. Equation (5-1)

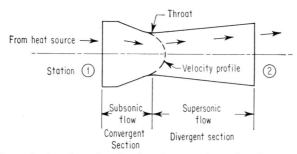

FIG. 5-2. Schematic drawing of a De Laval type of nozzle. It converts thermal energy into thrust.

applies to perfect gases being expanded through a nozzle with no heat loss or addition. For the isentropic flow process in the nozzle

$$\frac{T_1}{T_2} = \left(\frac{p_1}{p_2}\right)^{(\gamma-1)/\gamma}$$ (5-2)

where p = pressure. Since $c_p - c_v = R/M$, where R = the universal gas constant, M = the average molecular weight of the gas, and $\gamma = c_p/c_v$,

$$c_p = \frac{1,000\gamma R}{(\gamma - 1)M}$$ (5-3)

Combining the preceding equations, we arrive at an expression for the fluid velocity at Station (2):

$$v_2{}^2 = \frac{2,000\gamma R T_1}{(\gamma - 1)M}\left[1 - \left(\frac{p_2}{p_1}\right)^{(\gamma-1)/\gamma}\right] + v_1{}^2$$ (5-4)

Since v_1 may be neglected in most rockets, Eq. (5-4) may be written as

$$v_2 = \left\{\frac{2,000\gamma R T_1}{(\gamma - 1)M}\left[1 - \left(\frac{p_2}{p_1}\right)^{(\gamma-1)/\gamma}\right]\right\}^{\frac{1}{2}}$$ (5-5)

* For references see Bibliography at the back of the book.
† See Table of Symbols at the back of the book.

The dependence of v_2 upon the ratio $\sqrt{T_1/M}$ has important implications in the performance of thermal engines. Everything possible must be done to increase the temperature of the working fluid as well as reduce its average molecular weight. The effects of varying T_1 and M are illustrated in Fig. 5-3, where the specific impulse, which is related to v_2 through the relation $I_{sp} = v_2/g_0$, is plotted as a function of T_1.

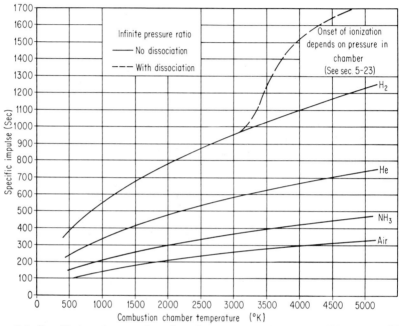

Fig. 5-3. Specific impulse as a function of temperature for several different working fluids. Note the effect of hydrogen dissociation at higher temperatures. Calculated from Eq. (5-5) for an infinite pressure ratio. See Fig. 5-19.

Except for the environmental thermal engines, where the momentum of the fluid taken aboard the vehicle must be included, the engine thrust in the vacuum of outer space is calculated from

$$F = \dot{m}v_2$$

With this brief introduction to the thermodynamics of heat engines, we conclude this generalized discussion. Next, some specific thermal propulsion systems which have applications in space flight will be reviewed.

AIR-BREATHING BOOSTERS

5-3. A New Application for the Turbojet Engine. The air-breathing turbojet engine is familiar to everyone. Since World War II, it has been employed in ever-increasing numbers in high-speed military and civilian aircraft.

The theory of turbojet operation, like that of the rocket, is simple in concept. Air, collected from the environment by an intake scoop, is first compressed by an axial compressor and fed into chemical combustor chambers where it is mixed with a low-grade hydrocarbon fuel (JP-4) and burned. The heated gases are next expanded through an axial turbine and nozzle. The turbine drives the compressor, and the expansion in the nozzle generates thrust on the aircraft. The components of the turbojet are shown in the cutaway view of the J-47 engine (Fig. 5-4).

A less familiar fact about the turbojet engine concerns its potential application to space flight. Since it requires air for its operation, its

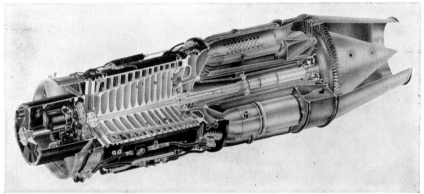

Fig. 5-4. A cut-away view of the J-47 turbojet engine. From left to right: axial compressor, chemical combustors, turbine, and nozzle. (*General Electric Co.*)

flight must be limited to the lower regions of the atmosphere. It is discovered, however, that this weakness may be its strength in the launching maneuver of space flight. Each kilogram of air taken in from the environment replaces propellant that would otherwise have to be launched from the ground and propelled to the altitude where it is consumed. The effective value of the specific impulse for the turbojet is approximately 1,500 sec, compared to 250 sec for conventional chemical rockets. If the air had to be carried along in the vehicle, the turbojet specific impulse would decrease to much less than 200 sec. The high effective specific impulse, combined with the high thrust-to-weight ratios of modern turbojets (about 10 for the engine alone), opens up a new area of application in the launching of space vehicles.

5-4. Turbojet Booster Performance. The most important space mission class discussed in Chap. 2 was the boosting or planetary surface mission. Space vehicles are currently launched into space through the use of large, multistage, chemical rockets. The possibility exists that the replacement of the first-stage chemical rocket with a recoverable, air-breathing turbojet stage may represent a cheaper, more flexible way to lift large payload masses into satellite orbits or escape trajectories.

A vehicle such as that shown in Fig. 5-5 might be used. The thrust from a large cluster of turbojets, possibly combined with the lift from wing surfaces, would enable such a vehicle to take off vertically (or

FIG. 5-5. A conceptual drawing of an air-breathing boost vehicle. Turbojet engines are located in the body of the vehicle and the three pods. The first stage may be detached, as shown in the upper portion of the illustration, landed, and used again. (*General Electric Co.*)

horizontally if winged) and fly through a first-stage mission profile like that illustrated in Fig. 5-6. At an altitude of about 24 km, the second-stage vehicle, perhaps a chemical or nuclear rocket or even a hypersonic air-breathing system, is activated and detached from the turbojet stage. The first stage is then landed and used again, while the second stage continues the launching maneuver.

Referring to Fig. 5-7, it is seen that the performance of modern turbojet engines as a function of altitude is sufficiently good to launch the second-

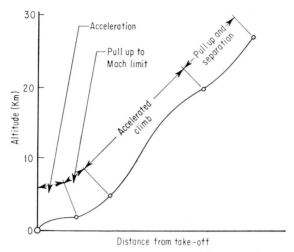

FIG. 5-6. Typical trajectory of a first-stage air-breathing boost vehicle.

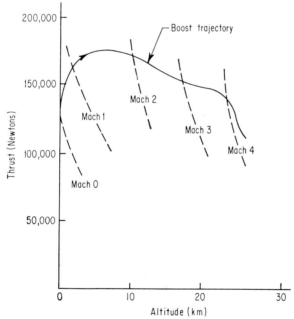

FIG. 5-7. Performance of a turbojet engine as a function of altitude.   The solid line shows the performance during a boosting mission.

stage rocket at Mach 5 at 24 km altitude (1,600 m/sec).   Note that high engine thrust may be maintained throughout the boost phase.   The launching velocity for the second stage, 1,600 m/sec, is quite low compared to what chemical rockets can achieve, but the air-breathing boost stage has not had to carry propellant along.   Figure 5-8 gives the mass breakdown for a typical air-breathing boost system. The mass of the second stage is considerably higher than that which could be carried to the same point and conditions by a chemical rocket with the same gross mass. Even with the low launching velocity, the second stage is above the bulk of the atmosphere, and it has sufficient mass to place an attractive fraction of the initial gross mass into orbit. Figure 5-8 shows how this payload-to-gross-mass ratio varies with the thrust-to-weight ratio.

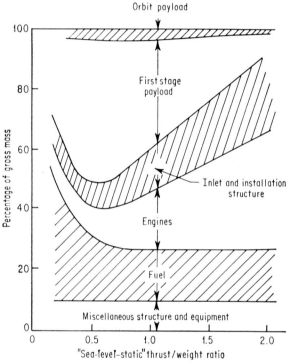

FIG. 5-8. Mass breakdown for air-breathing boosted systems as a function of the initial thrust-to-weight ratio. Horizontal take-off $T/W < 1$ yields the largest first-stage payloads.

These curves also show that thrust-to-weight ratios less than one, implying horizontal take-off with winged vehicles, yield the highest first-stage payloads.

The performance figures just reviewed for the air-breathing boost concept show that it can theoretically perform the first-stage launching maneuver and propel competitive payloads out into space. Unfortunately, the pure performance figures do not reveal many important points.

5-5. Evaluation of Air-breathing Boost. Along with its performance advantages, there are several qualifications and disadvantages that must be stated in connection with air-breathing boosters.

The recovery of the first-stage booster leads to economic advantages only if it can be used several times.   The cost of turbomachinery is considerably higher per pound of thrust than for contemporary chemical rockets.   Reuse is based on the assumption of successful separation of the first and second stages in flight.   This critical maneuver may prove damaging to the first-stage vehicle if it cannot be quickly removed from the vicinity of the second-stage jet.   It is also uncertain how applicable the air-breathing booster will be in the launching of nuclear second stages. One of the important advantages of nuclear rockets over three- and four-stage chemical rockets is their simple, single-stage operation.   In addition, nuclear rockets require a complex start-up procedure, involving a comparatively slow reactor power build-up.   The approach to full reactor power is a delicate matter, perhaps lasting minutes even after criticality has been attained.   Contamination of the first-stage vehicle and the hazards involved with the aborting of a nuclear second stage at high altitudes also make it difficult to envisage launching nuclear rockets from airborne pads.

Although turbojet engines have been developed to a point where they are reliable and long-lived, they must still be clustered or combined in multiple units to match the high thrusts available from large, liquid, chemical rockets.   In considering their use for the boosting maneuver, the question of absolute size must be examined.   By the time an air-breathing boost system is operational, we shall wish to launch payloads of 10,000 kg and more into orbit.   From Fig. 5-8, gross launching masses of 100,000 kg are inferred.   The largest jet engines existing today produce thrusts between 5,000 and 10,000 kg.   The implication is that, for vertical take-off, clusters of 10 or more turbojets will have to be employed. Even horizontal take-off will require six or more engines.   The complexity of the many-engine first-stage vehicle may lead to problems of control, start-up, and reliability.   This aspect of the use of turbojet boost has not been adequately probed.

The recoverable air-breathing boost concept offers one more competing high-thrust propulsion system for the coming era when frequent launching missions from earth into space are commonplace.   (Note that the turbojet is not appropriate for any of the other mission classes described in Chap. 2.)   The concept is now being studied by most turbojet manufacturers as a possible supplement to the chemical and nuclear rocket launchers.   While air-breathing first stages can theoretically compete with chemical rockets, they are several years behind in development as operational launchers.   Chemical rockets in the million kilogram thrust range are now being developed, but so far turbojets have been used very sparingly for the launching of missiles, particularly high-payload space-bound vehicles.   This lag in development added to the inherent complexity of large clusters of turbojets may effectively rule this approach out for space propulsion.

CHEMICAL ROCKETS

5-6. The Conventional Space Engine. For decades, space flight has centered around the chemical rocket. These engines placed the first satellites into orbit and will probably power the first manned lunar and interplanetary expeditions into space. The chemical rocket is truly the work horse of space flight as it is known today.

Ostensibly, the chemical rocket operates in a very simple fashion. Solid or liquid fuel is placed in a combustion chamber with an oxidizer and burned. The combustion gases are expanded through a nozzle to produce thrust. As any rocket engineer will testify, when this simple concept is translated into actual equipment, the result is a complex and sometimes unreliable engine. While the small rocket weapons (antiaircraft and ground-support rockets) have attained fair reliability, large chemical rockets of the size needed for space expeditions are less tractable. The main difficulties seem to arise from the malfunctioning of small, conventional components like valves, relays, and actuators which are profuse in any real rocket. As the state of the art improves with the accelerated development of space flight, we may expect million kilogram thrust rockets to launch payloads of 10 and more metric tons into space on a routine basis. Currently, orbital payloads in the vicinity of one and two metric tons are possible (Table 2-3) but hardly on a scheduled basis.

There exists abundant literature on the subject of chemical rockets (Refs. 1-16 and 5-22). They will be reviewed only briefly here in deference to the more advanced concepts. No inference that chemical rockets will play a minor role in space flight is intended; rather, the converse is true.

The two basic types of chemical rockets are the solid- and liquid-fuel varieties. Solid-fuel rockets are more reliable but have poorer specific impulses. Experience with very large solid rockets is not yet available; it is also more difficult to control their burning periods and thus program their flight. Table 5-2 summarizes the performances of both types in terms of their attainable specific impulses for different fuel-oxidizer combinations. The specific impulse is somewhat misleading since the fuel and oxidizer densities will affect the size of the tanks strongly. Many of the advanced fuel-oxidizer combinations have not been developed into operational systems. The Vanguard rocket (Fig. 5-9) represents an advanced liquid-chemical rocket. It obtains a specific impulse of about 250 sec. Figure 5-10 is an estimate of how the specific impulse of chemical rockets will vary with state of the art. With liquids, specific impulses

FIG. 5-9. The Vanguard rocket. An example of 1958 state of the art. First-stage specific impulse is 250 sec. (*General Electric Co.*)

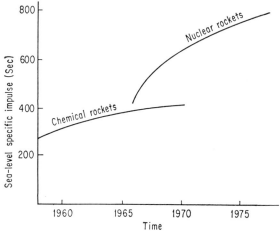

FIG. 5-10. Projected sea-level specific impulses obtainable with thermal engines as a function of time.

145

close to 400 sec are theoretically obtainable at sea level, with 480 sec possible at high altitudes. Beyond this point, performance is limited by two factors: the inherent weakness of the chemical bond, and the relatively heavy molecular weights of the combustion products. New materials and cooling techniques must be found to even attain the goal of 400 sec. For values of specific impulses beyond 400 sec, nuclear rockets and more advanced, nonchemical propulsion systems must be developed.

TABLE 5-2. PERFORMANCES OF CHEMICAL ROCKET FUELS

Liquids*		Chamber at 34 atm		
Oxidizer	Fuel	T_0, °K	M	I_{sp}, sec
Hydrogen peroxide...........	Gasoline	2930	21	248
Nitric acid...................	Gasoline	3120	25	240
Oxygen.....................	Alcohol	3340	22	259
Oxygen.....................	Hydrazine	3240	18	280
Oxygen.....................	Hydrogen	2760	9	364
Fluorine....................	Ammonia	4260	19	306
Fluorine....................	Hydrogen	3090	9	373

Solids†

Propellant system	Flame temp, °K	M	I_{sp}, sec
$KClO_4$ and C_2H_4O...........	1800–3030	25–35	165–210
NH_4ClO_4 and C_2H_4O.........	1800–2150	22–25	175–240
Nitrocellulose and nitroglycerine, miscellaneous..........	2360–3140	22–28	205–230
Asphalt and perchlorate.......	2360–2640	30	180–195

* Ref. 5-18.
† Ref. 1-16.

5-7. Evaluation of Chemical Rockets. An examination of the payload-carrying capabilities of chemical rockets indicates that the payload-to-gross-mass ratio cannot exceed 0.01 for escape missions even with the best fuel-oxidizer combinations. In spite of these low ratios, the chemical rockets remain the only propulsion systems presently capable of performing the planetary surface class of missions. It is likely to remain the sole contender until at least 1970, when nuclear-heat-transfer rockets may be sufficiently developed.

Manned voyages to the moon and instrumented probes to the nearby planets are certainly feasible with chemical rockets, although they are expensive in terms of propellant mass consumed. The more ambitious trips to the stars and manned interplanetary voyages will necessitate nuclear propulsion systems. By the time the other facets of space technology have progressed to this stage, these more advanced engines will probably be available. Chemicals could also power satellite propulsion systems. Although the thrust levels would be small in this application, the engine must operate over extended periods of time. Chemical rockets will be able to perform most of the anticipated maneuvers but will probably be limited to under 100 hr of thrust production because of excessive consumption of fuel and oxidizer. See Eq. (2-13). Electrical and nuclear thermal propulsion systems will probably outperform chemical rockets in some satellite and interplanetary mission classes, but the dividing line is not well defined at the present time (Chaps. 2 and 10). The most complimentary thing that can be written about the chemical rocket is that it is here now, it works, and it can perform most of the missions at hand.

Chemical rockets can be represented on the summary plots for thermal engines, Fig. 5-31, by a maximum specific impulse of about 400 sec and thrust-to-weight ratios of 10 and less.

THE RECOMBINATION RAM JET

5-8. Energy from the Ionosphere. In the regions of the ionosphere, beginning at 80 km and continuing out to the difficult-to-define edge of space, potential energy exists in the form of dissociated oxygen and nitrogen. Mention of this storehouse of free energy has already been made several times (Secs. 3-7 and 4-10). Figure 4-16 plots the amount of energy available per unit volume as a function of altitude. Is this energy sufficient and can enough of it be extracted from the atmosphere to make a useful propulsion system? In attempting to answer this question, numerous, rather risky assumptions concerning free radical recombination rates, high altitude drag and lift, and engine heating rates must be made. Experimental data concerning these phenomena are almost nonexistent. In general, the techniques and assumptions of Baldwin and Blackshear (Ref. 4-2) will be used in this treatment of ionospheric ram jets although several other investigators are also studying this concept.[*]

Figure 4-16 illustrates that the energy density available in the ionosphere is extremely small. This fact leads to the satellitelike ram-jet configuration diagrammed in Fig. 5-11. The most obvious feature of the vehicle is the extremely large scoop needed to collect sufficient energy from the environment for sustained flight. Conceptually, recombination occurs in the narrow section of the throat shown in the schematic. In

[*] At Rensselaer Polytechnic Institute, P. Harteck; at the University of Minnesota, R. Hermann; at Aerojet-General Corp., S. Demetriades and C. Kretschmer.

this region, heat is released in the recombination of the free radicals, and the enthalpy of the air is increased. Subsequent expansion of the hot gases through the nozzle generates the desired thrust.

The picture formed of the recombination ram jet, then, is that of a vehicle shaped like a large funnel, hurtling around the earth at an altitude and velocity where sufficient environmental energy is collected to offset drag losses and provide for some maneuverability. Lift and centrifugal forces, particularly the latter, will balance gravitational forces.

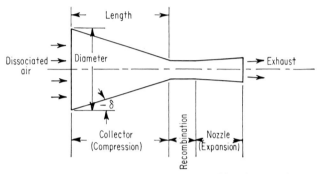

Fig. 5-11. Schematic drawing of a recombination ram jet.

5-9. Drag versus Thrust. The first calculation that must be made for the recombination ram jet compares the magnitude of the thrust available with the drag forces acting on the entire vehicle. The thrust-to-drag ratio must exceed or equal one, or sustained flight will be impossible. The thrust is approximately given by

$$F \cong \dot{m}v_e = \frac{2}{v_e} P_e = \frac{2}{v_e} (e\rho_E A V) \tag{5-6}$$

Therefore,

$$\frac{F}{A} \propto e\rho_E \tag{5-7}$$

where e = engine efficiency

$\dfrac{F}{A}$ = thrust-to-area ratio

ρ_E = energy density of environment

V = vehicle velocity relative to the atmosphere

A = vehicle frontal area

v_e = exhaust velocity

The drag per unit frontal area may be calculated for a variety of collector sizes and shapes. Assuming simple conical nacelles, Fig. 5-12 compares the thrust available with drags calculated for various cone angles and length-to-diameter ratios from Ref. 4-2. The curves shown are computed for orbiting velocities and 100 per cent engine efficiencies. Figure 5-12 shows clearly that sustained flight is definitely possible (within the

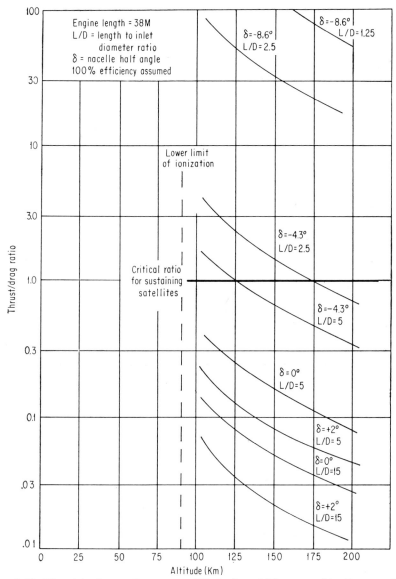

FIG. 5-12. Thrust-to-drag ratios versus altitude for orbiting recombination ram jets of various configurations. See Fig. 5-11 for definition of dimensions. (*Adapted from NACA TN 4267.*)

149

assumptions made) for wide-mouthed (negative angle) conical collectors
with small length-to-diameter ratios.   Following the conclusions derived
from these curves, the subsequent analysis will be confined to ram jets
of the type shown in Fig. 5-11 orbiting at 100 km.

5-10. Thermodynamics.   Cycle analysis for the ionospheric ram jet
is hampered by the scarcity of data on atmospheric conditions at 100 km
and the recombination rates of dissociated oxygen and nitrogen.

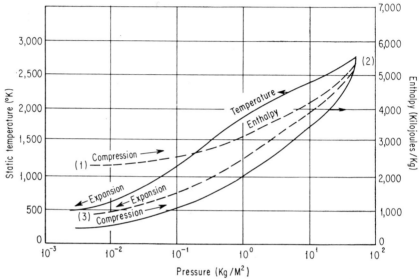

FIG. 5-13. A possible recombination ram-jet cycle.   (*Adapted from NACA TN* 4267.)

With the discussion restricted to orbital vehicles, an all-supersonic
cycle should be analyzed.   Baldwin and Blackshear consider the following
processes:

1. Frozen composition compression, where the relative amounts of free
radicals and undissociated molecules remain fixed
2. Attainment of chemical equilibrium for the compressed gas
3. Chemical equilibrium exhaust expansion to the ambient pressure

Inherent in these processes are the assumptions of a zero recombination
rate in the collector (process 1) and a high rate of recombination during
process 2.   These mutually contradictory assumptions may be made more
plausible through the use of a catalyst lining the expansion chamber.
The use of gold has been suggested by Harteck (Ref. 5-21).   The cycle
diagram corresponding to these three processes is presented in Fig. 5-13.
Energy is being recovered from the atmosphere during the transition
between points 1 and 2 in Fig. 5-13.   The difference in enthalpy between
points 1 and 3 measures the total energy recovery.

The heating of the internal and external surfaces of the engine will be a serious problem. Calculations show that radiation to space is adequate to cool all external surfaces (Ref. 4-2). Internal heating is a more difficult matter. The recombination reaction must be a three-body reaction to preserve momentum and energy. Thus, the inner lining of the thrust chamber localizes the heating, since it serves as a focus for recombination. The high heating rates at this point in the engine may require some sort of transpiration cooling to keep temperature down to acceptable values.

5-11. Evaluation of the Recombination Ram Jet. The several investigators of the recombination ram jet arrive at quite different engine sizes. Baldwin and Blackshear recommend large engines. Typical inlet radii of 6 m and engine lengths of 32 m are suggested. Actual thrusts would be under 10 kg in design, but this is still several times the drag forces. Engine efficiencies of 50 per cent seem attainable with inlet-to-exit-area ratios of 7. Baldwin and Blackshear consider the recombination ram jet to be a marginal device. This is emphasized by the many optimistic assumptions that must be made to even achieve the performance quoted above. Note that these investigators concentrated on orbiting ram jets where most of the system weight is balanced by centrifugal force.

Other studies of this engine (Ref. 5-21) have considered lifting surfaces on the vehicle. The results indicate that sustained flight at 100 km can be maintained below orbiting velocity providing extremely lightweight structures can be fabricated. Minute vehicles with total masses of 150 g are visualized. The payloads for these craft would be on the order of only a few grams. Corresponding inlet areas would approach a square meter. Clusters of these small engines could be formed to create vehicles with more practical payload-carrying capabilities.

In spite of the different approaches taken by various investigators, there is uniform agreement that the recombination ram jet shows some small promise. There is no clear-cut analytical proof that success is inevitable, but neither is a negative conclusion possible. This situation is not uncommon in space technology. Frequently, the state of knowledge concerning key physical phenomena is inadequate. It is general practice to make optimistic assumptions in lieu of concrete data. The result is a host of marginal devices, like the recombination ram jet, awaiting further facts to confirm or deny feasibility.

Assuming for the moment that the recombination ram jet will work, what missions of significance can it perform? Clearly, it will not have take-off and landing capabilities. Just as surely, it cannot operate outside the atmosphere on interplanetary and interstellar missions. It is then restricted to satellite or quasisatellite missions where some lift or thrust is required. All of the applications listed in Sect. 2-11 for satellites are feasible with this type of engine. The vehicle will, of course, have to be launched by a separate propulsion system like any passive satellite. The recombination ram-jet principle, then, permits the design of satellites or near-satellites operating near the altitude of 100 km, which will have sustaining and possibly some maneuvering capabilities at the edge of the earth's atmosphere.

In placing the recombination ram jet on a $F/W-I_{sp}$ performance chart (Fig. 5-31), it is interesting to find that the effective specific impulse may approach infinity. Since all of the propellant and energy is derived from the environment, the ratio $F/g_0\dot{m}$ may have a vanishing denominator. The mass flow would be greater than zero only if an engine-cooling fluid is used and ejected along with the matter ingested from the atmosphere. The thrust-to-weight ratio of a realistically designed recombination ram jet would probably be between 10^{-4} and 10^{-3}.

NUCLEAR-FISSION ROCKETS

5-12. The Application of Nuclear Power to Rockets. The thermal engines based on chemical fuels are ultimately limited by both the weakness of the chemical bond and the high molecular weight of chemical combustion products. See Eq. (5-5). By introducing nuclear power into rocket propulsion, both limitations may be overcome. The high energy densities of nuclear-heat sources are limited only by our ability to remove the thermal energy that is generated. In addition, great freedom in the choice of propellant is permitted since chemical combustion is unnecessary. Both of these advantages combine to make nuclear-fission rockets the prime contenders for the roles now played by the chemical rockets in space technology. The potentially large improvement in rocket performance has stimulated energetic nuclear-rocket development at Los Alamos Scientific Laboratory and the Rocketdyne Division of North American Aviation as part of the joint Atomic Energy Commission–National Aeronautics and Space Administration ROVER Project.

The application of nuclear power to rockets is, in many ways, more logical than its use in air-breathing engines for conventional aircraft. There are three major problems that plague the designers of nuclear aircraft. These largely disappear with the nuclear rocket.

1. High power-plant weights. A large portion of the weight in a nuclear plane is devoted to personnel shielding. This weight is eliminated in unmanned rockets and greatly reduced in manned systems because of the use of shadow shielding.

2. Long-lived design under the influences of high temperature and nuclear radiation. Because of the short operating life of the nuclear-rocket engine, these constraints are relaxed.

3. Ground-handling problems. Since the nuclear rocket will generally

be used but once and is not radioactive before launching, ground handling is considerably simplified in comparison with nuclear aircraft though certainly not in comparison with chemical rockets.

Not only are the problems just mentioned greatly reduced in importance, but the many positive advantages of nuclear power, such as high

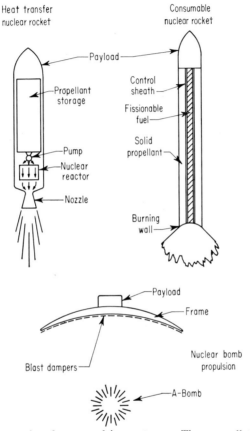

Fig. 5-14. Three types of nuclear propulsion systems.   These are all thermal engines.

specific impulse and high energy density fuel, combine to make the nuclear rocket a highly attractive space propulsion system.

There are three basic types of nuclear rockets.   They may be classified by the manner in which the nuclear reaction is contained (Table 5-1). The so-called "heat-transfer nuclear rocket" is no more than a nuclear-reactor core through which propellant is passed and heated.   Figure 5-14 illustrates this type schematically.   The second type is the consumable nuclear rocket.   Here the nuclear fissioning occurs directly in the working fluid. Both unfissioned fuel and fission products are released in the exhaust. This type is conceptually midway between the heat-transfer reactor and an atomic bomb. The final type of nuclear rocket is the controlled-explosion type. It is shown in Fig. 5-14 in the firecracker-under-can configuration. Each of the three shows promise as an eventual space propulsion system. It remains to evaluate and more fully describe their operation.

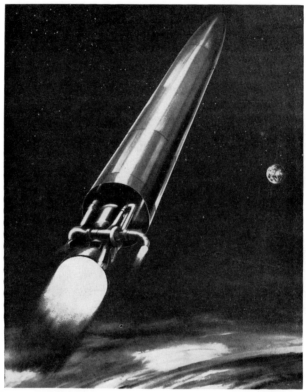

FIG. 5-15. Conceptual drawing of a nuclear-heat-transfer rocket vehicle. (*Rocketdyne Division, North American Aviation, Inc.*)

5-13. Heat-transfer Nuclear Rockets. The arrangement of the components in a heat-transfer nuclear rocket is very similar to that in the liquid-chemical rocket. The vehicle is projectile-shaped, such as shown in the conceptual drawing in Fig. 5-15, with the propellant tank occupying much of the vehicle volume. The nuclear reactor occupies a position identical to that of the chemical combustion chamber. Propellant is pumped through the hot core, vaporized, heated to high temperatures, and then expanded through a nozzle to produce thrust. The designation *heat transfer* comes from the fact that the great bulk of the heat generated in the fuel elements is transferred to the propellant by the conventional heat-transfer mechanisms of conduction and convection.

During the firing of the rocket, turbopumps drive the propellant from the tanks into the core header under high pressure. Pressures up to 100 atm and flows of 1,000 kg/sec are typical of many designs (Ref. 5-11). The heart of the heat-transfer nuclear rocket is the reactor itself. Figure

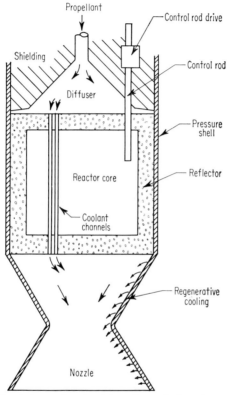

FIG. 5-16. Schematic of the nuclear-heat-transfer rocket engine. Heat is transferred from the solid fuel elements to the working fluid through conduction, radiation, and convection. Propellant turbopumps and piping for regeneratively cooled nozzle are not shown. Shielding keeps propellant from overheating.

5-16 illustrates one possible arrangement. Propellant under high pressure from the header enters the many coolant channels drilled in the core matrix material. Heat produced by fission within the matrix is conducted to the surface of the holes and then to the fluid itself by convection. Somewhere along its passage through the core, perhaps even before it leaves the top reflector piece, there will be a propellant phase change. When this occurs, heat-transfer coefficients will also change markedly. From this point on, the major problem in core design is the provision of the immense, extended heat-transfer areas needed to convey the heat generated in the elements to the gas. Many thousands of square meters of core area will be required in large rockets. The least blockage of coolant flow will cause hot spots to develop with possible vaporization of core material and the release of hazardous fission products to the exhaust. The reactor core is a region of intense energy production, perhaps 10,000 Mw/m³. It is exceedingly sensitive to the smallest variations in the heat-transfer process.

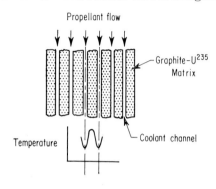

An alternate core configuration also seems attractive. Instead of massive blocks of core material pierced with propellant channels, myriads of tiny fuel elements may be used with good effect. Figure 5-17 shows enlarged sketches of both approaches. Note that the temperatures peak to extreme values in the heat-producing regions. The core material may soften or even melt and vaporize in these regions. In both configurations, the core pieces or elements are supported by solid stringers and support plates.

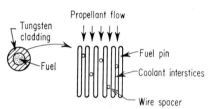

Fig. 5-17. Detailed views of two possible types of core structure applicable to the nuclear-heat-transfer rocket.

Since little heat is generated internally in these unfueled parts, they have more structural strength than the fueled regions. All structural loads are ultimately carried to the chamber or pressure-shell wall. The pressure drop across the core is so high (tens of atmospheres) that high loadings occur at localized parts of the pressure shell.

Examining the reactor from the standpoint of nuclear physics, the core is a source of high-energy neutrons, a certain fraction of which must be retained within the core to sustain the chain reaction. In the reactor shown in Fig. 5-16, the core is shown surrounded by a neutron reflector. The addition of a fraction of a meter of reflector material will substantially reduce the core dimensions and critical masses by reflecting escaping neutrons back into the core. In the nuclear rocket, the reflector might be cooled by a propellant flow path in series with the core. The heat generated in the reflector by gamma-ray absorption and neutron slowing down would have to be removed to preclude overtemperaturing.

The materials applicable to nuclear-rocket cores are the ceramics and refractory metals. They are used for their high-temperature properties in spite of their usual brittleness and sensitivity to thermal shock. It is extremely difficult to make fuel elements with adequate surface-to-volume ratios which will also withstand the high thermal and mechanical stresses produced during the firing of the rocket. The fuel, in the form of UO_2 or UC, may be dispersed through the matrix materials or possibly loaded as ceramic pellets. Since many of the ceramics are also good moderating and reflecting materials, the core structure, fuel matrix, and reflector may all be made from the same basic material. Such reactors would probably be slow or epithermal because of the good moderating properties of the materials. On the other hand, if a refractory metal like tungsten is employed, a reactor with a fast neutron spectrum should be designed because of the high absorption cross section of tungsten for slow neutrons. The three materials just mentioned, BeO, W, and graphite, are all highly important to nuclear-rocket technology. The properties of these materials are summarized in Table 5-3. As might be expected, the best developed material BeO is the least interesting from a performance point of view because of its poor properties at very high temperatures. The true significance of materials technology to nuclear-rocket performance can be seen by comparing the temperatures shown in Table 5-3 with the specific impulses obtainable with various propellants in Table 5-4.

Reactor control can be achieved through the use of axial control rods containing a neutron poison like boron carbide. The axial control rods shown in Fig. 5-16 are common in most nuclear reactors. Upon start-up,

TABLE 5-3. PROPERTIES OF SOME NUCLEAR ROCKET CORE MATERIALS*

Property	BeO	Graphite	W
Melting point.......	2800°K	3900°K, sublimes	3650°K
Density at 20°C.....	2.7	1.7	19.1
Short-time tensile strength, psi......	1,000–4,000, at 1500°K	3,000–6,000, at 2780°K	5,000–9,000, at 2780°K
Macroscopic thermal absorption cross section, cm^{-1}......	0.0006	0.00037	1.17
Probable rocket efflux temperature in 1970.............	1700°K	2300°K	2300°K
Comments.........	Comparatively well developed. Can be hot-pressed into almost any shape	Properties are anisotropic. Easily worked	Difficult to fabricate. Expensive

* Adapted from Ref. 5-2.

the rods would be withdrawn allowing the reactor power to build up at a rate consistent with the thermal stress and shock limitations of the core materials.   Of course, propellant flow past the fuel-bearing regions must be programed along with the reactor power changes.   The start-up procedure may take as long as several minutes if damage to the core is to be avoided.   This single fact constitutes one of the major problems of the heat-transfer nuclear rocket.   *Ready-to-go capability* is limited, and propellant must be provided from an auxiliary supply to remove heat while the power is being brought up to the design level.   Difficulties are also encountered during reactor shutdown because coolant must be directed through the core even after the chain reaction has ceased.   Unless this afterheat, a result of radioisotope decay, is removed, the rocket reactor will be destroyed and reuse will be impossible.

TABLE 5-4. SPECIFIC IMPULSES OF NUCLEAR ROCKETS*

Propellant	Sea-level thrust chamber specific impulse at the indicated gas temperature for 43 atm		
	1650°K	3300°K	4950°K
Hydrogen............	627 sec	890 sec	1216 sec
Helium...	395	540	653
Ammonia....... ...	307	431	577
Water.............	222		

* Ref. 5-11.

Most nuclear rockets will be unmanned, at least during the first years of their use.   For this reason, shielding will be a minor problem.   Only a few radiation-sensitive components, like transistorized electronic equipment, will have to be protected from the intense burst of radiation occurring during the short operating lifetime of the reactor.   It is also essential to place some shielding between the reactor and the propellant tank to prevent excessive heating of the propellant by the absorption of nuclear radiation.   Small temperature rises in the cryogenic propellant can cause severe cavitation problems in the propellant turbopump.   For the eventual nuclear rockets with a human cargo, enough shielding must be placed between the reactor and the crew compartment to bring the total dose integrated over the mission down to perhaps 10 rem.   The crew must also be protected from the neutrons and gamma rays that may be scattered into their compartment from the atmosphere.   Scattering will be important only during the initial flight phase.   It may be that the shielding necessary for human passage through the radiation belt surrounding the earth will be adequate for air-scattered reactor-produced radiation.

The direct and scattered radiation consists of two components: the gamma rays, which are best attenuated by high-density substances like lead and tungsten, and the fast neutrons, which should be stopped by light atoms like those present in water, the hydrides, and the organics.   Fortunately, the propellant inventory and tankage will *shadow-shield* the crew compartment very effectively during much of the rocket's ascent.   The long column of propellant and metallic structure will shield against both radiation components until just before rocket burn-out.   As in the case of nuclear turboelectric power supplies (Chap. 4), shielding depends so much upon the specific mission and vehicle at hand that generalizations cannot easily be made.   The reader is referred to more complete treatments of this subject (Ref. 5-2).

The superior performance of the nuclear-heat-transfer rocket over chemical rockets comes about not through higher temperatures in the working fluid but rather through the greater freedom in propellant choice that is available.   Until free radicals and metastable compounds become practical fuels, chemical rockets will be limited in sea-level specific impulse to about 400 sec (Table 5-2).   Nuclear heat-transfer rockets, using the same chamber temperatures as chemical rockets (2500 to 3000°K), will at least double this value.   The increase is obtained through the choice of lighter propellants.   Table 5-4 indicates the potentialities of different propellants at different reactor efflux temperatures.   This table is more practical than Fig. 5-3 since it does not contain the idealizations of perfect nozzles and zero friction loss.   Hydrogen is obviously the best fluid to use from the standpoint of specific impulse, with helium and heavier fluids following.   Unhappily, hydrogen and helium are cryogenic fluids.   Storage, handling, and pumping problems are severe. If *instant readiness* is a system requirement, as for AICBM weapons, then it is doubtful whether these two propellants would be useful.   Table 5-4 also shows that the more tractable propellants (H_2O, NH_3) seriously reduce the performance of the nuclear rocket because of their high molecular weights.   In the final analysis, the fluid chosen will be dictated by the mission requirements.   The actual margin of improvement over chemical rocket will depend upon just what compromises have to be made. Hydrogen is the almost universal choice of propellant for the nuclear heat-transfer rocket.

Table 5-5 illustrates some interesting points about nuclear heat-transfer rockets.   The example using helium rather than hydrogen does not realize the full potential of the nuclear rocket.   No significant increases in performance over the chemical rocket are apparent.   The payload-to-gross-mass ratio is 0.0525 compared with projected and current ratios of 0.03 to 0.002 for staged chemical rockets.   Hydrogen propellant promises better performance, of course.   Hydrogen-using nuclear rockets can put more than 10 per cent of the gross mass into a low orbit.   The reactor thermal power levels are truly impressive: 14,600 and 24,000 Mw.   This is 100 to 1,000 times the thermal power of submarine and stationary nuclear power plants.   Great advances in reactor design will have to be made to achieve these power levels for even the few minutes required during the rocket firing.   Finally, the propellant mass, 97,000 kg of helium, represents an impractical quantity of this rather rare element.

TABLE 5-5. SAMPLE NUCLEAR-ROCKET PARAMETERS

State of the art	1975	1975
Core material	Graphite	Graphite
Core-efflux temperature	3300°K	3300°K
Propellant	Hydrogen	Helium
Chamber pressure	43 atm	43 atm
Exhaust velocity	8,900 m/sec	5,400 m/sec
Specific impulse	890 sec	540 sec
Reactor thermal power	24,000 Mw	14,600 Mw
Propellant mass flow	257 kg/sec	424 kg/sec
Gross mass	114,000 kg	114,000 kg
Propellant mass	84,000 kg	97,000 kg
Reactor mass	7,000 kg	6,000 kg
Structural mass	5,000 kg	5,000 kg
Payload into low satellite orbit	18,000 kg	6,000 kg
Sea-level thrust	228,000 kg	228,000 kg

The high-thrust nuclear rockets extend the area representing the chemical rockets on the $F/W-I_{sp}$ plane (Fig. 5-31) up to about 1,000 sec specific impulse.   Their maximum thrust-to-weight ratios will probably be somewhat less than those of chemical rockets due to the desire to keep the reactor power level (and thus the heat-transfer areas) as low as possible.

In spite of the concentrated AEC nuclear-rocket program (the first prototype nuclear rocket, KIWI-A, Fig. 5-18, was successfully tested at the AEC test site in Nevada in 1959), it is doubtful whether nuclear heat-transfer rockets will become operational before 1970.   There are a great many real barrier problems that must be overcome before this type of propulsion system reaches fruition.   The fuel elements must maintain their integrity under the intense thermal stresses in spite of the notorious tendencies of ceramics to spall and crack.   Any deviation of coolant distribution, because of channel blockage by core fragments, will cause burnout with its attendant release of fission products.   The reactor start-up and control problem is as difficult as any.   Similarly, the erosion of the core, resulting in fuel element damage and the release of radioactivity, is an unevaluated hazard.   The launching sites of nuclear rockets may be seriously contaminated because of this release of radioactivity (Ref. 4-43). Even with such a difficult path ahead, the promise of the nuclear heat-transfer rocket, as portrayed by the potential design parameters shown in Table 5-5, makes the development of this propulsion system a necessity. It is the most promising replacement for the chemical rocket for the boosting and interplanetary classes of missions.

5-14. Low Pressure Nuclear Heat-transfer Rockets. A much-neglected type of nuclear rocket is the low-pressure version of the heat-transfer variety described in the preceding section. To illustrate the importance of low pressures, the specific impulse of a hydrogen nuclear rocket is plotted versus temperature in Fig. 5-19 for very low chamber pressures. Note that the phenomenon of dissociation causes sharp increases of specific impulse as the average molecular weight of the exhaust

Fig. 5-18. The KIWI-A nuclear-rocket experimental engine at the Nevada test site. The KIWI-A was successfully tested in 1959. (*Los Alamos Scientific Laboratory, University of California.*)

decreases. If isothermal, rather than isentropic, expansion proves feasible (Ref. 5-20), it is conceivable that specific impulses of over 1,500 sec and more might be attained with the pure thermal engine. Such performance would make this propulsion system a prime candidate for highly maneuverable military satellites and for some interplanetary vehicles. Thrust-to-weight ratios would probably fall between 0.01 and 0.001. Among the problem areas of this type engine are the difficulties in transferring the heat from the fuel region to the rarified gas and the high void fractions in the reactor core. Figure 5-20 illustrates how the low pressure and isothermal expansion principle might be combined. There will be problems in attaining critical assemblies with such high length-to-diameter ratio cores. Still, the potential of both of these principles warrants further study and development.

5-15. The Consumable Nuclear Rockets. A very logical way to solve the materials problems of the nuclear heat-transfer rockets is to allow the hottest parts of the rocket to be consumed and expelled as part of

the exhaust.   In a propulsion system of this kind, the nuclear fissions
occur directly in the working fluid.   The solid structure of the rocket
engine is protected from the hot reaction zone by a buffer layer which
maintains a high temperature differential between the two.   With such
an approach, temperatures many times the melting points of even the
most refractory substances can be obtained in principle.   The greatest
drawbacks of such rockets are the loss of fissionable fuel and the dispersion

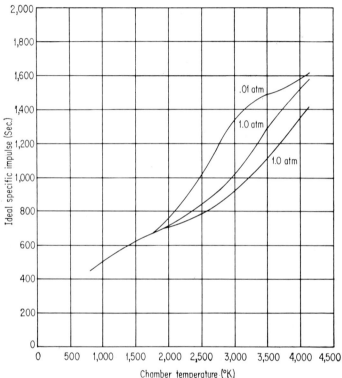

FIG. 5-19. Specific impulse of low-pressure nuclear-heat-transfer rockets as a function
of chamber temperature.   The effects of hydrogen dissociation are clearly evident.

of dangerous fission products to the environment.   Obviously, schemes
which promise fuel and fission product retention are highly desirable.   A
few of these techniques will be discussed in this section.

    There are two basic types of consumable nuclear rockets.   These are
the solid and liquid varieties, as in the case of chemical rockets.   In the
first, all of the necessary ingredients—fuel, propellant, and structure—are
present in the solid mass.   The nuclear reaction is initially prevented by
the presence of neutron absorbers which are withdrawn upon firing.   In
the liquid type, the reactants are initially separated into noncritical

volumes. They are mixed together in a common chamber to create a critical region when the rocket is launched. The advantage of these more radical kinds of nuclear engines is their high potential performance. A host of development problems need to be solved before any one of them becomes a reality. Obviously, none has been built except on paper.

An example of the solid type is shown in Fig. 5-21. The U-235 fuel is concentrated in a rod running the length of the rocket. A good neutron absorber, such as cadmium, surrounds the fuel. Around this there is a thick layer of propellant, perhaps lithium hydride. To fire the rocket, a

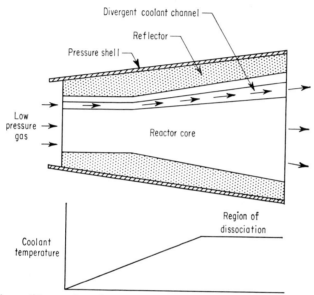

FIG. 5-20. A possible core for a low-pressure nuclear-heat-transfer rocket utilizing isothermal rather than isentropic expansion in the nozzle. Heat must be generated in the nozzle in this case.

section of the cadmium sheath is pulled off the bottom of the fuel cylinder causing the neutron chain reaction to begin. In the region where cadmium is absent, the nuclear reaction will flash the solid materials into a high temperature vapor. The anisotropic expansion of the vapor will produce a forward thrust on the rocket. The average molecular weight of the vapor will be dictated by the relative proportions of uranium and propellant in a given cross section. Usually the ratio of masses will be about 100 kg of propellant for each kilogram of fuel. Once the reaction begins, it will proceed up the body of the rocket as the neutron temperature rises high enough to make the cadmium an ineffectual neutron absorber. Unfortunately, no way has yet been found to prevent the reaction from traveling at velocities exceeding 100 m/sec. The consequence of this fact is that inordinately long rockets would be needed to obtain reasonable accelerations and burn times.   For manned systems, it is desirable to keep accelerations below 10 g.   Burn times between 10 and 100 sec are satisfactory for many launching missions.   If this fundamental problem of slowing down the reaction can be solved, the solid, consumable nuclear rocket is simple and attractive in operation.

The liquid type of consumable nuclear rocket (also called *plasma core, fizzler,* or *cavity reactor* rocket) makes use of the fact that a critical nuclear assembly may be made from a gaseous core and solid or liquid reflector

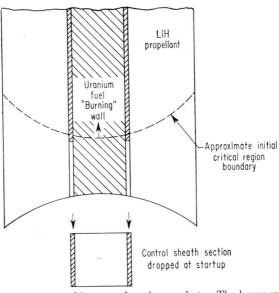

LiH
propellant

Uranium
fuel
"Burning"
wall

Approximate initial
critical region
boundary

Control sheath section
dropped at startup

Fig. 5-21. The solid consumable type of nuclear rocket.   The lower end of the rocket "fizzles" or vaporizes to release high-velocity propellant.

(Ref. 5-12).   Figure 5-22 shows how this concept may be factored into the design of a nuclear rocket.   Note that reasonable diameters of 1 to 2 m may be obtained using this principle.   The vortex configuration shown in Fig. 5-22 is in many respects similar to that employed by the plasma jet of Sec. 5-22.   Cold propellant is introduced tangentially along the periphery of a thick-walled pressure vessel and spirals in toward the rocket axis.   U-235 fuel is injected at some point to create the core region.   In the hot core, the propellant and fuel are heated to perhaps 50,000°K and expelled through an orifice or nozzle.   The relative proportions of core materials are kept constant by matching the inflow of fuel and propellant with the flow through the nozzle.   The wall of cool propellant surrounding the hot core is at once the neutron reflector, the pressure vessel coolant, and the radiation shield protecting the wall from thermal and nuclear radiation. Very high pressures are needed in this system to reduce the physical size of the core. Nuclear calculations show that core diameters of 2 to 3 m are appropriate for temperatures of 30,000°K and 5,000 atm pressure. These pressures necessitate immense pressure vessels, which in turn control the minimum sizes of consumable rockets. Aside from the question of absolute magnitude, the real technical problems center around the attainment of a high-opacity fluid or vapor to protect the pressure vessel wall from the intense thermal and nuclear radiation being emitted by the core. Present indications are that the opacity of available materials is at least an order of magnitude too low.

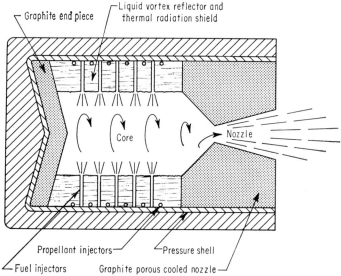

FIG. 5-22. Schematic of a gaseous core, consumable nuclear rocket. The vortex action of the spinning propellant causes some retention of the heavy uranium atoms.

Although the thickness of the buffer layer may be increased to compensate for low opacity, it cannot be made larger by a factor of 10 without making the rocket over-all dimensions unwieldy. Buffer layer thicknesses of several meters seem necessary to sufficiently attenuate the radiation.

Both liquid and solid consumable nuclear rockets must deal with two seemingly intractable problems. The first is the release of radioactive fission byproducts. Although the energy needed to boost a 100,000-kg gross-mass nuclear rocket out of the gravitational influence of the earth is only a small portion of that released in a large nuclear explosion, and the total amount of fission products correspondingly less, the political resistance to any *dirty* nuclear rocket would be difficult to overcome. It is easy to predict that international bans against bomb testing will be made to apply to consumable nuclear rockets, although the heat-transfer type would probably be allowed. The hazards connected with the launching of consumable nuclear rockets may be alleviated by first boosting them to altitudes so high before firing that most of the radio-activity will have disappeared by the time atmospheric circulation (a 10-year cycle has been measured) brings them back to earth. This technique is possible in theory, but, in practice, the start-up and control of the rocket on a mobile launching pad are impressive and probably preclude this kind of solution. The second problem common to all consumable nuclear rockets is the waste of expensive fissionable material. Nuclear bombs, reactors, and rockets generally utilize less than 20 per cent of the fissionable fuel mass in the original critical assembly. The rest is dispersed and lost. (In the case of stationary power reactors, it is reprocessed and refabricated into new fuel elements.) In the rocket where retention of fuel is nil, we may expect that approximately 1 kg of U-235 will be expended for each 100 kg of propellant in most designs. The ratio may be made more favorable only by considerably enlarging the size of the core in the liquid type. U-235 costs about \$20,000 per kilogram at the prices set by the Atomic Energy Commission. For the zero-retention case, it turns out that the consumable rocket can be competitive with chemical rockets in terms of dollars per kilogram placed in orbit. We calculate about \$50 to \$200 per kilogram for each kind of rocket. However, the situation is competitive only when the absolute size of the nuclear rocket is very large. Typical designs call for gross masses of 100,000,000 kg and uranium investments in the billions of dollars.

The cost factor can be relieved somewhat by attempting to retain the unburnt uranium within the rocket. One scheme for retention, using electromagnetic fields, assumes that the temperatures in the core are high enough to singly ionize all the atoms. The electrically conducting mass is then spun by rotating electromagnetic fields like the armature of an induction motor. The uranium atoms are concentrated near the periphery of the chamber because their masses are so much higher than those of the propellant ions. The electromagnetic, viscous, and centrifugal forces, in theory, tend to concentrate the fuel in an annular layer surrounding the core of the rocket. Propellant ions are introduced tangentially and spiral inwardly, picking up heat from the fissioning uranium ions. Although the electromagnetic forces on the propellant ions are the same as those on the uranium ions, the centrifugal forces are much less. Finally, the propellant picks up a strong axial component of velocity through the thermal expansion process and is expelled through the nozzle. Retention may approach 100 per cent through the use of externally generated fields, but the necessity for heavy electrical equipment greatly reduces the over-all performance of the system. In addition, it has not been conclusively shown that electromagnetic retention can be made to work without the use of impractically large magnetic fields.

Hydrodynamic retention of fuel also promises some interesting possibilities. By injecting the propellant and fuel into a vortex (Fig. 5-22) at high tangential velocities, the heavier uranium atoms will tend to be centrifugally separated from the lighter propellant atoms. If the radial concentrations of fuel and propellant are calculated, a high concentration of uranium will be found peaking near the periphery. Although no electrical equipment is needed here, practical difficulties include many of those common to all consumable nuclear rockets. Nozzle erosion, low opacity of the buffer zones to thermal and nuclear radiation, and nuclear control are important examples.

So little is known about the consumable or partially consumable nuclear rockets that it is difficult to estimate their real place in space propulsion. Not only must these engines be proven basically feasible, but retention schemes must also be made to work if really attractive propulsion systems are to be generated. Thrust-to-weight ratios for consumable nuclear rockets can probably be made greater than one so that planetary surface missions may be considered. There is even the possibility that extremely powerful, controlled-explosion nuclear rockets could perform the first interstellar missions. Specific impulse–wise, the higher temperatures expected should boost the limits on purely thermal engines to 3,000 sec. There is much to be learned in studying these radical rocket concepts, but they are a long way from fruition. There does not seem to be any way of avoiding the large physical sizes required by such systems. The rewards of successful development of high-thrust, high-specific-impulse thermal engines are so great that the U.S. government and private industry are studying these concepts seriously, despite the many difficulties inherent in them. Such work is being pursued at Oak Ridge, Los Alamos, Livermore, Lockheed, Convair, General Electric, and many other companies.

5-16. Nuclear Bomb Propulsion. Although nuclear bombs are customarily thought of as inefficient devices so far as the utilization of nuclear fuel is concerned, they actually do convert several per cent of the potential energy available from the U-235 fuel into heat, radiation, and shock waves. In the consumable nuclear rockets, the approach was to slow the nuclear reaction down to a point where the energy is released in seconds rather than microseconds. In bomb propulsion, some attempt is indeed made to slow the reaction rate of bomb down, but the emphasis is on the spreading out in time and damping of its effects on the vehicle. The situation is also different in the matter of temperature. The core of the bomb, of course, reaches many millions of degrees, but the explosions are kept external to the vehicle. Distance thus acts as an effective insulator for the vehicle as far as high temperatures are concerned.

In what ways can a nuclear explosion impart kinetic energy to a space vehicle? Many configurations are possible, but the simplest is that shown in Fig. 5-23. When a bomb is exploded at the focal point shown, an intense burst of electromagnetic energy is first emitted. Traveling at the speed of light, it is the first influence to reach the vehicle. The partial absorption of this energy by the vehicle surface immediately vaporizes a thin layer of material. The absorption of energy plus the

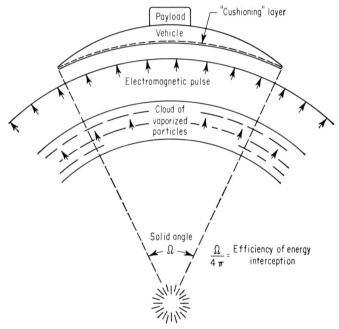

FIG. 5-23. One possible kind of nuclear-bomb propulsion.

rearward expulsion of the hot vapor gives the vehicle an impulse in the desired direction. The second interaction occurs, assuming a vacuum and no shock waves, when the physical particles that constituted the original bomb arrive at the vehicle surface. They will have very high velocities and, upon collision, will impart momentum to the vehicle. In this fashion, each explosion gives two impulses to the spaceship. A long series of such explosions, perhaps several hundred, could conceivably boost a large payload from the earth's surface. The whole process might be compared to a many-staged rocket built up from powerful, short-burning stages.

Again, the greatest drawbacks are the waste of unfissioned material and the spread of radioactive fission products. The very short high-intensity shocks from the series of bombs are also mechanically difficult to handle. Uncontrolled, these sharp impulses could wreck the vehicle and its contents even though the average acceleration might be small. Several methods of smearing out the impulses have been suggested. These include the cushioning of the vehicle by spring-mounted plates (Fig. 5-23) and the use of elastic absorbing surfaces. Interesting though these ideas may be, there has been no real proof of feasibility for bomb propulsion in the unclassified literature. One other problem is that of focusing the bomb's energy so that more of it will be intercepted by the vehicle. Finally, stability during flight might be extremely difficult to maintain with a configuration like that shown in Fig. 5-23. The arrangement is naturally unstable, and fine precision in locating the explosion focal point is necessary if the vehicle is to be kept on course.

The criticisms that can be leveled against nuclear bomb propulsion are manifold. Yet, like the other wasteful, hazardous nuclear engines that have been described, immense increases in performance are assured if the barrier problems are ever solved. Bomb-propelled vehicles may achieve effective specific impulses of 1,000 to 3,000 sec, but this performance is applicable only to systems comparable in absolute size with the consumable rockets previously discussed. Even though the government is sponsoring work at Los Alamos, Livermore, and General Dynamics (Project-Orion), nuclear bomb propulsion must be regarded as highly problematical. The development of small, efficient, clean, directional, nuclear bombs would make bomb propulsion more attractive.

THERMONUCLEAR ENGINES

5-17. Power from Fusion Reactions. In the fission of U-235, energy is released when a neutron splits the heavy uranium nucleus into smaller fragments. The total mass of all fission fragments is less than that of the original uranium nucleus plus neutron. Mass has been converted into energy in this process. It is also possible to produce energy by fusing light nuclei to make heavier ones. Again, the reaction products weigh less than the sum of the original light particles. This latter process has been dubbed *fusion*. It is still another way of tapping the potential energy available in the universe.

The most important fusion reactions are those listed below.

$$_1D^2 + {_1}D^2 \rightarrow {_2}He^3 + {_0}n^1 + 3.25 \text{ Mev}$$
$$_1D^2 + {_1}D^2 \rightarrow {_1}T^3 + {_1}p^1 + 4.0 \text{ Mev}$$
$$_1T^3 + {_1}D^2 \rightarrow {_2}He^4 + {_0}n^1 + 17.6 \text{ Mev}$$

Although any of these reactions may be produced in a cyclotron by the bombardment of a suitable target by deuterons, this procedure will not result in any net generation of power because of the excessive losses incurred by the nonproductive absorption and scattering of the incident particles. Almost all present-day fusion research is being directed down the *thermonuclear* path. In a thermonuclear reactor, temperatures are high enough so that the most energetic of the particles, deuterons, and perhaps tritons will have sufficient energy to overcome the coulomb repulsive forces surrounding each nucleus. Temperatures on the order of 10^8 °K must be created before net power can be produced. The fundamental problems facing thermonuclear power are the attainment of these high temperatures and the confinement of the high-temperature reacting plasma. These problems have not been solved in spite of the ambitious programs underway in many countries. While no insurmountable obstacles have yet appeared, it has become evident that practical thermonuclear power will not be forthcoming until late in this century.

A variety of ways have been proposed whereby thermonuclear temperatures might be reached. The techniques involving the *pinch effect*, *magnetic mirrors*, and *magnetic pumping* are all characteristic of the ways in which hot plasma can be confined and have energy added to it. In every scheme now under scrutiny, the hot ionized gas or *plasma* is prevented from touching the solid container walls by use of an electromagnetic bottle. It is still premature to pick the system that will eventually prove successful.

All the material that follows concerning thermonuclear engines for space propulsion is predicated on the assumption that successful thermonuclear reactors will eventually be built. While it might seem unrealistic to even discuss the use of fusion power when it has not yet been proven possible, sufficient facts are known about the basic fusion processes so that a very generalized treatment of potential thermonuclear engines can be given. The reader is referred both to Chap. 6 in this book and the articles by Post (Refs. 4-23 and 5-10) and Teller (Ref. 4-36) for further information on the fusion reaction itself.

5-18. Propulsion-system Design Considerations. In designing a thermonuclear propulsion system, one usually first assumes the possibility of obtaining a self-sustaining fusion reactor and then a specific containment scheme. Once this is done, attention can be directed to the problems of transferring the heat generated to the working fluid, protecting the structure from nuclear and thermal radiation, design of controls, and the means by which the large amounts of electrical power needed for the confining mechanisms can be generated. All the propulsion-system designs so far reported in the literature are conceptual in nature. That is, they only suggest how the fundamental obstacles can be overcome without proof of feasibility.

A glance at the three most common fusion reactions listed in the pre-

vious section shows some interesting points.   First, there will be intense
nuclear radiation emitted from the reaction zone in spite of the confining
electromagnetic fields.   Neutrons are given off in copious quantities.
In fact, a large portion of the reaction energy appears as neutron kinetic
energy.   While the protons and other charged particles will usually be
retained by the action of the fields, the neutrons escape, carrying off
energy and creating a radiation hazard to humans.   A neutron-absorbing
layer surrounding the reaction zone would perform two functions: shielding and energy absorption.   The same layer of material could also absorb
the large quantities of thermal radiation and *Bremsstrahlung* that will be
given off by the reactions.   The shielding and heat-sink layer might be
made from some liquid metal like lithium, which would be circulated
to a turboelectric power plant to generate electric power.   These few

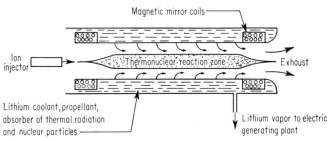

Fig. 5-24. A thermonuclear rocket utilizing magnetic mirrors.   Heat is conveyed to
the external working fluid by radiation, both thermal and nuclear.

basic concepts are sufficient to begin generating conceptual propulsion
systems using fusion energy.

5-19. Systems with External Working Fluids.   This approach is perhaps the most obvious.   A hot reaction zone is created, perhaps by magnetic mirrors (Chap. 6).   The fusion energy generated is transferred to
the surrounding absorbing layer of lithium by thermal and nuclear radiation.   Figure 5-24 shows the essentials of this scheme.   The lithium
blanket is both the propellant and working fluid for auxiliary power
generation.   Lithium from the blanket is introduced close to the reaction
zone, is heated as it moves axially past the fusion zone, and finally is
expelled through the nozzle with high axial velocity.   Lithium vapor is
also channeled off to run the turboelectric power plant which supplies
the confining electromagnetic fields and auxiliary equipment.   Thrust,
of course, is produced upon expansion of the hot vapor in the nozzle.

It is conceivable that very high specific impulses might someday be
obtained with this type of engine.   The limit in performance is reached
when structural materials become overheated in spite of the flow of
lithium coolant.

As with all designs projected this far into the future, little is said or can be said about size, precise configuration, and practical considerations like controls and reliability. Even weights are almost impossible to estimate for thermonuclear engines. Once a self-sustaining thermonuclear reactor has actually been built, more facts about fusion for space engines will become available. The engine just described, if actually feasible, would in all probability be immense. If the thermonuclear machines now being built, like the Model C Stellerator, are any criteria, then thermonuclear space engines might be tens or hundreds of meters long. It must also be exceedingly heavy by virtue of its size, metallic absorbing layer, and shielding. The advantages of such machines would be the high energy density of the fuel and the high specific impulses that are expected. Some estimates for the latter quantity run as high as 3,000 sec. Thrust-to-weight ratios might be made greater than one, but this is unlikely.

From the standpoint of categorization, the thermonuclear rocket just described combines the features of both thermal and electrical engines. Working fluid is heated in a thermal engine and then expanded through a nozzle to produce thrust. The fact that large amounts of electrical power must be generated, necessitating conversion equipment and possibly radiating surfaces, ascribes to this engine some of the disadvantages of the purely electrical systems. The resulting performance, reasonably enough, is somewhere in between the two basic types. Specific impulses are between 2,000 and 3,000 sec for most of the proposed highly conceptual designs. Thrust-to-weight ratios will probably be on the order of 0.1.

5-20. The Leaky Magnetic Bottle. The plasma in the core of a thermonuclear reactor will have a temperature greater than 10^8 °K. If a portion of this extremely hot fluid could be expanded and used to create thrust, very high specific impulses could be obtained. In fact, one can estimate from the proportionality of I_{sp} and $\sqrt{T/M}$ that specific impulses with deuterium propellant would be in the neighborhood of 350,000 sec. Such a high value is desirable if it is not coupled with unusably low thrust-to-weight ratios, as it would be in the case of purely electrical propulsion systems, see Eq. (2-19). If the engine power is not proportional to engine mass or power-plant specific masses are small, then a promising propulsion system might be developed from this concept.

The magnetic bottles that have been constructed as part of the Sherwood Project are naturally leaky, as any experimentalist might expect. The problem resolves itself into the provision of controlled plasma leakage, with a net momentum transfer out of the system. The linear magnetic mirror configuration (Chap. 6) lends itself admirably to the requirements of propulsion. The mirror at one end of an arrangement, such as that shown in Fig. 5-24, can be made less reflecting by reducing the magnetic field strength in that region. High-speed particles will escape through the mirror to provide the propulsive forces. Of course, energy will still escape the bottle through the departures of neutrons and photons. Their energies can be collected and diverted to sustaining the thermonuclear reaction and for auxiliary power. One can only guess at the over-all performance of a concept like this one. While specific impulses will be greater than 10^5 sec, thrust-to-weight ratios will probably be less than 10^{-5}.

The development problems of any of the thermonuclear propulsion systems are imposing. The basic problem of the self-sustaining thermonuclear reaction has not yet been solved. Based on current progress, fusion power for space propulsion will not be available for at least 20 to 30 years; then the machines will be enormous in physical size.

PLASMA JETS

5-21. Introduction to the Plasma Jet. The plasma jet is a hybrid thermal-electrical propulsion system. In both operational concept and performance, it is located in the transition range between the purely thermal jets (chemical and nuclear rockets) and the totally electrical engines (ion drives). Although the plasma jet relies upon the expansion of a hot plasma for the bulk of its thrust, its energy is supplied electrically, rather than from chemical combustion or nuclear fission and fusion.

Plasma jets have a long and interesting history. Hans Gerdien, back in the early 1920s, was one of the first to construct a true plasma jet, or *fluid-constricted-electric arc* as they are sometimes called. These interesting devices remained little more than laboratory curiosities until very recently when they became potent instruments for high temperature research. In connection with reentry-nose-cone studies, the plasma jet has been called upon to produce tens of thousands of degrees for periods up to a few minutes in duration. Although materials research is the primary purpose of the plasma jet at the moment, it is easy to predict other applications. These include hyperthermal wind tunnels, high temperature chemistry, plasma sources, and finally propulsion (Ref. 5-5).

In the next few sections, we shall describe the operation of the plasma jet and how it can be used as a thrust generator in outer space. Like many of the other propulsion systems that have been described, the plasma jet is far from being an operational propulsion device at the present time. Many extrapolations of contemporary technology will be made in what follows to predict the propulsive capabilities of this potential space engine.

5-22. Description of Operation. A somewhat idealized schematic of the plasma jet is shown in Fig. 5-25. It consists of a cylindrical chamber with electrodes at either end. The negative electrode may be a plate with an orifice in it or an actual nozzle. The positive electrode is rod-like, possibly with an automatic feeding mechanism to replace material that is consumed in the hot arc.

During start-up, a d-c voltage is built up across the electrodes. At some potential difference, depending on the pressure and proximity of the electrodes, an arc will be struck between the electrodes, and the region in the chamber core will become a good electrical conductor by

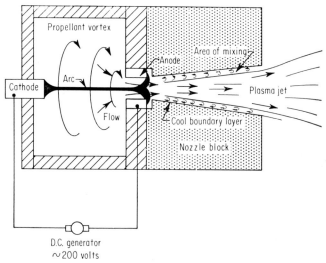

Fig. 5-25. Schematic of a plasma jet with nozzle.

virtue of the presence of positive ions and electrons in the arc. In actual practice, the arc generally is started by placing the electrodes very close together at first and then separating them after the arc has been struck. In the arc, electrical energy is being consumed in the ionization process, in molecular dissociation, and in increasing the temperature of the material in the region of the arc. Energy leaves the arc in the form of electromagnetic radiation, as kinetic energy of escaping particles, and in the potential energy of ionization and dissociation. So far, only an ordinary arc discharge in air has been described. Such an arc, using the chamber shown in Fig. 5-25, would produce little thrust in itself, but it does represent an admirable heat source.

To make a plasma jet from this device, a propellant-coolant must be introduced along with a means of protecting the surrounding solid structures from the high temperatures created in the arc. The propellant-coolant can be made to perform the latter task by introducing it at high tangential velocity around the periphery of the cylindrical chamber. In this fashion, the introduced fluid will cool the walls and also act as a radiation shield. As the propellant fluid swirls closer and closer to the arc, it naturally gets hotter and hotter as it absorbs heat energy from the arc. It is first vaporized (if it is a liquid), then dissociated, and finally ionized. Each of these three processes tends to cool the outer surface of the arc. The cooling causes the current to concentrate in the hotter, more conductive central regions of the arc. This constriction and resulting concentration of energy makes the arc much hotter than it would be without the fluid vortex surrounding it. Temperatures as high as 50,000°K have been obtained with modern plasma jets. With the generation of high temperatures and the formation of large quantities of vapor, conditions exist for production of thrust through the expansion of the hot, gaseous coolant-propellant. The orifice or nozzle comprising the negative electrode will permit the escape of some of the hot plasma, and a propulsion system is created. The acceleration of the hot fluid is accomplished thermally; pressures of several atmospheres exist in the usual plasma jet chamber. Electromagnetic forces play a very small role in accelerating the propellant in this propulsion system.

One of the greatest drawbacks of the plasma jet in space propulsion is its present short operating lifetime. Plasma-jet operation shows that the expelled propellant includes many particles and atoms of the electrode materials. The hot plasma rapidly erodes away the orifice and nozzle where the jet is formed unless protective measures are taken. Most present-day plasma jets can operate for only a few minutes before the electrodes must be replaced. The pinch effect, discussed in Chap. 6, may possibly be used in large plasma jets to reduce electrode consumption and thus lengthen its operating lifetime, but the use of electrolytic electrodes, transpiration cooling of the orifice and nozzle, and the development of ablating materials may eventually extend the operating lifetimes of plasma jets to 100 hours and more. A modern, high-power plasma jet is illustrated in Fig. 5-26.

In summary, the use of an electric arc for a heat source and a vortex of fluid for cooling and radiation shielding permits the attainment of chamber temperatures far in excess of those possible with chemical heat sources and conventionally cooled reaction chambers. These high temperatures give rise to the high specific impulses of interest to space propulsion.

5-23. Plasma-jet Physics. The physics of plasma jets is not perfectly understood. Still, it is possible to discuss two subjects with some degree of assurance. These are the phenomena of dissociation and ionization.

As the arc of a plasma jet gets hotter, an increasing fraction of the electrical energy supplied to the plasma-jet terminals is converted into the potential energy of dissociation and ionization. Unless this energy can be recovered and converted into expellant velocity, it will represent a serious waste of power. Saha's equation may be used to estimate the frac-

FIG. 5-26. A large plasma jet used for creating high temperatures. It consumes about 15 Mw of electricity and can produce temperatures up to 14,000°K. (*General Electric Co.*)

tion of molecules dissociated and atoms ionized. It is represented by three separated equations.

$$\left(x_i = \frac{a}{a+p} \right)^{1/2} \qquad a = 10^b$$

$$b = -\frac{5{,}050 E_i}{T} - 6.5 + 2.5 \log_{10} T \qquad (5\text{-}8)$$

where x_i = fraction of atoms ionized
   p = pressure in atmospheres
   E_i = ionization or dissociation potential in ev
   T = temperature
Saha's equation should be used only for low fractions of ionization.

Figures 5-27 and 5-28, plotted for hydrogen and helium plasma jets, are very revealing. As the temperatures of the gases are raised by the heating action of the arc, energy is at first mostly converted into the kinetic energy of the gas molecules. At about 3000°K, dissociation becomes important in hydrogen, and most of the added energy is consumed by this phenomenon until 5000°K is reached. At 10,000°K, the ionization of hydrogen begins to be dominant, and energy is funneled into this degree of freedom. This stored energy may not be available for thrust production. The different regions of the graphs show the relative

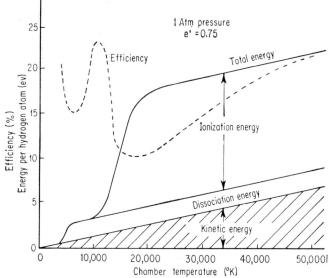

FIG. 5-27. Estimate of how the energy is divided in a hydrogen plasma jet. Note the effects of dissociation and ionization (Ref. 6-12).

importance of the phenomena as functions of temperature. Helium, being monatomic, does not show any effects due to dissociation. In both hydrogen and helium plasma jets (Figs. 5-27 and 5-28), efficiencies drop to low values beyond 20,000°K unless the energy stored in ionization and dissociation can be recovered.

Pressure in the chamber has an important bearing upon dissociation and ionization. High pressures suppress both ionization and dissociation. The peaks and valleys in Figs. 5-27 and 5-28 would tend to be smoothed out by higher values of chamber pressure.

Another factor affecting the use of the plasma jet in propulsion is the loss of energy from the arc by electromagnetic radiation. Although the inwardly swirling propellant absorbs some of the photons streaming from the arc, a high flux will impinge on the walls. As long as this energy can be used in heating the propellant, no inefficiencies will result.   Generally, the energy lost in radiation will be less than 10 per cent (Ref. 5-4).

Important as the problem of energy recovery in a nozzle may be to propulsion, a solution has not been worked out.   The times required for reassociation and deionization are practically unknown under the conditions that prevail in the jet of the plasma jet.   Illustrative of the many difficulties besetting the complete understanding of the plasma jet is the fact that thermal equilibrium is seldom attained in the jet, making inadequate the theoretical approaches which depend upon the assumption of

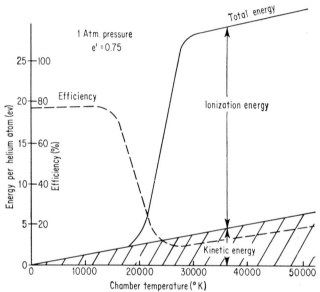

FIG. 5-28. Estimate of how the energy is divided in a helium plasma jet. There is no dissociation (Ref. 6-12).

thermodynamic equilibrium.   Experimental data concerning the propulsive properties of plasma jets is also wanting.   The best data presently available originated at the Gianinni Research Laboratory (Ref. 5-4).

All subsequent performance calculations will be made on the conservative basis that energy recovery in the nozzle is impractical.   The justification for such an assumption is that particle velocities are extremely high in the plasma jet (on the order of 10,000 m/sec); even recombination times of milliseconds would infer impractically long nozzles.   Further experimentation may show this assumption to be very pessimistic.

5-24. Plasma-jet Performance.   From the discussion of the preceeding sections, it is evident that the high-temperature plasma jets and the use of low-atomic-weight propellants will produce specific impulses that are significantly higher than those achieved by contemporary chemical rockets and even the more distant nuclear heat-transfer rockets. These improvements in specific impulse are purchased with higher power requirements—electrical power requirements with attendant conversion equipment masses. With the material developed in the beginning of this chapter, specific impulses may be computed. Using the specific mass data presented in Chap. 4, approximate thrust-to-weight ratios for plasma-jet propulsion systems may also be found. In spite of the fact that thermodynamic equilibrium is probably not attained in the jet itself, Eq. (5-5) is usually employed to compute exhaust velocity and specific impulse. Thrust levels, of course, are found from $F = \dot{m}v_2$. These relationships

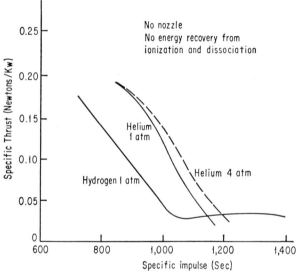

FIG. 5-29. Specific thrust versus specific impulse for hydrogen and helium plasma jets (Ref. 6-12).

may be used to construct graphs of specific thrust as a function of specific impulse. This has been done in Fig. 5-29 for hydrogen and helium. Note the rapid drop off of specific thrust at high specific impulses. The consumption of power by the parasitic modes of dissociation and ionization accounts for the fast reduction in specific thrust. If the combination energy is found to be recoverable in nozzles, the specific thrust curves will drop off less rapidly.

Naturally, it is unreasonable to assume that all of the electrical input is converted directly into jet power. A 75 per cent coupling efficiency between the input terminals and the total energy in the jet (including both directed kinetic energy and potential energy stored in ionization and dissociation) has been assumed. The energy still unaccounted for (25 per cent) is consumed by radiation losses, plasma leakage, and poor collimation of the jet.   These optimistic figures for projected plasma-jet efficiency have not yet been approached in the laboratory.

Table 5-6 has been included to indicate the present state of the art in plasma-jet propulsion.   Both experimental data and the corresponding theoretical calculations are shown.   There are obvious discrepancies between theory and experiment.   The data do show room for optimism in the matter of performance.   Certainly, very few other thermal engines can boast the measured specific impulse of 590 sec shown for the helium plasma jet.   The beneficial effects of even a short nozzle upon perform-ance are also evident.   It seems quite likely that the curves in Fig. 5-29 are conservative.   Probably the plasma jet will be able to produce specific impulses of 2,000 to 3,000 sec, at which points the plasma tem-peratures will be limited by radiation and other losses.

TABLE 5-6.   RESULTS OF TYPICAL RUNS WITH PLASMA THRUST DEVICES*

Parameter	Argon					Helium
Nozzle length, in....................	$\frac{1}{8}$	$\frac{1}{8}$	$\frac{1}{8}$	$\frac{5}{4}$	$\frac{5}{4}$	$\frac{3}{4}$
Input pressure, psig................	20.0	40.0	80.0	80.0	80.0	80.0
Electrical power, kw................	34.5	40.0	43.2	30.7	45.6	80.0
Mass flow, kg/sec $\times$ 10³.............	2.98	5.07	9.06	5.04	4.66	1.29
Thrust, newtons....................	1.76	2.36	3.58	8.25	8.90	7.46
Measured exit velocity, m/sec........	580	470	370	1250	1450	4,500
Calculated exit velocity, m/sec.......	1800	1600	1300	1240	1420	4,850
Measured specific impulse, sec.......	58	47	40	164	195	590
Calculated specific impulse, sec.......	293	261	212	166	198	647

* Ref. 5-4.

When the plasma jet is incorporated into a vehicle, it is possible to calculate thrust-to-weight ratios fairly precisely.   In general terms, how-ever, only limiting values can be given.   Using the specific mass data from the previous chapter and making nominal allowances for propellant tankage and payloads, it is found that plasma jet thrust-to-weight ratios will fall between 10^{-3} and 10^{-5}.   Table 5-7 gives the parameters of a plasma jet of advanced state of the art designed specifically for propulsion. From the standpoints of thrust-to-weight ratio and specific impulse, the plasma jet is an admirable propulsion system for satellite maneuvering and attitude control.   As the following paragraphs will point out, per-formance alone is not sufficient information upon which to base pro-pulsion-system choices.

5-25. Auxiliaries and Barrier Problems of the Plasma Jet.   In addi-tion to the nozzle, there are several other extra pieces of equipment which may or may not be used on a plasma-jet propulsion system.   One is a current limiting resistance to protect the plasma jet from excessive cur-

TABLE 5-7. SAMPLE PLASMA-JET PARAMETERS

State of the art...................... 1965
Propellant........................... Hydrogen
Thrust............................... 50 newtons, 11.2 lb
Specific impulse...................... 1,000 sec
Exhaust velocity...................... 9,800 m/sec
Thrust-to-weight ratio*............... 7.5×10^{-4}
Mass flow rate........................ 0.0051 kg/sec
Beam power........................... 245 kw
Power input.......................... 1 Mw
Propulsion unit efficiency............. 24.5%
Chamber pressure..................... 1 atm
Power-supply mass, 5 kg/kw........... 5,000 kg
Propellant mass, 100 hr.............. 1,840 kg
Average efflux temperature........... 3500°K

* Excluding vehicle, but including propellant for 100 hr of operation.   No recovery of combination energy.

rents arising from the negative temperature characteristics of arc discharges.   As the temperature of the plasma jet arc rises, its electrical resistance drops, causing it to draw more and more current.   In the earth-bound plasma jets now operating, this current limiting resistance is usually a large and heavy component.

It has been suggested that some sort of *magnetohydrodynamic** booster or augmentation unit may be added after the plasma-jet nozzle.   This device would create additional acceleration of the plasma through the interaction of its magnetic fields and the conducting plasma (Chap. 6).   Such augmentation is possible in principle, but it has not been theoretically or experimentally demonstrated that any appreciable gains in performance are possible.   The electrical equipment necessary for the generation of the magnetic fields would be massive.   In addition, it will probably be difficult to affect the core of the plasma column with the magnetic fields because of the high conductivity of the surface of the column.   These difficulties seem to limit the value of this otherwise attractive approach.

5-26. Evaluation of the Plasma Jet.   The fact that the plasma jet is basically a thermal engine limits the maximum obtainable specific impulses to about 2,500 sec.   Above this value, temperatures are so high that the propulsion unit efficiency drops to low levels because of the loss of power by radiation and through the expulsion of uncombined ions and atoms.   Since the plasma jet is also electrical in the sense that it requires electrical energy for the production of its high temperatures, the thrust-to-weight ratio suffers because of the heavy electrical conversion

* See Glossary of Terms at the back of the book.

equipment. The maximum thrust-to-weight ratio for an advanced plasma jet will be about 10^{-3} at 1,000 sec specific impulse.

The ultimate operating lifetime of the plasma jet is still open to question. While it seems certain that they can be run for hours without seriously eroding the nozzle and orifice, further tests must be completed to show whether plasma jets will be able to operate successfully for the thousands of hours required for space flight. The degree to which the energy locked up in ionization and dissociation may be recovered cannot be answered conclusively at the present time. The answers to both of these questions will greatly affect the applications of the plasma jet in space.

The plasma jet will probably be most useful in satellite missions where bursts of thrust, at high specific impulse, will be needed for attitude control and orbit adjustment.

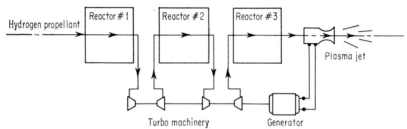

Fig. 5-30. A hybrid nuclear-electric propulsion system.   (*After J. Ackeret.*)

5-27. A Nuclear-electric Hybrid Space Engine.   J. Ackeret of the Swiss Federal Institute of Technology has suggested the space propulsion system illustrated in Fig. 5-30. The concept embodies an open-cycle nuclear power plant in series with an electric exhaust heater. The propellant from the storage tanks enters the first of two or more reactors and is heated to the maximum temperature permitted by the fuel element materials. Some energy is then extracted by an open cycle turboelectric generating system which produces electricity for the electrical heater. This process of heating and cooling the gas may be repeated several times with the accumulated electrical energy finally being fed into the propellant stream by a plasma jet upon emerging from the last reactor.

There are two extremely important advantages of such a system. First, the propellant may be heated to a higher temperature than that possible in a pure heat-transfer nuclear rocket. Second, the great disadvantage of the electrical engines, the radiator vulnerability to meteoroids, is nonexistent with the open-cycle power-generating system.

The specific impulse and thrust-to-weight ratio limits of this scheme are about the same as the plasma jet. The great reduction in vulner-

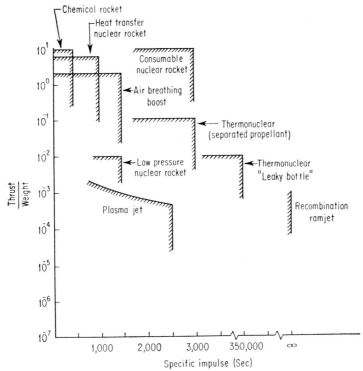

Fɪɢ. 5-31. Summary graph showing the approximate performance limits of the thermal propulsion systems.

ability makes this hybrid space propulsion system more promising than the pure plasma-jet power plant. Its potential applications are also very similar.

EVALUATION OF THERMAL ENGINES

5-28. Final Comparisons. All the chapters in this book dealing with the various classes of propulsion systems will be concluded in the same fashion. The numerical performance factors, the specific impulse, and the thrust-to-weight ratio will be plotted on the summary graph, Fig. 5-31, in this chapter. The more difficult-to-calculate factors, such as state of the art, barrier problems, special advantages and disadvantages, and areas of applications, will be collected in a final summary table. For the thermal propulsion systems discussed in this chapter, Table 5-8 performs this function. In addition, Chap. 10 provides an over-all comparison of all space propulsion systems, in which the thermal engines are compared with the other classes of space propulsion systems.

TABLE 5-8. SUMMARY OF THERMAL SPACE-PROPULSION SYSTEMS

Engine type	State of the art	Major advantages and disadvantages	Potential applications
Air breathing boost	Turbojet well developed, but no large cluster experience available	Complexity of large clusters. Most of the working fluid taken from the environment	First-stage launching
Chemical rockets	A great deal of experience available with engines in the 10^5-kg thrust class	Limited by weakness of chemical bond. Fair reliability. Cheap to manufacture and well developed	All planetary surface missions, nearby interplanetary missions, short-time satellite maneuvers, and attitude control
Recombination ram jet	Poorly understood. No experience or test data available	Energy and propellant extracted from the environment. Must be boosted to high speeds and altitudes	Satellite sustaining and maneuvering
Nuclear-heat-transfer rocket	Not operational. Limited experimental data available	High specific impulses. Best propellants are cryogenic. Radiation hazards may be serious. Low-pressure chambers may push I_{sp} to 1,500 sec.	All planetary surface, interplanetary, and satellite missions
Consumable nuclear rocket	Conceptual. No proof of feasibility	Very high specific impulses. Immense sizes. Difficult to protect solid structures from nuclear and thermal radiation. Expulsion of fuel and radioactive propellant	All planetary surface and interplanetary missions
Nuclear-bomb propulsion	Conceptual only. No proof of feasibility	Waste of fuel. Nuclear hazards. High instantaneous accelerations	All planetary surface, interplanetary, and possibly interstellar missions
Thermonuclear rockets	Conceptual. Basic thermonuclear reaction not yet attained	High performance. Cheap fuel. Need for large amounts of auxiliary electric power	All planetary surface, interplanetary, and interstellar missions
Plasma jet....	Some experience as a laboratory high-temperature device	Short operating lifetimes. Erosion of electrodes and nozzles. Requires high-grade electric power	All satellite missions and possibly some interplanetary missions

The thermal engine is fundamentally a high-thrust low-specific-impulse device when compared to the electrical engines (Chap. 10). Its development, however, is relatively far advanced. The thermal engine is also simple and relatively invulnerable to the environment. These qualifications often tend to override the specific-impulse limitations. The thermal engine will undoubtedly perform the great majority of all space missions undertaken in this century.

CHAPTER 6

ELECTRICAL PROPULSION SYSTEMS

6-1. Introduction to Electrical Propulsion Systems. In spite of the simplicity and unquestioned utility of thermal space propulsion systems, it is electromagnetic propulsion that captivates the imagination. The generation of thrust by the thermal acceleration of matter is somehow crude compared with the action of electromagnetic fields on charged particles. It is esthetically more satisfying to think of the ordered progress of ions or plasma down an accelerating tube rather than the helter-skelter motion of gas atoms through the nozzle of a thermal engine. This chapter is devoted to the many ways in which electromagnetic fields may be used to eject matter at high velocities from space vehicles.

Most of the thermal systems described in the preceding chapter displayed only modest specific impulses; generally, they were less than 3,000 sec. While such engines possess many uses and are now the dominant class of space engines, it is not difficult to foresee the need for propulsion systems with specific impulses an order of magnitude higher. In particular, the satellite and interplanetary classes of missions present excellent opportunities for the application of the high specific impulses* and low thrust-to-weight ratios that are typical of the electrical propulsion systems.

Perhaps the key performance characteristic of the electrical engine is its inability to launch itself from the earth's surface. The requirement of electrical rather than thermal power for thrust production is the fundamental reason behind this disadvantage. First, thermal energy must be converted into electrical energy; second, electrical energy is changed into the kinetic energy of the exhaust particles in the jet stream. The two-energy conversion steps in series add an extra burden of weight to the engine. The thrust-to-weight ratios of electric engines are generally less than 10^{-3} for this reason. Similarly, the ultimate performance and usefulness of these engines depend not only upon the development of electrical power supplies of low specific mass but also upon the design of highly efficient propulsion units. Figure 6-1 illustrates the effects of specific impulse and specific mass upon the thrust-to-weight ratio.

* See Glossary of Terms at the back of the book.

186

Although the electrical engines more nearly fit the mind's pictures of the space engines of the future, there are a great many practical difficulties ahead in their application. They must be made reliable enough to run for years without mishap. They must overcome the immense development lead and ever-improving performance of the thermal engines. In this chapter, we shall try to evaluate the progress that has already been made and the future potentialities that exist for electrical space engines.

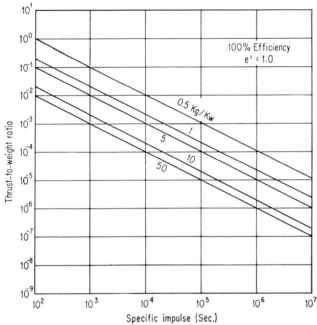

Fig. 6-1. Thrust-to-weight ratio versus specific impulse for electrical propulsion systems with power supplies of different specific mass. See Eq. (2-19).

6-2. Electromagnetic Fields. The application of electrical energy to propulsion permits the acceleration of matter to velocities much higher than those attainable in the temperature-limited thermal engines. While electrical energy may be used to heat the working fluid, as in the plasma jet, the true electrical engines call upon electrostatic and electromagnetic fields to accelerate electrically-charged particles. In a sense, the presence of electrical charge on a particle or ion is a *handle* by which the electromagnetic fields can grasp and accelerate it to velocities approaching that of light itself. Before discussing the more complex subject of *magnetohydrodynamics*, where the hydrodynamic as well as the electromagnetic properties of ionized fluids must be combined, a brief review of the behavior of isolated charged particles in electrostatic and magnetic fields is in order.

The force on a charged particle due to electromagnetic fields is given by

$$\mathbf{F} = q(\mathbf{E} + \mathbf{v} \times \mathbf{B}) \tag{6-1}$$

where $\mathbf{F}$ = force
q = charge
$\mathbf{E}$ = electric field intensity
$\mathbf{v}$ = particle velocity
and $\mathbf{B}$ = magnetic induction*

The force component due to the electric field intensity is always in the direction of the field, while the component due to the magnetic field is always normal to both the particle velocity and the magnetic field. When $\mathbf{B} = 0$, the charged particle is given the acceleration

$$\mathbf{a} = \frac{q\mathbf{E}}{m} \tag{6-2}$$

where m = the mass of the particle. If $\mathbf{E} = 0$ and $\mathbf{B} \neq 0$, a particle will trace a circle of radius

$$r = \frac{mv}{qB} \tag{6-3}$$

Various combinations of parallel and crossed electrostatic and magnetic fields may be employed to generate complex particle motion. The simple notions just discussed permit a qualitative understanding of several interesting physical phenomena. The magnetic bottle and magnetic mirror will be used as examples. Both were mentioned in Chap. 5 in connection with thermonuclear engines.

One type of magnetic bottle is illustrated in Fig. 6-2. The electric current in the windings creates a strong magnetic field parallel to the bottle axis. Particles which possess an electric charge and have velocity components perpendicular to the bottle axis will be deflected back into the bottle as shown. A qualitative explanation of the behavior states that the charged particles are tied to the magnetic lines of force. The ions and electrons, in this case, describe helical paths around the lines of force. If the spatial density of the charged particles is so great that hydrodynamic effects begin to be important, Eqs. (6-1), (6-2), and (6-3) are inadequate. The equations of magnetohydrodynamics must then be used.

Figure 6-3 illustrates the magnetic mirror concept. The apparatus is merely a magnetic bottle which narrows down at each end because of the presence of much stronger magnetic fields in these regions. Most of the

---

* The rationalized MKS system of units is used in this book. See Table of Symbols at the back of the book.

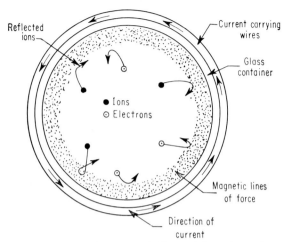

FIG. 6-2. A magnetic bottle. The magnetic lines of force turn charged particles of both signs back into the center. High-temperature plasmas can be confined in this manner.

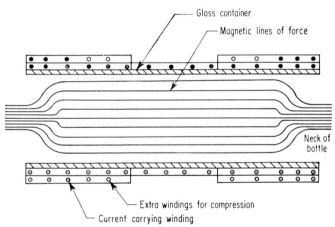

FIG. 6-3. Longitudinal section of a magnetic bottle with magnetic mirrors at each end. The magnetic lines of force are compressed in the mirror regions because of the presence of additional windings. Activation of the other windings shown will move the mirrors together, compressing the plasma.

charged particles are prevented from escaping through the sides of the bottle by the confining mechanism portrayed in Fig. 6-2. The ends of the bottle, the magnetic mirrors, reflect charged particles because the magnetic lines of force in these regions have components which are both parallel and perpendicular to the bottle axis. In theory, all particles, except those traveling on the axis and parallel to it, will be turned back into the bottle cavity by the converging magnetic lines of force shown in

Fig. 6-3. In thermonuclear mirror machines, the plasma in the bottle may be heated by compression by electrically moving the mirrors inward. The additional windings, shown in Fig. 6-3, would be activated in such a compression and create a pistonlike action. Of course, neither the mirrors nor the sides of the bottle are perfectly tight. Some high-energy ions will always have velocities sufficient for escape. Likewise, charge exchange processes may permit some neutral matter to leak out. Magnetic fields, however, have proven to be excellent containers of hot plasma and are widely used in thermonuclear research. As a quantitative bench mark, typical magnetic bottles with magnetic fields of 5 webers/m^2 (50,000 gauss) may contain a plasma at 100 atm (Ref. 6-28).*

The simple notions just discussed are excellent for obtaining a physical understanding of the microscopic events occurring in plasmas. However, the most general descriptions of plasmas, including their interactions with externally and internally generated magnetic fields, require the welding together of the two disciplines of electromagnetics and hydrodynamics. This synthesis is called *magnetohydrodynamics, magnetogasdynamics,* or *hydromagnetics.*

6-3. Magnetohydrodynamics (MHD). Undoubtedly, MHD is one of today's most exciting fields of scientific endeavor. Not only is it of importance to space propulsion, but the subjects of atmospheric reentry, astrophysics, and thermonuclear power call upon MHD for insight into their respective complex high-temperature phenomena. New as MHD is, abundant literature is already in existence (Refs. 6-1, 6-11, 6-18, 6-23, and 6-25). A few paragraphs will be devoted here to preparing the groundwork for the plasma or MHD propulsion systems to be discussed in more detail later in the chapter.

The basic working material of MHD is plasma. Although simple ions are useful in describing concepts, a concentration of like-charged particles is an unnatural occurrence. Matter prefers to be neutral, and special pains must be taken to produce a beam or assemblage of ions of the same sign. A more natural state of matter is plasma. Plasma is a macroscopically neutral mixture of ions, electrons, and neutral atoms. Random microscopic variations may create local charge concentrations, but there are enough electrons present to neutralize each positive charge. Plasma may be generated in plasma jets (Chap. 5), gas discharge tubes, shock tubes, and by exploding wires. We shall want to know how plasma can be efficiently produced and accelerated to high velocities for propulsive purposes.

Plasma, being composed of charged particles and subjected to external as well as internally produced magnetic fields, must obey the laws of electromagnetics. It is also a gas and thus must observe the laws of gas

* References are listed in the Bibliography at the back of the book.

dynamics. The two sets of laws are coupled through the velocities of the charged particles. To better illustrate the concepts embodied in MHD, we shall write down the basic equations governing plasma behavior. In these formulations, the plasma is assumed to behave as a continuum in which no nuclear or chemical reactions occur. Furthermore, there must be no energy loss or gain through radiation mechanisms (Ref. 6-25).

Maxwell's equations describe the basic phenomena of electromagnetics. Ampere's law is the first of these. It describes the magnetic field that is generated by an electric current.

$$\frac{\partial \mathbf{D}}{\partial t} + \mathbf{J} = \boldsymbol{\nabla} \times \mathbf{H} \tag{6-4}$$

where $\mathbf{D}$ = displacement
t = time
$\mathbf{J}$ = current density
$\mathbf{H}$ = magnetic field intensity

Next, Faraday's law of induction measures the electric field created by a time-varying magnetic field.

$$\frac{\partial \mathbf{B}}{\partial t} = -\boldsymbol{\nabla} \times \mathbf{E} \tag{6-5}$$

Maxwell's equations are completed by adding

$$\boldsymbol{\nabla} \cdot \mathbf{B} = 0 \tag{6-6}$$
and
$$\boldsymbol{\nabla} \cdot \mathbf{D} = \rho_e \tag{6-7}$$

where ρ_e equals the electric charge density. Maxwell's equations describe the different characteristics of the electric and magnetic fields. For example, magnetic lines of force are nondestructible, while the electric field may originate or terminate on charged particles.

Usually, Eq. (6-1) is added to Maxwell's equations at this point; however, it and Maxwell's equations are still not adequate to describe the behavior of a plasma. They do not account for hydrodynamic effects. The so-called "momentum equation" must be used.

$$\rho \frac{\partial \mathbf{v}}{\partial t} + \rho \mathbf{v} \cdot \boldsymbol{\nabla} \mathbf{v} = \mathbf{J} \times \mathbf{B} - \boldsymbol{\nabla} p + \mu_1 \boldsymbol{\nabla}^2 \mathbf{v} \tag{6-8}$$

where ρ = gas density
p = pressure
μ_1 = viscosity

Equation (6-8) adds the Lorentz force $\mathbf{J} \times \mathbf{B}$ to Euler's equation from gas dynamics. Equation (6-8) assumes an incompressible gas, constant viscosity, and a negligible charge density. The coupling between electromagnetics and gas dynamics through the velocity is obvious in this equation. Ohm's law and the charge conservation equation are added to the list next.

$$J = \sigma(E + v \times B) \tag{6-9}$$

$$\frac{\partial \rho_e}{\partial t} + \nabla \cdot J = 0 \tag{6-10}$$

where σ equals electrical conductivity. Next, we take two equations from gas dynamics. They are the well-known equation of continuity and equation of state.

$$\frac{\partial \rho}{\partial t} + \nabla \cdot v\rho = 0 \tag{6-11}$$

$$p = f(\rho, T) \tag{6-12}$$

Finally, the energy equation completes the list.

$$\rho \left[\frac{\partial (c_p T)}{\partial t} + v \cdot \nabla (c_p T) \right] - \frac{\partial p}{\partial t} - v \cdot \nabla p = \nabla \cdot k \nabla T + \frac{J^2}{\sigma} \tag{6-13}$$

where c_p = specific heat at constant pressure
k = Boltzmann constant

Again in Eq. (6-13), the coupling of gas dynamics and electromagnetics is observed in the ohmic heating term at the far right. Equation (6-13) is merely a statement of the law of conservation of energy neglecting viscous, dissipative forces.

Together, the 10 equations from Eq. (6-4) through Eq. (6-13) complete the formal mathematical description of MHD. An insight to some of the intricacies of MHD may be found in some rather simple reasoning from this imposing array of laws.

Following Clauser (Ref. 6-9), if the displacement current can be neglected and the conductivity is constant throughout the region, we can obtain from Eqs. (6-4), (6-5), (6-6), and (6-9) the following result:

$$\frac{\partial B}{\partial t} = \nabla \times v \times B + \frac{1}{\sigma \mu_0} \nabla^2 B \tag{6-14}$$

where μ_0 equals the permeability of free space and B equals $\mu_0 H$. The conductivity σ turns out to be a key factor in fixing the interaction between the electromagnetic fields and the plasma. If it is high,

$$\frac{\partial B}{\partial t} = \nabla \times v \times B \tag{6-15}$$

and the magnetic field is effectively locked into the fluid and follows its motion. In the case of low conductivity, the magnetic field diffuses through the fluid.

The concept of magnetic pressure is extremely important in the discussions of MHD propulsion systems to follow. If a conducting fluid, liquid metal, or ionized gas has a high electrical conductivity, it is possible to create a magnetic field that is strong enough to pump, confine, or accelerate it. From Eqs. (6-4) and (6-8), neglecting displacement currents and viscosity, we obtain

$$\rho \frac{\partial \mathbf{v}}{\partial t} + \rho \mathbf{v} \cdot \nabla \mathbf{v} = -\frac{1}{\mu_0} \frac{\nabla B^2}{2} + \frac{(\mathbf{B} \cdot \nabla)\mathbf{B}}{\mu_0} - \nabla p \qquad (6\text{-}16)$$

Now if the gradient of the magnetic field vanishes, Eq. (6-16) becomes

$$\rho \frac{\partial \mathbf{v}}{\partial t} + \rho \mathbf{v} \cdot \nabla \mathbf{v} = -\nabla \left(p + \frac{B^2}{2\mu_0} \right) \qquad (6\text{-}17)$$

From this equation, we see that the magnetic pressure is just the term $B^2/2\mu_0$. Magnetic fields can be made strong enough to confine plasma at pressures of thousands of atmospheres.

Neutral gases lose energy through electromagnetic radiation and conduction to the surroundings. Hot plasma not only loses energy in these ways but also through emission of *Bremsstrahlung* radiation. This kind of electromagnetic radiation is generated when high-velocity charged particles are decelerated by the coulomb fields of heavy ions in the plasma. Kinetic energy is converted to electromagnetic energy in this process. Losses by thermal radiation are much smaller than those due to Bremsstrahlung in very hot plasma. This is due to the fact that the blackbody radiation laws do not hold for the plasmas created in laboratory apparatus. This unusual behavior of plasmas has its origin in the absence of thermal equilibrium in most laboratory experiments. The mean free paths of the photons are larger or of the same order of magnitude as the dimensions of the confining equipment. Instead of the usual Stefan-Boltzmann equation, where the radiant emittance is proportional to the fourth power of the temperature, we have the law for hot plasmas stating that their radiant emittance is proportional to the square root of the electron temperature.

Perhaps the best known phenomenon of MHD is the *pinch effect*. It occurs when a very strong current is sent through a plasma. Figure 6-4 illustrates this phenomenon, although toroidal as well as cylindrical containers have also been used. The high currents that are necessary are usually obtained by discharging large condenser banks through the apparatus. As the current builds up in the plasma, it creates strong magnetic fields which give rise to an inwardly directed magnetic pressure. The current column thus tends to constrict itself without the use of externally generated magnetic fields. Figure 6-4 shows how the magnetic field varies across the discharge. Evidently the interior of the current column is shielded somewhat by the high surface currents. The pinch effect turns out to be an unstable phenomenon. Any kinking or nonuniformities in the current column tend to increase the perturbations and either drive the plasma into the walls or completely pinch off the discharge.

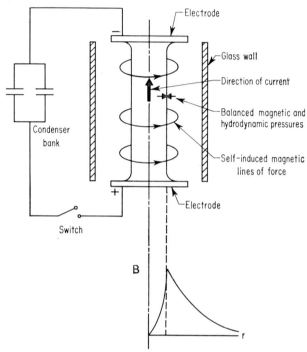

Fig. 6-4. Schematic of a pinch apparatus. Self-induced magnetic fields pinch the plasma away from the solid walls. The magnetic field is strongest at the surface of the current column.

Although the pinch effect is described here mainly to illustrate MHD effects, it conceivably could be used in propulsion systems to protect nozzles and orifice walls from the effects of very hot fluids in plasma propulsion systems.

The preceding paragraphs give a very simplified treatment of a complex and poorly understood subject. In practical applications, such as thermonuclear reactors where energy is being generated internally, more refined approaches must be evolved. In the sections to follow, we shall proceed from the relatively simple ion drive, which may be treated using the techniques from Sect. 6-2, to the more complicated plasma or MHD propulsion systems.

ION DRIVES

6-4. Introduction to Ion Propulsion. The ion drive or rocket is the oldest and most respectable of the many electrical propulsion systems that have been proposed for space travel. The use of electrostatic fields for electron acceleration in radio tubes was early extrapolated into a thrust-producing ion gun. Ion propulsion systems have been repeatedly proposed over the last three decades. Ion propulsion is just now emerging from the study phase into prototype development. Although it is difficult to imagine ion beams that are powerful enough to propel spaceships, the present governmental support for hardware development substantiates the practicality and usefulness of the concept for low-thrust missions.

In examining the physical laws applicable to ion propulsion, we discover that the basic knowledge necessary for the design and construction of ion drives has been available for a half century. If this is so, why have such engines not been developed before? The answer, of course, is that no practical use for low-thrust high-specific-impulse propulsion systems existed before 1958. Now that payloads of thousands of kilograms can be launched into orbit, low-thrust space propulsion systems begin to have some practicality. Reviewing the missions described in Chap. 2, it is apparent that very low thrust-to-weight ratios (10^{-4}) are adequate to sustain, maneuver, and control the attitude of satellites and possibly even provide thrusts for orbit-to-orbit trips to the farther planets.

The physical concept behind the ion drive is simplicity itself. Put a charged particle in an electrostatic field, and it will be accelerated according to Eq. (6-2). This direct procedure has esthetic appeal, and the equations descriptive of the phenomenon are readily understood. A closer look at any ion accelerator uncovers an impressive array of practical nuts-and-bolts problems. Ion-drive development is just entering the stage where the simplicity of the original concepts is being replaced by the complexities of the workable machine.

6-5. The Basic Ion Drive. Every ion propulsion system has three basic elements. These are:

1. The emitter, consisting of some sort of device to ionize neutral matter and separate the positive ions from the electrons for subsequent separate acceleration.

2. The accelerator, which takes the ions produced by the emitter and electrostatically accelerates them to the velocity specified by the mission specific-impulse requirements.

3. The beam neutralizer is the final element. It recombines the positive ions and electrons to ensure that the net charge of the propellant leaving the vehicle is neutral. It forestalls the build-up of space charge on

the vehicle and consequent reduction of propulsion-system performance.

Numerous ingenious mechanisms have been proposed for each of the three fundamental ion-drive components. Although it may be feasible to combine some of the elements, most of the designs that have been proposed have them well separated.

The ion drive is in actuality an immense ion gun of the same basic type as that used in the physics laboratory. Much of the design philosophy used for high-energy particle accelerators can be carried over bodily to this new application. There are, however, many places where the similarity ends. For example, the term "ion gun" brings to mind a cylindrical device with a high length-to-diameter ratio which accelerates ions to energies of many million electron volts. It is soon discovered that the ion gun for propulsive uses has a low thrust-to-area ratio. Ion-drive configurations tend to be thin and flat. They have very low length-to-diameter ratios in contrast with most other reaction engines.

It is also interesting to compare ion and plasma propulsion systems. Different philosophies are embodied in each. The ion drive takes neutral matter, separates the differently charged particles, accelerates each separately, and recombines them at the exit port. The plasma machines have a clear-cut advantage over the ionic systems in that the separation and recombination of charges is not necessary. The emitter and neutralizer must be added to the ion drive because the electrostatic field cannot accelerate neutral plasma or un-ionized matter. This difference in the way in which the propellant is handled would be important only if lower performance and higher mechanical risks accrue to the ionic systems.

6-6. The Emitter. The ion drive demands a copious source of uniformly charged ions. These ions must be generated as efficiently as possible, since every watt expended in ion generation must be subtracted from the potential beam power. All energy not appearing as ion kinetic energy or energy of ionization must be disposed of by radiation to outer space or through an auxiliary cooling loop. Most of the ion sources used in the laboratory for experiments in particle physics first create a plasma, by an arc discharge, and then separate the ions from the electrons by the application of electromagnetic fields. Contemporary ion sources, however, measure their output in fractions of an ampere, whereas the ion drive will require tens and hundreds of amperes for the production of usable thrusts. Likewise, present equipment is notoriously inefficient in the production of ions. Table 6-1 indicates the potentialities of several ion sources. Clearly, some major advances in efficient ion production must be made before the practical ion drive becomes a reality.

Three types of plasma sources are common today: the plasma jet, the electric arc, and the radio frequency (r-f) sources. The first of these was described in some detail in Chap. 5. The arc source is probably best exemplified by the ion source used in the *calutron*. The calutron was used extensively during the Manhattan Project in producing uranium ions for the electromagnetic separation of U-235 from natural uranium. Figure 6-5 shows the operating configuration of the calutron's source. In the r-f source, high-frequency electromagnetic energy is pumped into a neutral gas and produces ionization by induction heating. Some r-f sources are presently used in some low-current ion accelerators in physics laboratories.

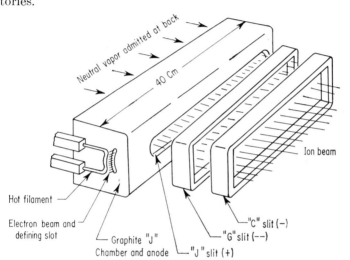

Fig. 6-5. The ion source for the calutron. Propellant vapor is ionized as it passes through the electron stream flowing from the filament through the *J* chamber. Focusing is achieved electrostatically through the different potentials on the *J*, *G*, and *C* slits (Ref. 6-2).

Once plasma is created, the electrons must be extracted for the subsequent ion acceleration processes. Usually, separation is accomplished electromagnetically, as in the case of the calutron. As long as one deals with small quantities of plasma, it is not too difficult to overcome the coulomb forces which oppose charge separation.

While the plasma sources used in conjunction with charge separators have the advantage of being readily available, Table 6-1 indicates that these processes are relatively inefficient compared with a different type of ion-producing process. This new scheme uses the fact that some of the alkali metals have first-ionization potentials which are lower than the work functions of several metals. This condition permits the contact ionization of the alkali metal vapors by metals like platinum and tungsten. The so-called "contact potential ion source" is the most popular ion source used in ion drive designs; and, if the efficiencies listed in Table 6-1 are born out in practice, it will be preferable over the more conventional ion sources from this standpoint alone.

TABLE 6-1. ION SOURCE EFFICIENCIES*

Type	Probable efficiency, kw/amp
Low-pressure arc source	10
Radio-frequency source	20
Plasma-jet source	0.025
Contact-potential source	0.5

* Ref. 6-12.

In the contact potential ion sources, which will be assumed in all later discussion, ions are created without the intermediate formation of plasma. There are no short-lived electrodes such as those in the arc source, and no heavy r-f generating equipment is needed. A simple model of the physical processes occurring during contact ionization involve, first, adsorption of the neutral atom on the high-work-function surface, second, capture of the outermost electron of the propellant atom by the surface, third, release of the singly ionized atom. The entire sequence, of course, happens in a fraction of a second. In actuality, the process is more complex, involving a shift in the equilibrium ionization of the plasma near the hot surface. Laboratory experiments indicate that ionization of the atoms of alkali metal vapors on hot tungsten surfaces occurs with nearly 100 per cent probability. The simplicity, lightness, and potential long life of the contact potential ion source make it the most likely candidate for ion-drive emitters.

Table 6-2 lists a few potential propellants and their properties. Some high-work-function pure metals are also added for comparison and as a guide to selecting attractive propellant-emitter metal combinations. The best combination from the standpoint of high contact difference of potential is that of cesium and platinum. Unfortunately, both of these substances are relatively expensive, though high demand might reduce their prices somewhat. Projected costs of cesium fall between $40 and $200 per kilogram in large quantities. Besides the cost and the magnitude of the contact difference of potential, the factors of material compatibility, high temperature properties, and atomic weight are important to the selection of materials. Naturally, the propellant and surface metal must be able to survive at high temperatures for thousands of hours of operation in the company of each other. Little experimental information exists to guide us in predicting the results of the unusual combinations of materials needed for the contact potential source. The wisdom of the nearly universal choice of tungsten and an alkali metal will be established only in the laboratory. Cesium is the most popular propellant choice, but rubidium and abundant potassium are close competitors.

TABLE 6-2. PROPERTIES OF PROPELLANTS AND HIGH-WORK-FUNCTION METALS

Propellant	First ionization potential, ev	Melting point, °C	Boiling point, °C	Atomic weight	Density, g/cm^3
Cesium............	3.89	28.5	670	133	1.87
Rubidium..........	4.18	38.5	700	85.4	1.53
Potassium.........	4.34	62.3	760	39.1	0.83
Sodium............	5.14	97.5	880	23.0	0.93
Lithium...........	5.39	186	1336	6.9	0.53

Metal	Work function, ev	Melting point, °C
Platinum............	5.32	1773
Iridium.............	5.30	2454
Rhenium............	5.10	3167
Nickel..............	5.03	1455
Palladium...........	4.98	1555
Rhodium............	4.80	1985
Carbon.............	4.60	3550
Tungsten...........	4.52	3370

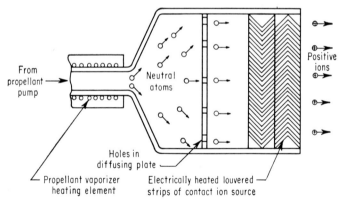

FIG. 6-6. Schematic diagram of a contact potential ion source. Exaggerated in the horizontal direction.

A physical picture of a possible ion emitter using the contact potential principle is shown in Fig. 6-6. The features include a liquid-metal boiler, a diffuser to distribute the vapor evenly to the ionizing surfaces, heater elements, and the ionizing surface itself. Note that electric power must be provided for boiling the propellant, separating the charges, and heating the emitter to a temperature sufficiently high to preclude the formation of a neutral layer of propellant over its surface. The last function is achieved by passing high current through the ionizing surface. Several possibilities exist for the construction of the emitter. It should present a path for the vapor atoms that is tortuous enough to ensure at least one collision with the hot surface before entry to the accelerator. The louvered strips shown in Fig. 6-6 are perhaps the simplest, and they lend themselves to easy electrical heating. A porous or packed granular mass or an optically dense woven mesh of the high-work-function material are

Fig. 6-7. Cesium contact potential ion source for ion propulsion equipment under test. (*General Electric Co.*)

also conceptually possible. Many organizations are now actively testing different ion emitters constructed along these lines. Figure 6-7 portrays an experimental packed-tungsten-granule emitter being tested by the General Electric Company. Current densities of 14 ma/cm^2 have been achieved by Electro-Optical Systems, Inc. with this type of source.

6-7. The Accelerator Section. Once a cloud of singly charged propellant ions is created at the exit port of the ion source, they must be quickly drawn off by the accelerating electric field and accelerated to the final desired velocity.

A phenomenon which occurs with any kind of ion source is the limitation of the ion beam current by the build-up of a *space charge* just outside the emitter surface. As the charged particles leave the emitter surface under the influence of the electric field, a column of like-charged particles will fill the space between the electrodes. The presence of the cloud of charges reduces the electric field intensity in the neighborhood of the emitter since electric lines of force terminate inside the charge cloud. Figure 6-8 illustrates the physical situation and also plots the potential energy of a charged particle in the space between the emitter and the accelerating electrode. There will be a critical voltage (Fig. 6-8) when

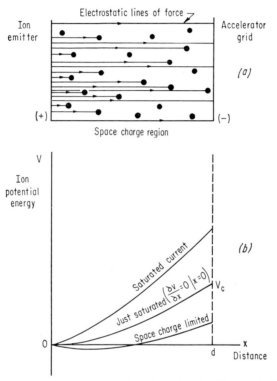

FIG. 6-8. Effect of space charge on electric potential. (a) Electrostatic lines of force terminate on the ions reducing the electric intensity in the region of the accelerating grid; (b) potential-energy curves for different conditions of ion emission.

all of the charges emitted are drawn off to the grid and there is no suppression of current. If the voltage is less than this value, the potential has a minimum in it, indicating a change of sign in the electric field intensity vector. In this case, the emitter current is space-charge-limited, and there will be a repulsion of some of the emitted ions back to the emitter surface. Above the critical voltage difference, the current is emission-limited, all ions leaving the emitter are drawn to the accelerating grid. By assuming plane geometry, a simple equation describing this phenomenon can be easily derived.   The three pertinent equations are:

$$qV = \frac{mv^2}{2} \tag{6-18}$$

$$J = \rho_e v \tag{6-19}$$

$$\frac{d^2V}{dx^2} = -\frac{\rho_e}{\epsilon_0} \tag{6-20}$$

The first equation gives the kinetic energy possessed by a particle of mass m and charge q after falling through a voltage V. Equation (6-19) is the definition of the current density J where ρ_e equals the charge density. The final equation is a one-dimensional form of Poisson's equation, where x equals distance and ϵ_0 equals the permittivity of free space.   Note also that m equals $A \times 10^{-3}/N_0$.

By solving Eqs. (6-18), (6-19), and (6-20) simultaneously and applying the following boundary conditions at the emitter,

$$\frac{dV}{dx} = 0 \quad \text{and} \quad V = 0$$

we arrive at Child's law

$$J = \frac{4\epsilon_0}{9} \sqrt{\frac{2q}{m}} \frac{V^{3/2}}{d^2} = \frac{4\epsilon_0}{9} \sqrt{\frac{2q}{mV}} E^2 \tag{6-21}$$

The fact that the current density J has a saturation value dependent on the voltage gradient E has an important ramification in the design of ion drives.   High current densities are desirable from the standpoint of compactness or, equivalently, high thrusts per unit area of emitter.   Figure 6-9 plots the current density as a function of accelerator voltage for potassium and cesium.   The high-voltage gradients that would permit the high current densities are limited by the voltage breakdown characteristics of the ion-filled spaces between the emitter and accelerator.   A thorough experimental study of the arc breakdown in the presence of alkali metal vapors of ion-drive accelerator sections has not been published.   One may expect, however, to achieve about 15,000 volts/cm in typical designs.   In addition, high-voltage differences lead to high specific impulses, possibly far higher than necessary.   Obviously, compromises between emitter area, design specific impulse, and the breakdown characteristics of the drive unit must be made.   One possible solution that has been adopted by many designers is the acceleration-deceleration technique where high-voltage gradients, as high as permitted by arc breakdown, are first used to keep the emitter area down; then, a decelerator grid is added to slow the ions down to the velocity desired for the target specific impulse.

Once the current density permitted from space charge considerations is fixed (Fig. 6-9), the design of the accelerator grids themselves must be examined. Usually, a single grid is sufficient for specific impulses up to 100,000 sec. This value is about the upper limit for useful electrical propulsion due to decreasing thrust-to-weight ratios (Fig. 6-1). The acceleration-deceleration approach requires an additional grid, and electrostatic ion-beam focusing may add other structures to the accelerator

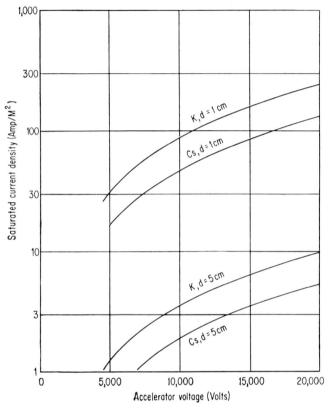

FIG. 6-9. Ion current density for plane geometry as limited by space charge effects. (Computed from Child's law.)

assembly. The position of the grids in the ion beam naturally subjects them to high levels of ion bombardment and the resultant heating. Ideally, electrostatic focusing would keep the total fraction of ions terminating on the grids down to less than 1 per cent. The practical ion drives will probably have at least 1 per cent interception. When ions do terminate on any structure within the drive unit, not only does heating result, but surface sputtering with consequent deterioration of the structure will occur. If the heating is small, radiation to space will be an adequate cooling mechanism. If it is larger than 1 per cent, it is advisable to cool the structures with the liquid-metal propellant in a manner analogous to regeneratively cooled chemical rocket nozzles.   The effects of sputtering on performance depend upon the ion energy, the type of surface, and the length of the mission.   Experimental determinations of the precise effects of the sputtering of heavy ions on grid structures are now underway at several locations.   Present indications are that sputtering will limit the number of ion terminations to a far lower fraction than the effects of grid heating, perhaps to 0.001 per cent (Ref. 6-14).

Electrostatic and possibly magnetic focusing of the ion beam may be used to minimize deleterious effects of ion impingement.   An ion beam, of course, has a tendency to disperse since it is made up of mutually repelling particles.   The principles of electrostatic beam focusing are exemplified by cathode ray tube design.   The heavy ions used for propulsion are more difficult to focus than the much lighter electrons, but the same techniques apply.   Figure 6-10 presents the cross section of an electrostatically focused accelerator tube.   This configuration makes use of the accelerate-decelerate concept as well as the so-called "Pierce gun" electrode arrangement.   The electrostatic lines of force connecting the grids and focusing electrodes tend to force ion trajectories away from physical structures.   It is also possible that some of the electric current destined for the emitter may be directed through the grid wires to generate magnetic fields around them.   Such fields would also suppress grid terminations.   Figure 6-11 is a photograph of a test assembly designed to probe the problems associated with the configuration shown in Fig. 6-10.

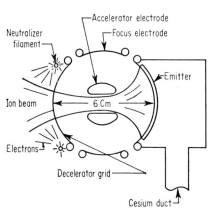

FIG. 6-10. A possible arrangement of ion drive components.   This is a Pierce gun configuration employing the accelerate-decelerate principle.   A cylindrical geometry is used to facilitate the supply of propellant vapor and grid construction (Ref. 6-13).

It is interesting to note that the design of an ion accelerator for propulsion is radically different from the design of particle accelerators for physical research.   Millions of volts potential difference are common in the latter, while thousands of volts are more appropriate for ion drives.   There is also a disparity in current handling capabilities.   The drive needs hundreds of amperes compared with milliamperes for physics research.   Perhaps the most unusual requirement of the ion drive is that of beam neutralization.   Ion beams in the laboratory are quickly neu-

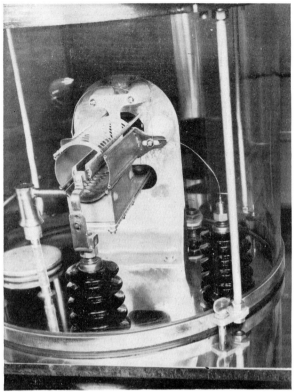

Fig. 6-11. An ion drive unit under test. This is the same configuration as that shown in Fig. 6-10. (*General Electric Co.*)

tralized in the air or target, but in outer space special precautions must be taken.

6-8. The Beam Neutralizer. If the ions emerging from the drive unit were shot out into space without neutralization, the build-up of space charge on the vehicle itself would soon force them to return because of the attracting coulomb forces that would be created. This effect can be prevented by discharging electrons into the beam immediately after it leaves the accelerator section of the drive. Electrons may be shot into the beam by small separate accelerators, in which case high electron velocities should not be attempted, for the electrons contribute very little thrust per unit of power. The most attractive way to neutralize space charge is to provide an electron source in the form of an electron-emitting filament (Fig. 6-10) and allow the space charge of the ion beam to pull the mobile electrons into itself. An equilibrium situation may ultimately be created where self-neutralization of the beam will occur. The penalty for this automatic action will be the reduction in performance caused by the creation of sufficient space charge to draw off the proper electron current. To some extent, the termination of ions on the grids will knock off secondary electrons which will aid in suppressing the space charge. If the ion beam is dense or of large dimensions, it is possible that the neutralizing electrons will have to be injected at velocities high enough to penetrate the beam so that localized space charges will not be created. Ion beams from the contact potential type of source will be so tenuous that the injected electrons may penetrate the charged beam, be attracted back, and oscillate through it many times before neutralization is accomplished. Analysis has also shown that electron and ion velocities should be closely matched for effective neutralization. Even thermionically emitted electrons may be moving faster than the much heavier ions. Such disparities in velocities lead to charge oscillations within the beam and additional problems in the neutralization process. Beam neutralization must occur quickly before the image charges created at the exit port of the accelerator can decelerate the ion beam and before the mutual repulsive forces within the beam can defocus it. Beam neutralization has emerged as one of the most critical problems in ion propulsion. Experiments in beam neutralization are urgently needed to confirm analysis and to suggest new techniques for producing a neutral propellant efflux.

6-9. The Integrated Propulsion Unit. Figure 6-10 shows the relationship of the emitter, accelerator, and neutralizer for one feasible type of design. While axially symmetric (parallel to the thrust vector) arrangements are possible, the most practical configuration is cylindrical with a cross section such as that in Fig. 6-10. A complete ion-drive unit would then consist of a long tube or bank of small units (Fig. 6-12). The ions would be emitted perpendicular to its axis. The accessory unit containing propellant pumps, transformers, heaters, and controls would be at its base. A great many other design variations are also quite feasible.

Although one usually thinks of the ion drive as a d-c device, there is no reason why the units cannot be made to operate on alternating current. By pairing units, a full-wave bridge circuit could be set up to take advantage of the lighter and more flexible a-c power equipment. Twice as many propulsion units would have to be provided, but their weight, in comparison with the power-generating equipment, is very small. Figure 6-13 is very revealing. In it are plotted estimates of the various power drains in an ion drive. Some losses, like that due to the heating of the source, are constant regardless of the specific-impulse level. Other losses are proportional to specific impulse. Because of the first type of losses, ion drives tend to be more efficient the higher the specific impulse or ion energy.

Several organizations are now working both on the basic element prob-

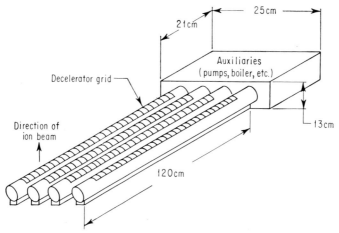

Fɪɢ. 6-12. Conceptual design of an 80-kw ion rocket. This unit operates as an a-c full-wave bridge (Ref. 6-13).

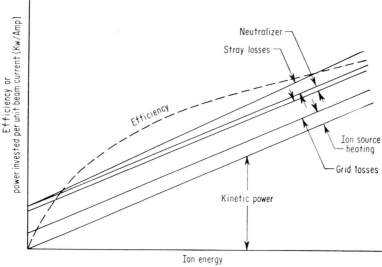

Fɪɢ. 6-13. Power losses in a representative ion drive. The efficiency improves with power because many of the losses are constant with increasing ion energy (Ref. 6-12). Power curves are cumulative.

lems as well as the construction of prototype ion propulsion systems. The General Electric Company, Rocketdyne Division of North American Aviation, Aerojet-General, Convair-Astronautics, and Thompson-Ramo-Wooldridge are all known to be engaged in such research. In addition, the NASA and the Livermore Laboratory of the University of California are sponsoring similar work. The first successful laboratory prototypes were operated during 1958 at the General Electric Company.

6-10. Propulsion Parameters. So far, little has been said about the thrust-producing capabilities of the ion drive. Even though ions are being expelled rather than the hot gases from a combustion process, the thrust equation $F = \dot{m}v$ still holds. We may factor in the electrical parameters by introducing the following equations:

$$P_e = IV \tag{6-22}$$

$$\dot{m} = \frac{IA}{1,000N_0qn} \tag{6-23}$$

$$v_e = \sqrt{\frac{2nqV}{m}} = \sqrt{\frac{2,000nqN_0V}{A}} \tag{6-24}$$

where P_e = exhaust power
$\quad\ I$ = ion current
$\quad\ V$ = voltage
$\quad\ A$ = atomic weight
$\quad\ N_0$ = Avogadro's number
$\quad\ n$ = degree of ionization

Equation (6-22) gives the beam power in terms of electrical quantities. Electron power is ignored because neutralizing electrons will generally not be given any appreciable acceleration. Equation (6-23) states the amount of mass transferred per second by each ampere of ions. Finally, Eq. (6-24) equates the kinetic energy of the ion with the energy extracted from the electrostatic field. The thrust is then

$$F = I\sqrt{\frac{2VA}{1,000nqN_0}} \tag{6-25}$$

This equation can be conveniently plotted for any specific propellant in the form shown in Fig. 6-14. An approximate expression for the thrust-to-weight ratio for an ion propulsion system can now be derived. First, one assumes that the total mass of the vehicle M_0 can be given approximately by

$$M_0 \cong M_{PS} \cong \frac{M_{sp}P_e}{1,000e'} \tag{6-26}$$

$$= \frac{M_{sp}IV}{1,000e'}$$

where M_{PS} = power-supply mass
$\quad\ e'$ = propulsion-unit efficiency

From Eqs. (6-25) and (6-26), it is apparent that the thrust-to-weight ratio is

$$\frac{F}{W} = \frac{F}{g_0M_0} \cong \sqrt{\frac{2,000e'^2A}{g_0^2M_{sp}^2nqN_0V}} \tag{6-27}$$

The other important performance parameter that may be related directly to the missions requirements (Chap. 2) is the specific impulse. It is obtained directly from Eq. (6-24).

$$I_{sp} = \frac{v_e}{g_0} = \sqrt{\frac{2,000nqN_0V}{g_0{}^2A}}$$ (6-28)

With the thrust-to-weight ratio and specific impulse expressed in terms of ion-drive parameters, a few interesting generalizations may be made.

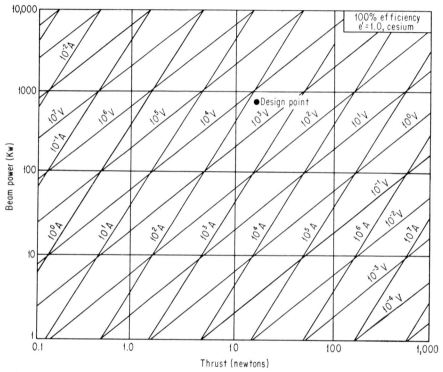

FIG. 6-14. Power-thrust curves for a cesium ion drive. The design point from Table 6-3 is indicated approximately.

The specific impulse will usually be fixed by the mission and the optimization of some system parameter (Chap. 2). Of the variables in Eq. (6-28), only the ratio V/A is under the control of the designer. The product nq is fixed by the characteristics of the contact potential ion source. The thrust-to-weight ratio, in contrast, has more parameters under the control of the designer. They are V, A, e', and M_{sp}. The propulsion unit efficiency e' is a complex function of the system design, the state of the art, and the design point of the drive. Obviously, it is made as high as possible. The specific mass of the power supply M_{sp} depends on the state of the art, mission duration, power level, and meteoroid vulnerability (Chap. 4). Naturally, M_{sp} is made as small as possible. The effective accelerator voltage and the atomic weight of the propellant appear in ratio form in both Eqs. (6-27) and (6-28). It is impossible to conclude from these equations alone what voltages and propellants are best for an ion drive. Once the specific impulse is fixed by the missions requirements, the ratio V/A will be determined but not the values of each parameter separately. Within the limits set by the variability of M_{sp} and e', the thrust-to-weight ratio of the propulsion system will also be set.

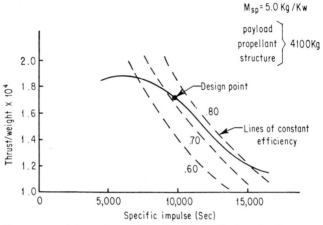

FIG. 6-15. Thrust-to-weight ratio as a function of specific impulse for a representative ion-driven spaceship. The thrust-to-weight ratio is reduced by decreasing efficiency at the low specific impulses and by increasing power-plant mass at the higher specific impulses.

If the resulting thrust-to-weight ratio is too low, one can conclude that ion propulsion is inappropiate for the mission under consideration. If it is too high, payload may be added or a power supply with a higher specific mass may be used. These analytical arguments should not conceal the fact that many practical factors must enter the picture. For example, Fig. 6-15 shows the variation of the thrust-to-weight ratio of a particular ion propulsion unit design as a function of the specific impulse. Although this curve is calculated rather than experimental, it does include the accelerator geometry, efficiency, and the variation of the power-supply specific mass with power level. Mathematically, this variation may be found by eliminating the ratio V/A from Eqs. (6-27) and (6-28). This procedure leads to

$$\frac{F}{W} = \frac{2,000e'}{g_0{}^2 M_{sp} I_{sp}} \tag{6-29}$$

which is identical with Eq. (2-19).

The ion drive can, in principle, produce specific impulses from zero up to a value limited by relativistic effects, 30,000,000 sec. Equation (6-29), however, sets a practical upper limit of 100,000 sec on ion drives because of unacceptable thrust-to-weight ratios above this value. For this reason, the possible values of V/A have a corresponding upper limit of about 220. The lower limit $V/A = 15$ is set by the competition of thermal engines (Chap. 5) below a specific impulse of 1,000 sec. This wide range in V/A permits the use of many propellants, even ionized dust or colloidal particles. For the more feasible propellants for use with the contact potential source, sodium ($A = 23$) through cesium ($A = 133$), the corresponding voltages limits are 300 and 300,000 volts. The propellant flexibility of the ion-drive principle is evident in these numbers.

Figure 6-16 plots the specific thrust of an ion drive with 100 per cent efficiency versus accelerator voltage for various propellants. As might be expected, the heavier ions give more thrust for a specified quantity of power. Equation (6-28) indicates that heavy ions reduce the specific impulse. The ultimate choice of propellant must be made from a carefully considered balance of performance (F/W and I_{sp}), propellant characteristics and availability, and the actual accelerator design. Most development work now underway centers around the cesium ion drive. Cesium is easily ionized by the contact potential type of source and yields desirable specific impulses (about 10,000 sec) for reasonable accelerator voltages ($\sim$6,000 volts).

Another quantity of interest in ion propulsion is the thrust per unit area of emitter surface. It is of importance because emitter areas must be kept as small as possible to reduce power loss by radiation and vulnerability to meteoroid damage. In addition, small structures are desirable from the standpoints of packaging and vehicle launching. The thrust-to-emitter-area ratio is determined by Eqs. (6-21) and (6-25). Since J equals I/A, where A equals area, the ratio F/A is easily derived.

$$\frac{F}{A} = \frac{8\epsilon_0 V^2}{9\,d^2} = \frac{8\epsilon_0 E^2}{9} \tag{6-30}$$

The thrust per unit emitter area is independent of the propellant properties. It is a function only of the electric field intensity. Substituting a reasonable value for E, 10^6 volts/m, we find that F/A is on the order of 10 newtons/m².

The ion drive is obviously a low thrust-to-area propulsion system. This fact accounts for its flat, thin configuration compared with the usual high length-to-diameter ratio engines used in atmospheric flight.

Many of the equations and figures presented in this chapter assume a propulsion unit efficiency of 100 per cent. We might inquire, at this

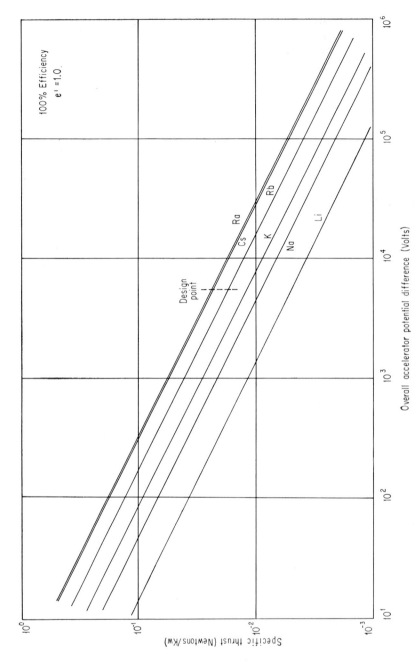

Fig. 6-16. Specific thrust for several ion-drive propellants as a function of accelerator voltage. Higher voltages produce higher specific impulses but require more power for a given thrust level. The specific thrust thus falls with higher accelerator voltages.

point, whether it is reasonable to assume high efficiencies for the ion drive. Analytical calculations, exemplified by Fig. 6-13, indicate that it is. If the analytical determinations of radiation losses, beam focusing, and ion-source power consumption are confirmed in the laboratory, eventually ion drives will probably be over 75 per cent efficient. This nearly perfect conversion of electrical energy into the directed kinetic energy of the propellant is essential if electrical propulsion is to play an important role in space propulsion. So far, the prospects are favorable. By the end of 1959 experimenters at General Electric had obtained total beam currents of 75 ma and propulsion-unit efficiencies of 15 per cent.

6-11. A Typical Ion Drive. Most of the ion propulsion systems that have been designed have specific impulses between 5,000 and 25,000 sec. Thrust-to-weight ratios range between 10^{-5} and 10^{-4}. Table 6-3 lists the major parameters of interest for a representative cesium ion propulsion system. While the figures presented in this table are the results of fairly sophisticated calculations, there has been no experimental verification of key factors, such as efficiency (in prototypes, $e' < 0.2$) and the thrust-to-weight ratio. Table 6-3 may be said to represent the projected state of the art in ion propulsion for 1965.

TABLE 6-3. DESIGN PARAMETERS FOR A TYPICAL ION DRIVE

Thrust	16 newtons
Efficiency	73%
Specific impulse	9,600 sec
Power consumed	1,000 kw
Propellant	Cesium
Propellant consumption	0.6 kg/hr
Design lifetime	10,000 hr
Thrust-to-weight ratio, including payload and propellant-structure allowance, 4,100 kg	1.7×10^{-4}
Mass of propulsion unit	500 kg
Mass of power supply	5,000 kg
Voltage	6,000 volts
Current in beam	121 amp
Beam power	730 kw

The space vehicle that utilizes an ion propulsion system will not be the sleek, streamlined spaceship of the science-fiction magazines. Instead, extensive radiator surfaces will dominate the configuration, with the ion engines being insignificant protuberances or perhaps internally contained (Ref. 6-27). While the unmanned, interplanetary, ion-driven probe will probably be a vehicle of only a few thousand kilograms, the manned, interplanetary spaceship will undoubtedly gross tens of thousands of kilograms. The conceptual design of such a vehicle is illustrated in Fig. 6-17.

6-12. Auxiliaries and Barrier Problems in Ion Propulsion.   In addition to the electrical power supply, the ion drive will require propellant storage facilities, equipment for melting and pumping the propellant, grid cooling systems with their own radiator sections, and separate power supplies for the emitters and beam neutralizers.   It seems quite likely that all of these pieces of equipment can be incorporated into small, modular assemblies with a specific mass of about 0.5 kg/kw of power delivered to the propulsion unit.

FIG. 6-17. Conceptual drawing of an ion-propelled spaceship.   Note the large radiator surfaces needed to reject waste heat.   (*Rocketdyne Division of North American Aviation, Inc.*)

Like every advanced propulsion concept, the ion drive has numerous problem areas associated with its development.   The more important of these are listed below:

1. Arc breakdown of the accelerator section in the presence of metallic propellant vapor.

2. Emitter lifetime under the corrosive action of the alkali metal propellant vapors.

3. Excessive heating of the accelerator structure because of terminations of high-energy ions.   Surface sputtering and loss of drive efficiency are attending problems.

4. Beam neutralization seems feasible, but experimental data are urgently needed to substantiate designs.

Despite the many unsolved problems connected with the development of the ion drive, this propulsion system has much to recommend it.   Of great practical import is the fact that ion propulsion technology is an extrapolation of the technology developed in the electronics and atomic energy fields.   Active research programs in the United States are rapidly providing the answers to the many questions raised by the above barrier problems.

Ion drives are extremely flexible in operation.   A great variety of propellants, even including charged dust, are feasible.   Voltages and currents can be easily varied to produce wide ranges of thrust and specific impulse with the same basic propulsion unit.   The ion propulsion system is one of the most interesting of all the electrical space engines.   It promises to be the most suitable propulsion system for the many low thrust-to-weight ratio, high-specific-impulse missions that are vital to successful space travel.

PLASMA ACCELERATORS

6-13. Plasma Acceleration.   Dozens of different techniques for accelerating neutral plasma have been proposed for propulsion as well as for fuel injection into thermonuclear reactors.   The field of MHD is in an explosive period of growth.   It is characteristic of this stage that most of the concepts that have been proclaimed in the literature have been analyzed only superficially.   Their real practicality as propulsion units remains unevaluated.   In contrast to the usual progression of concept formulation, feasibility study, basic experimentation to prove out design ideas, and final prototype development, the evolution of electromagnetic plasma thrust generators has apparently reversed this procedure.   Laboratory models of experimental plasma accelerators have emerged full blown with a minimum of theoretical work.   It has proven to be very easy to collect a few pieces of equipment and assemble a plasma gun, but the analytical description and the theoretical understanding of the phenomena are much more difficult.

All plasma drives differ from the ion engines in that they use electromagnetic fields to accelerate a macroscopically neutral mass of gas rather than the purely electrostatic acceleration of separated charges.   The processes of initial ion separation and final beam neutralization are eliminated.   Only the steps of plasma generation and acceleration remain.   The plasma may be produced either by arc discharge or by electrodeless induction heating.   In all cases, the electromagnetic acceleration of plasma may be explained in terms of the concepts developed earlier in this chapter.   In particular, the concept of magnetic pressure is useful in understanding the basic physical processes.

The variety of plasma propulsion systems is impressive.   It is difficult to categorize them.   The universally common feature is the use of electromagnetic fields for plasma acceleration.   The method of plasma generation and the mode of source operation are distinguishing features, however. In addition to the two basic methods of plasma production just mentioned, the sources may operate in a pulsed or continuous fashion. Table 6-4 separates out the major varieties of plasma propulsion systems and lists their important characteristics. Figure 6-18 displays these major types schematically (Ref. 2-15). In the following sections, a more

TABLE 6-4. CHARACTERISTICS OF PLASMA ACCELERATORS

Basic type	Ionizing mechanism	Mode of operation
Plasmoid guns..................	Arc	Cyclic
Traveling-wave tube.............	Induction	Continuous
Plasma pumps..................	Induction	Continuous
Kolb tubes.....................	Arc	Cyclic
Transient magnetic field..........	Induction	Cyclic

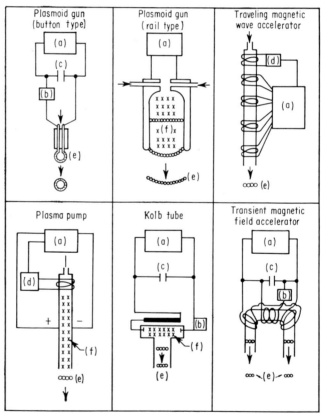

FIG. 6-18. Six types of plasma accelerators. (a) Power source; (b) switching circuits; (c) capacitor; (d) r-f induction plasma source; (e) plasmoids; (f) magnetic lines of force. (Adapted from W. E. Moeckel, "Propulsion Methods in Astronautics.")

complete description of operation and an evaluation of each major type will be given.

Although complete data is wanting, all the MHD propulsion systems have very similar performance characteristics. The thrust-to-weight ratios approach an upper limit of 10^{-4}, while the specific impulses are generally around 10,000 sec. They are all, therefore, intercompetitive and challenged by the ion drive. This similarity of performance among all of the electrical propulsion systems may be regarded as a distinctive family characteristic.

6-14. Plasmoid Guns. One class of plasma accelerators is made up of the *plasmoid guns*. These devices create small clumps of plasma

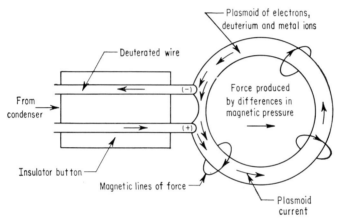

FIG. 6-19. Plasmoid gun, button type.

(plasmoids) and accelerate them with the electromagnetic fields that are generated by the discharge itself. Externally produced magnetic fields are also sometimes used. One of the earliest plasmoid guns was constructed by Bostick (Refs. 6-4, 6-5, and 6-6). This gun (Fig. 6-19) expels doughnut-shaped plasmoids at extremely high velocities. A pulse of high voltage, applied to the two wires piercing the insulator, causes the formation of an arc discharge across the ends of the wires. The explosive effect of the high current drawn between the wires boils metallic atoms from the surfaces of the wires. The wires may be deuterated or doped with other light atoms. In these instances, the plasmoid will consist of light ions as well as ions of the basic wire. Under the impetus of its self-generated magnetic fields (Fig. 6-19), the plasmoid is shot away from the ends of the wires at high speeds. During the formation of the doughnut, the magnetic field created by the current in the wires and the arc itself impresses a strong acceleration on the plasma. One may also think of the phenomenon in terms of a high differential magnetic pressure existing between the inside and outside of the partially formed doughnut. The differential forces will push the plasmoid away from the source. Once the doughnut is completely detached from the wires, its integrity is maintained by high circulating currents in the plasmoid. These currents generate magnetic fields which resist the hydrodynamic forces tending to disperse the plasma.

Some of the faults of the simple plasmoid gun for use in propulsive applications have their origin in the ringing of the capacitor circuits after the discharge owing to poor circuit damping. The I^2R losses may be severe because of this effect. In addition, the plasma ejected from this type of gun is poorly collimated, an effect which reduces the system efficiency. Some design parameters for an advanced plasmoid gun are listed in Table 6-5. Actual experiments show that propulsion unit efficiencies e' are usually less than 1 per cent. Some improvements over these crude prototypes will of course be forthcoming.

The plasmoid gun in its present form is a low-current pulsed propulsion system. To make it suitable for propulsion in outer space, it must be fed propellant wire continuously, arrayed in large numbers for reasonable thrust levels, and it should be operated at high frequencies. For example, to obtain 1 newton of thrust, the gun described in Table 6-5 must operate at 10,000 cycles/sec, assuming perfect collimation of the plasmoids.

TABLE 6-5. PROJECTED PLASMOID-GUN CHARACTERISTICS

Plasmoid mass	10^{-9} kg
Plasmoid velocity	10^5 m/sec
Specific impulse	10^4 sec
Pulse frequency	10^4 1/sec
Thrust per gun	1 newton
Projected efficiency	40%
Mass flow	10^{-5} kg/sec
Specific thrust	8×10^{-3} newton/kw
Power input	125 kw
Thrust-to-weight ratio for power supply alone, 10 kg/kw	8×10^{-5}

The difficulties encountered with the button-type of plasmoid gun has led to the design of a rail-type plasmoid gun. Figure 6-20 illustrates its general configuration. Here, the plasmoid maintains electrical contact between the rails as it is accelerated by the differential magnetic pressure across it. By extending the wires of the button source into rails, the magnetic forces can be made to act on the plasmoid for longer periods of time. The rail gun is, in effect, a linear electric motor. Any conducting substance, even solid metal pieces with sliding contacts, may be accelerated in electromagnetic guns of this nature. Plasmoid velocities of 10^5 m/sec have been demonstrated in the laboratory with the rail gun.

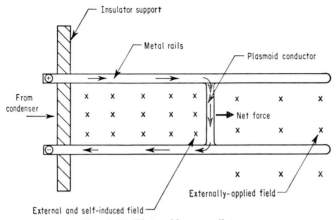

Fig. 6-20. Plasmoid gun, rail type.

A feeling for the dimensions and circuit parameters of the rail gun may be obtained from Table 6-6. The two columns show the projected capabilities of the rail gun with and without externally imposed magnetic fields.

TABLE 6-6. PROJECTED PLASMA-RAIL-GUN CHARACTERISTICS*

Characteristic	Series motor	Series-shunt motor
External magnetic field, webers/m^2.............	0	1
Plasmoid velocity, m/sec......................	4.6×10^5	1.5×10^6
Specific impulse, sec.........................	4.6×10^4	1.5×10^5
Length of rails, m............................	0.23	0.73
Plasmoid mass, kg............................	10^{-10}	10^{-10}
Current, amp.................................	10^4	10^4
Input energy per pulse, joules.................	22	140
Plasmoid energy, joules.......................	10.6	106
Potential efficiency, per cent..................	48	76
Load impedance, ohms........................	0.42	2.8
Ratio of wire separation to wire radius.........	10	10

* Ref. 6-4.

While it is apparent that the plasmoid guns, both the button and rail types, are sources of extremely high velocity plasma, sufficient development work has not been done to accurately establish the propulsion parameters. As Table 6-5 suggests, it is expected that the performance may eventually approach that of the ion drive. It is anticipated that the thrust-to-weight ratios will be somewhat lower than those of the ion drive because of the addition of capacitors and switching equipment. Of particular importance is the reliability and lifetime of the propulsion unit.

These critical factors have not been determined as yet for any of the electrical propulsion systems. It is probable, though, that reliability and lifetime would be affected adversely by pulsed modes of operation. Even though efficiencies of 40 per cent are eventually expected, this is only about half the estimated efficiency of the ion drive.

An interesting variation of the rail gun has been built by Patrick (Ref. 6-22). It is illustrated in Fig. 6-21. The device is fundamentally

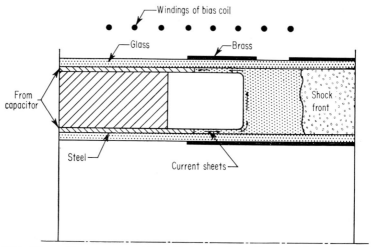

FIG. 6-21. Plasmoid gun, concentric cylinder configuration. (*Adapted from R. M. Patrick, "A Description of a Propulsive Device Which Employs a Magnetic Field as the Driving Force."*)

a rail gun with cylindrical symmetry. An arc is first created by a high voltage impressed across the concentric cylinders. The bias coils produce a magnetic field which keeps the electrons in the arc-created plasma circulating in the annulus so that they uniformly ionize the hydrogen gas, which is used as the propellant. As in the case of the simple rail gun, the magnetic field produced by the current sheets between the cylinders (Fig. 6-21) builds up enough magnetic pressure behind the shock front to accelerate the plasma to velocities in the order of 10^5 m/sec. The overall thrust-to-weight ratios obtainable with this device will be between 10^{-5} and 10^{-4}, while propulsion unit efficiencies may ultimately reach 50 per cent.

6-15. Traveling wave Accelerators. Few data exist concerning this kind of electromagnetic plasma accelerator. The basic concept is shown in Fig. 6-18. To better illustrate the accelerating action of the traveling waves, a longitudinal section through a conceptual accelerator tube is presented in Fig. 6-22. The magnetic waves, which are forced to travel down the tube by varying voltages across the tube coils, are analogous to magnetic mirrors which are continuously generated and accelerated down the tube. Bunches of plasma, created by a continuous r-f induction source, are fed into the tube and caught between the moving magnetic mirrors (Ref. 6-20).

By assuming accelerator lengths of 1 m and exhaust velocities of 10^5 m/sec, the acceleration of the magnetic waves can be found to be 5×10^9 m/sec^2. The frequency of the waves would probably be about

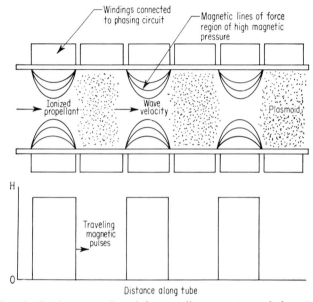

FIG. 6-22. Longitudinal cross section of the traveling-wave type of plasma accelerator.

10^4 cycles/sec. There is little experimental information available on this type of plasma generator at the present time. One can predict that great difficulties would be encountered in providing lightweight phasing circuits with the high power capacities needed for electrical space propulsion. In addition, the r-f induction source will probably be heavier than the arc-type of plasma source, since the conversion of low frequency power from the generator to the high frequencies needed for induction heating involves heavy and inefficient equipment. Although working models of this type of accelerator have been constructed at Los Alamos (Fig. 6-23 and Ref. 6-20), there are grave doubts whether the over-all thrust-to-weight ratios will be competitive with the other plasma accelerator units and ion drives described in this chapter. It is also expected that the r-f induction equipment and the electronic components which generate and control the traveling-wave acceleration will be short-lived and relatively unreliable. The specific impulses obtainable with the traveling-wave tube will be comparable with those of the other electric space engines, but the other aspects of performance are quite certain to be poorer.

6-16. Plasma Pumps or E × H Accelerators.   When any conducting fluid, whether it be a liquid metal or ionized gas, is subjected to crossed electrostatic and magnetic fields, a force at right angles to both of the applied fields is produced on each volume element of the fluid.   This

Fig. 6-23. Laboratory model of a traveling-wave plasma accelerator.   (*Los Alamos Scientific Laboratory, University of California*) (*Adapted from J. Marshall, "Acceleration of Plasma into Vacuum."*)

force can be used to pump and accelerate the fluid.   The electromagnetic liquid-metal pumps used in the nuclear-energy field represent a practical application of this principle.   Since plasma may be a good conductor, if the degree of ionization is sufficiently high, the crossed field accelerator can be used in plasma propulsion systems.

The configuration of the plasma pump is shown in the schematic of Fig. 6-18.   A magnetic field is impressed across a duct filled with plasma by external field coils.   Then, electrodes, perhaps constituting parallel sides of the duct, are connected to a d-c power supply.   The difference in potential between the electrodes will cause current to flow transversely across the duct.   The current is composed of ions and electrons moving in opposite directions.   When these charged particles move perpendicular to the magnetic field, a force normal to the electrostatic and magnetic fields is produced.   The force on each charged particle is $q(\mathbf{E} + \mathbf{v} \times \mathbf{B})$.

This approach is particularly attractive since a continuous acceleration of plasma is possible. An r-f induction plasma source preceding the accelerator section can be used to provide a steady, uniform flow of ionized propellant.

Some analytical studies of the acceleration of a compressible plasma in a uniform duct have been reported (Ref. 6-23). The plasma pump has not been thoroughly investigated experimentally. The contemporary liquid-metal pumps are the only $E \times H$ accelerators operating today. Some of the experimental difficulties foreseen include electrode construction and arc breakdown, losses of efficiency due to Joule heating, and the heating of the duct walls by recombining plasma.

The $E \times H$ accelerator can certainly be made to work with plasma, but the extent of this accelerator's success as a propulsive device is still in doubt. The magnitude of the specific impulse obtainable and the system weights are undetermined. There is a strong probability that this type of propulsion equipment will not be competitive with the other electrical space engines because of the heavy mass of the magnetic field coils. From a development standpoint, the $E \times H$ accelerator is comparable with the traveling-wave tube.

6-17. Kolb Tubes. The Kolb tube (Fig. 6-18) is a pulsed plasma accelerator using an arc discharge to generate the plasma propellant. An externally produced magnetic field is employed to add energy to the burst of hot ionized gas which is ejected down the stem of the T-shaped tube. The Kolb tube is used extensively in experimental MHD because it provides a simple, compact source of high-velocity plasma. The velocities obtainable are also high enough to make the Kolb tube interesting for space propulsion applications.

Referring to Fig. 6-18, when the capacitor shown is discharged across the electrodes located in the top of the T, the cold gas initially residing there is ionized by the arc. The capacitor discharge current is also directed through the conducting strap or coil placed just outside the top of the tube. The current flow in the strap produces a strong magnetic field which is perpendicular to the stem of the T. In effect, the presence of the field produces a high magnetic pressure in the top of the tube and adds to the thermally-created forces driving the plasma down the stem of the tube. Kolb's experiments show that the presence of the strap can increase the velocity of the plasma by a factor of 4 (Ref. 6-17).

One of the Kolb tubes reported in the literature (Ref. 6-17) has a stem length of 20 cm and a tube diameter of 2 to 4 cm. The applied voltage is 20,000 volts; the capacitance, 5 μf; and the circuit ringing frequency, 115 kc. The initial gas pressure in the tube is 10 mm Hg. Although high gas temperatures and velocities may be obtained through ohmic heating without the use of the magnetic fields generated by the strap, the magnetic augmentation is needed to produce the high specific impulses of interest in space propulsion. With the strap, plasma velocities of 10^5 m/sec have been measured in the laboratory. The corresponding specific impulse is 10^4 sec.

A photograph of an experimental plasma accelerator based on the Kolb-tube principle is shown in Fig. 6-24.

FIG. 6-24. Kolb-tube plasma accelerator. The T tube is shown at the right. The ejected plasma can be seen through the port in the center of the picture. (*General Electric Co.*)

Few measurements have been reported on Kolb tubes designed specifically for propulsion. Specific impulses may be expected to be in the same range as those of the other electrical propulsion systems, 10^4 sec. The thrust-to-weight ratio will depend, to a large extent, upon just what efficiencies can be obtained. Good energy coupling, corresponding to propulsion unit efficiencies of 50 per cent, will probably be obtained in the future. At present, experimental Kolb tubes show efficiencies of less than 1 per cent. The thrust-to-weight ratios will probably be somewhat lower than those of the ion drive because of poorer efficiencies and the mass associated with the electrical storage and switching circuits.

6-18. Transient Magnetic Field Accelerators. The U-shaped tube shown in Fig. 6-18 utilizes induction heating to create a plasma from the cold propellant gas which is introduced into the top of the tube. By applying a strong magnetic field with the coils located at the elbows of the tube, the plasma will be given an extra push down each arm of the U-tube. The action is very similar to that employed in the Kolb tube. The effect of the magnetic field is to squeeze the plasma out of the top of the tube into the arms of the U. The location of the windings on the curved portions of the tube also aids in turning the plasma flow into the straight arms.

No propulsion data are available for this device. The estimated performance shows that the transient magnetic field accelerators will be on a par with the rest of the plasma propulsion systems described in this chapter.

6-19. Evaluation of Plasma Propulsion Systems. Reviewing the various devices that have been proposed for plasma acceleration, it is found that the majority is represented by working laboratory models. None of them, however, are well understood theoretically. Some of the concepts are paper propulsion systems with no experimental backing. The transient magnetic field accelerator falls into this category. Even where plasma accelerators have been demonstrated in the laboratory, it is usually the case that no measurements have been made of parameters of interest in propulsion. We may conclude that both the experimental and theoretical aspects of plasma propulsion are in an unsatisfactory state. The rapid growth of MHD will undoubtedly remedy this situation in the near future.

The lack of accurate propulsion data is exemplified by the specific-impulse measurements that have been made. Usually, the experimenter has measured the plasma velocity by a time-of-flight technique. In this manner, the velocity of the fastest particle is obtained. It is very apparent from the design of many plasma experiments that much of the plasma and even some neutral gas is ejected at velocities much smaller than the maximum. Even knowledge of the average propellant velocity is not sufficient. In many of the devices that have been proposed, there is a considerable dispersion of the propellant at the end of the unit. Since the specific impulse is defined by $F/g_0 \dot{m}$, collimation effects must also be included. The use of the equation $I_{sp} = v_e/g_0$ will lead to spurious results unless the low-velocity expellant (*dribble effect*) and collimation are included.

In plasma propulsion, there is a profusion of concepts and laboratory devices which can propel matter at velocities high enough to be of interest in space technology. Although the real specific impulses, measured by $F/g_0 \dot{m}$, are in doubt, it is certain that additional development will produce equipment that will generate both high specific impulses (10^4 sec) and high efficiencies (50 per cent). The upper limit to the thrust-to-weight ratios for plasma propulsion systems is about 10^{-4}, but, in reality, most systems will be far below this value. The mass of the switching and storage equipment, the mass of the magnetic field coils, and the inefficient

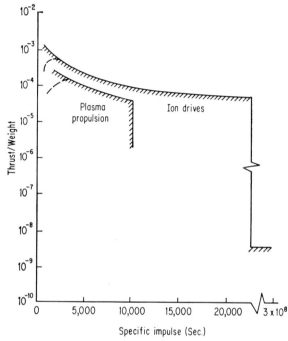

Fig. 6-25. Summary graph showing the approximate performance limits of electrical propulsion systems. Reduced propulsion unit efficiencies will usually cause the thrust-to-weight ratios to fall at very low specific impulses. This is indicated by the dotted lines. At electrical power levels under 100 kw, the thrust-to-weight ratios will be even lower than shown due to the rapid increase in power supply specific mass as the power level is reduced.

performance of the plasma sources will lead to thrust-to-weight ratios that are at least a factor of 2 below those of the ion drives. The periodic operating characteristics of several of the plasma accelerators will confer low reliability. In the next few years, as better data and understanding of plasma propulsion become available, it is probable that most of the plasma devices described here will fall within the performance ranges shown in Fig. 6-25. Plasma propulsion will be applicable to extended satellite maneuvers and possibly to long-range interplanetary probes. The over-all performance of plasma propulsion systems will be somewhat below that of the ion drives.

EVALUATION OF ELECTRICAL PROPULSION SYSTEMS

6-20. Final Summary. Following the lead of Chap. 5, the electrical propulsion systems presented in this chapter have been summarized by plotting the performance parameters F/W and I_{sp} on Fig. 6-25. Table 6-7 has been provided to recapitulate the qualitative factors that cannot be included on a $F/W–I_{sp}$ graph.

TABLE 6-7. SUMMARY OF ELECTRICAL SPACE-PROPULSION SYSTEMS

Engine type	State of the art	Major advantages and disadvantages	Applications
Ion drive.....	Prototypes available by 1960. Operational units by 1962	Requires charge separation and beam neutralization. High-power levels needed for useful thrust-to-weight ratios. Must be able to operate reliably for thousands of hours	Satellite sustaining, maneuvering, and attitude control. Unmanned interplanetary probes
Plasma accelerators	Various types now operating experimentally at low efficiencies	Many types require pulsed operation. Externally generated magnetic fields frequently necessary. Neutral matter may be accelerated. Must be able to operate reliably for thousands of hours	Satellite sustaining, maneuvering, and attitude control. Unmanned interplanetary probes

An important generalization concerning the performance of electrical propulsion systems arises from the direct proportionality of power level and power-supply mass. The power level is also proportional to the specific impulse, so that the thrust-to-weight ratio for an electrical propulsion system is inversely proportional to the specific impulse. See Eq. (6-29). Figure 6-25 is correct for a 1,000-kw electrical power supply with a specific mass of approximately 10 kg/kw. When lower thrusts, and, consequently, lower power levels, are desired, the higher specific masses indicated in Fig. 4-41 should be used. For example, a 1-kw ion drive would have its thrust-to-weight ratio reduced by a factor of 50 compared to the 1,000-kw system.

To summarize the place of electrical propulsion systems in space travel, they are inherently low thrust-to-weight ratio high-specific-impulse systems. The thrust-to-weight ratio is inversely proportional to the specific impulse and also drops as power levels are reduced below 100 kw. The development work now underway on electrical propulsion in almost every aircraft company promises that operational units will be available in the early 1960s. Despite the value of high specific impulse, the low thrust-to-weight ratios of the electrical engines relegate them to satellite and some interplanetary missions. Electrical propulsion systems seem to be superior to other space engines for unmanned probes and possibly manned expeditions to the planets beyond Mars and Venus, providing they can be made sufficiently long-lived and reliable. The high payload-to-gross-weight ratios possible with the high-specific-impulse electrical propulsion systems also make them attractive for unmanned interplanetary logistics missions where the time duration of the voyage is of secondary importance.

CHAPTER 7

NUCLEAR-PARTICLE GENERATORS

7-1. Nuclear-particle Emitters for Propulsion. The preceding two chapters have discussed how thermal and electrical energy can be transformed into the directed kinetic energy of a propulsive jet. Besides these two basic types of propulsion systems, there are several other ways in which jet thrust can be obtained from energy sources. In this chapter, we shall analyze space engines which can generate an anisotropic flux of nuclear particles and thus provide thrust for space missions.

Although nuclear particles like protons, alphas, and electrons can be accelerated by electrical propulsion systems, this chapter concerns only those nuclear particles arising directly from nuclear reactions. The most important of these for propulsion are the alpha particles and fission fragments. A great variety of nuclear reactions are available to generate the alphas, while fission fragments originate only in the fission of uranium, plutonium, and a few other heavy elements. Naturally, it is desirable to utilize only the lightest, cheapest, and most powerful of the nuclear reactions. The most obvious sources of nuclear energy for propulsion are the fission, fusion, and radioactive decay reactions.

Generally nuclear particles are emitted with very high velocities, velocities so high that extreme specific impulses are possible. For example, a 1-Mev alpha particle travels at 7×10^6 m/sec, corresponding to a specific impulse of 700,000 sec, providing the particle is directed parallel to the axis of the propulsion system. Such a high specific impulse is useful only if it is not associated with an unusably low thrust-to-weight ratio. A recollection of the jet-power equation $P_e = F g_0 I_{sp}/2$ indicates that immense power must be provided the propulsion unit to sustain useful thrusts at such high specific impulses. Since high power levels infer high power supply masses, it should be expected that nuclear-particle generators will also have rather low thrust-to-weight ratios.

Furthermore, nuclear-particle generators are hampered by three additional difficulties:

1. Nuclear reactions expel particles isotropically, and no thrust will result unless they can be focused or preferentially absorbed in a given direction.

2. Nuclear particles, especially the alphas and betas, are readily

absorbed by very small thicknesses of material. The dimensions of nuclear-particle generators are therefore limited in the direction parallel to the thrust axis. Nuclear-particle propulsion systems consequently tend to be flat and very thin.

3. Alphas, betas, and fission fragments will carry electrical charge away from the propulsion system. The residual charge left behind on the propulsion system will eventually reduce the effectiveness of the propulsion unit unless neutralization of the emitted particle flux can somehow be accomplished. Charged particles are easily neutralized in matter, even in gases, but, in outer space, there will be no natural neutralization. Therefore, the space-charge problem may restrict the use of particle generators for propulsion.

It is fairly easy to calculate the approximate performances of the different nuclear-particle engines. In the following pages, they will be categorized according to the type of nuclear reaction that produces the particles.

7-2. Fission Reactors as Particle Emitters. The fission of U-235, U-233, and Pu-239 yields both neutrons and heavy fission fragments. The neutrons possess about 2.5 per cent of the total energy released in the form of kinetic energy. The fission fragments are approximately half the mass of the fissioned nucleus, are usually highly charged, and possess about 85 per cent of the 200 Mev given up in the fission reaction. Both the neutrons and fission fragments can be used for propulsion. The neutrons are highly penetrating, but the fission fragments have ranges of only 10^{-5} m in solids because of their high mass and charged state. The fission fragments can be used for propulsion only if the nuclear reactor can be made thin enough to permit the escape of a significant proportion of the fission fragments over one hemisphere.

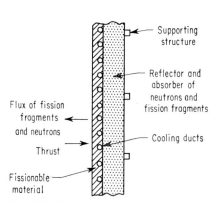

Flux of fission fragments and neutrons ←

Thrust →

Fissionable material

Supporting structure

Reflector and absorber of neutrons and fission fragments

Cooling ducts

FIG. 7-1. Conceptual drawing of a thin plane reactor for the production of an anisotropic flux of fission fragments. The thick reflector on one side absorbs the fission fragments over one hemisphere.

Figure 7-1 illustrates schematically how a thin, plane reactor might be constructed for propulsive purposes. A thick reflector on only one side of the reactor permits the escape of neutrons and fission fragments only over one hemisphere. The greatest drawback to this concept is the difficulty in achieving a flat, thin, critical assembly of fissionable material. The thickness of the reactor should be small enough to permit the escape of at least 10 to 20 per cent of the fission fragments and yet large enough to retain sufficient neutrons to carry on the chain reaction. These two conditions are obviously contradictory. Although a flat plane reactor can theoretically be made, the critical masses are unacceptably high or the dimensions are too thick to permit the escape of enough fission fragments for good thrust-to-weight ratios. Reactor control would, of course, be very difficult. In addition, the heat produced by the fission fragments which do not escape must be removed from the core and rejected by radiation to prevent melting of the core. The manifold disadvantages of this type of propulsion system make its use in space propulsion very unlikely.

Upper limits to the potential performance can be easily calculated. Assuming an equal split in the mass and energy of the U-235 fission reaction, the maximum velocity of an escaping fission fragment would be about 1.3×10^7 m/sec. The corresponding specific impulse is 1,300,000 sec. If one-sixth of the fission fragments leave the system shown in Fig. 7-1 in a direction parallel to the thrust axis, the specific thrust will be about 2×10^{-5} newton/kw. The neutrons may be ignored in these rough calculations. Taking the lowest reactor specific mass from Fig. 4-9, 0.1 kg/kw and estimating the mass of shielding, radiators, pumps, fluids, and structure, an over-all specific weight of 10 newtons/kw seems reasonable. Note that the power density of a nuclear reactor is so high that very little of the heat generated can be radiated away from its surface. If it is to remain a solid, a separate radiator and heat-transfer fluid must be provided. The maximum thrust-to-weight ratios that can be expected for a fission-reactor particle generator will be less than 10^{-6}.

To this poor performance must be added the almost insurmountable problems described earlier in the chapter. In particular, the space charge built up on the vehicle will prevent successful operation of the unit unless neutralization can be accomplished. Even with the optimistic assumptions made above, feasibility cannot be shown for the nuclear-particle generator using fission fragments directly. It must be concluded that this is not an attractive propulsion system.

7-3. Radioisotope Particle Sources. Radioisotopes are not subject to the geometrical restrictions placed upon the fission-reactor particle sources by criticality conditions. Consequently, some improvement in performance and feasibility may be expected.

The use of radioisotopes for the production of space power was discussed in Sec. 4-5. Many of the criteria developed there are also useful in analyzing radioisotope particle production for propulsion. The thrust-to-weight ratio is again a critical parameter. For this reason, the specific mass of the radioisotope is extremely important. The more interesting of the radioisotopes from the viewpoints of specific mass and availability

are the alpha and beta emitters listed in Table 4-3.   In making a choice
between the alpha and beta emitters for application to the type of propulsion discussed in this chapter, it is important to realize that, for a given
disintegration energy, the alpha emitters will produce higher specific
thrusts and higher over-all thrust-to-weight ratios.   These facts are
apparent from the large disparity in particle masses, 7,350 to 1 for alphas

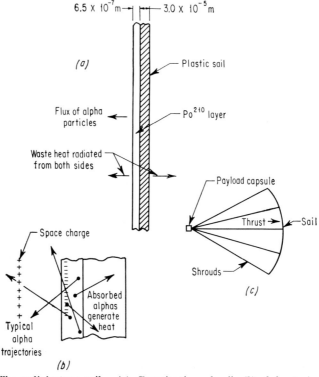

FIG. 7-2. The radioisotope sail.   (a) Constitution of sail; (b) alpha trajectories; (c)
unfurled sail and vehicle.

and betas.   The alpha emitters are usually chosen for radioisotope particle propulsion because their specific impulses are more than adequate,
although lower than those for beta emitters, and their thrust-to-weight
ratios are significantly higher.

As in the case of fission-fragment sources, a flat and thin geometry is
desirable for best performance.   With the radioisotopes, criticality is
unnecessary and extremely thin films of fuel may be used without penalty.
The so-called "radioisotope sails"* combine the lightweight properties of
the sail concept with the low specific masses of the radioisotopes.   Figure
7-2 shows the construction of a propulsion system of this type.   The

* See Glossary Terms at the back of the book.

radioactive nuclei coating one side of the sail undergo disintegration and emit alpha particles with an isotropic distribution.* Zero net thrust will result unless the alpha particles can be given an anisotropic distribution so that some net amount of momentum leaves the vehicle. A thin absorbing layer on one side of the sail accomplishes this. A sheet of plastic or metal will suffice to stop most of the alpha particles. Here, the alpha emitters have an advantage over the beta emitters. The shorter ranges of alphas in any material lead to thinner absorbing layers and higher thrust-to-weight ratios.

As an example, the performance parameters of a Po-210, plastic radio-isotope sail will be calculated. Table 7-1 lists the properties of Po-210 and

TABLE 7-1. PROPERTIES OF A RADIOISOTOPE SAIL

Density of Po-210	9.2 g/cm³
Mass of the alpha particle	6.7×10^{-27} kg
Half-life of Po-210	138 days
Decay constant for Po-210	5.8×10^{-8} 1/sec
Alpha energy for Po-210	8.5×10^{-13} joule
Alpha velocity	1.6×10^{7} m/sec
Alpha range in air	3.6 cm
Density of plastic	2.0 g/cm³
Stopping power for Po-210	5,500
Stopping power for plastic	1,200
Thickness of Po-210 layer	6.5×10^{-7} m
Thickness of plastic layer	3.0×10^{-5} m
Sail weight per unit area	0.66 newton/m²
Thrust per unit area	2.6×10^{-5} newton/m²
Thrust-to-weight ratio for sail	4.0×10^{-5}
Effective specific impulse	800,000 sec
Thrust-to-weight ratio including vehicle and auxiliaries	10^{-5}

plastic pertinent to such computations. The thickness of the plastic layer needed to stop the alpha particles may be calculated from the known *stopping power* of plastic. The stopping power of a substance is the ratio of the particle range in air to the range in the material under considera-tion. For alphas in plastic, it is about 1,200. Referring to Table 7-1, the range of the alpha particle in plastic will be $3.6/1,200 = 3 \times 10^{-5}$ m. Figure 7-2, which shows the make-up of the sail, uses a plastic film just 0.003 cm thick. It is also necessary to prescribe a layer of Po-210 that is thin enough so that appreciable self-absorption does not occur. Taking a stopping power of 5,500 for the polonium layer, it is found that a thick-ness of 6.5×10^{-6} m will stop one of its own alphas. For a crude design, a layer one-tenth this thickness will be assumed. This thickness is small enough to permit most alphas to escape the polonium layer without losing

* Recent experiments showing the lack of conservation of parity give a glimmer of hope that the direction of particle emission may some day be controllable.

much of their kinetic energy. The weight of the sail per unit area is easily calculated. The results are shown in Table 7-1.

The next step is to find the force generated per unit area by the escaping alphas. The thrust is given by the familiar $F = \dot{m}v_e$. The rate of mass ejection per unit area may be found using the law of radioactive decay.

$$\frac{dN}{dt} = -\lambda N = -\frac{1{,}000\lambda N_0 \rho}{A} \tag{7-1}$$

where N = number of radioactive nuclei per unit volume
$\quad \lambda$ = decay constant
$\quad t$ = time
$\quad N_0$ = Avogadro's number
$\quad \rho$ = density
$\quad A$ = atomic weight*

Assuming that half of the alpha particles will escape from the thin layer of radioisotope used in the example, the upper limit to the mass flow per unit area $\dot{m}_A$ will be:

$$\dot{m}_A = \frac{1{,}000\lambda N_0 \rho x m_\alpha}{2A} \tag{7-2}$$

where m_α = mass of alpha particle
$\quad x$ = thickness of the layer

The velocity to be used in the force equation is the alpha-particle velocity projected onto the thrust axis and averaged over the hemisphere. Assuming no degradation of velocity due to collisions within the radioisotope layer, this effective velocity turns out to be just one-half the actual alpha velocity. The thrust per unit area of sail F_A for the thin geometry assumed here is

$$F_A = \frac{1{,}000\lambda N_0 \rho x \sqrt{2E m_\alpha}}{4A} = 2.6 \times 10^{-5} \text{ newton/m}^2 \tag{7-3}$$

for the example. In Eq. (7-3), E equals the alpha energy. By dividing F_A by the sail weight per unit area, the thrust-to-weight ratio for the sail alone is found to be 4.0×10^{-5}. If an allowance is made for payload and supplementary structure, the thrust-to-weight ratio would drop to about 10^{-5}. The upper limit to the specific impulse is one-half the maximum alpha velocity divided by $2g_0$. In this case, it is 800,000 sec.

One of the barrier problems expected for the radioisotope sail involves space-charge neutralization. There is conservation of charge in radioactive decay, and the charged alpha particles will eventually return to the sail under the influence of the negative charges left behind, unless steps are taken to neutralize the flux of positive ions leaving the sail.

* See Table of Symbols at the back of the book.

The heat produced by the alphas that are absorbed in the polonium and the plastic must somehow be dissipated. In the example, this amounts to about 0.04 watt/m². This small amount of heat is easily radiated away if the sail is only a few degrees above the sink temperature of space. From Chap. 3, this is about 300°K near the earth. Thicker layers of Po-210 will yield higher thrust-to-weight ratios but will make the heat-removal problem much more serious with the low melting point plastic sails.

The radioisotope sail offers a simple propulsion system of low meteoroid vulnerability. The over-all performance is somewhat low but acceptable for some space missions (unmanned probes). The practical problems,

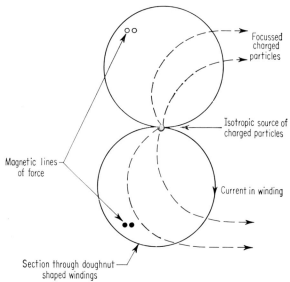

FIG. 7-3. The charged particles emitted from a small isotropic source could be focused with the magnetic field generated by a toroidal winding.

the space charge, the scarcity of radioisotopes, the lack of control over the heat source, and the reduction of thrust level as the radioisotope decays, militate against the use of radioisotope sails. It is also difficult to conceive of packaging and launching a hot, radioactive plastic sail. The radioisotope sail is a marginal propulsion system from the standpoints of feasibility and performance.

7-4. Magnetic Focusing of Charged Particles. One other method of controlling the particle flux distribution emitted from any source is through the use of magnetic fields. The concept is shown in Fig. 7-3. A small piece of alpha-emitting radioisotope is placed at the center of a doughnut-shaped coil. The magnetic field inside the toroid, if of the proper strength, can bend all of the charged particles emitted from an isotropic, monoenergetic point source into a uniform beam. This idea is interesting but impractical. The weight of the windings, power supply, and the extra power consumption would so reduce the thrust-to-weight ratio of any particle-emitting system that the scheme is of academic interest only.

7-5. Thermonuclear-particle Generators. There are several fusion reactions which produce charged particles. One of the most interesting is

$$_3Li^6 + {}_1D^2 \rightarrow 2{}_2He^4 + 22.4 \text{ Mev}$$

If this reaction could be tamed and confined in a small volume, an ideal source of charged particles would be the result. However, not even the

TABLE 7-2. SUMMARY OF NUCLEAR-PARTICLE GENERATORS

Engine type	State of the art	Major advantages and disadvantages	Applications
Fission.........	None	Space-charge buildup. Incompatibility of criticality and geometry requirements	Not a feasible propulsion system
Radioisotope....	None	Space-charge buildup. Packaging and launching of hot, radioactive sails. Decay of thrust. Lack of control. Poor availability of fuel	Not a feasible propulsion system
Thermonuclear..	None	Basic technology not developed to the point where realistic designs can be made	Not a feasible propulsion system

simplest thermonuclear machine has been constructed to date. Until fusion reactions are made self-sustaining in the laboratory and their basic features determined, there is little point in discussing thermonuclear space engines.

7-6. Summary of Nuclear-particle Generators. The fundamental concept of using the particle energy produced in the nuclear reaction directly without intervening equipment is highly attractive. The three basic methods of producing nuclear reactions in abundance have been investigated. None shows high performance. Feasibility has not been demonstrated for any of the propulsion systems proposed. It may be concluded that the nuclear-particle generators, including the radioisotope sail, will not compete with the thermal and electrical space propulsion systems.

Table 7-2 and Fig. 7-4 summarize the capabilities and drawbacks of each type of propulsion system described in this chapter. The perform-

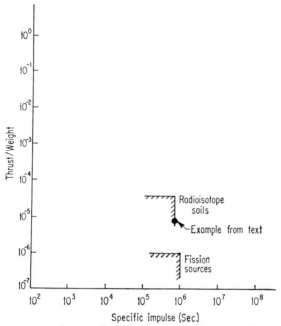

FIG. 7-4. Summary graph showing the approximate performance limits of the nuclear-particle generators. These systems are not feasible.

ance shown on the F/W–I_{sp} graph (Fig. 7-4) are upper limits, assuming that the solution of the many barrier problems listed in Table 7-2 may someday be obtained.

CHAPTER 8

PHOTONIC PROPULSION SYSTEMS

8-1. Introduction to Photonic Propulsion Systems. Up to this point, all of the propulsion systems described in this book have relied upon the acceleration and subsequent expulsion of mass to provide thrust. The force exerted on the vehicle has always been calculated from $F = \dot{m}v$, where $\dot{m}$ equals the propellant mass flow rate whether it is comprised of atoms, ions, nuclear particles, or any aggregation of substance-possessing mass. It is now reasonable to ask whether thrust can be generated through the interaction of the vehicle with electromagnetic radiation.

This question can be answered affirmatively. Several physical phenomena illustrate the effects of radiation pressure. These effects might conceptually be employed to propel spaceships. The most common examples of light pressure are the radiometer from the physics laboratory and the repulsion of the tails of some comets by sunlight. Such phenomena are described in classical physics through the interaction of the electric and magnetic components of electromagnetic waves with the electrons in the object of interest. In quantum mechanics, the same phenomena are treated by ascribing momentum to each quantum of electromagnetic energy. Both interpretations indicate that a thrust-producing device may be constructed by properly controlling the emission or absorption of electromagnetic radiation by space vehicles. The vehicle thrust would, of course, still be given by Newton's second law $F = dp/dt$ where p equals momentum; however, no massive particles would be released, and the momenta of the electromagnetic quanta would generate the thrust.

The photon drive, exemplified by Fig. 8-1, operates like an immensely magnified flashlight. It is often called the ultimate in reaction engines, since it apparently ejects no mass while still producing thrust. As we shall see, mass really does leave the vehicle so that an infinite specific impulse is not produced as long as the photons are produced on the vehicle itself. Still, the specific impulse of the ideal photon drive is 30,000,000 sec. This is the highest attainable specific impulse for propulsion systems which do not derive their propellant from the environment. Purely from an academic viewpoint, photonic propulsion systems are worthy of study.

Their extreme specific impulses have made the photon drives or photon rockets popular subjects for discussion in space technology. Like most other space propulsion systems, the photon drive is not a new idea. It has been mentioned frequently in the astronautical literature for many years. One of the latest students of this type of space engine is E. Sanger, in Germany, who has published numerous interesting articles on the subject (Ref. 8-2).* In this chapter, we shall examine the photon drive and

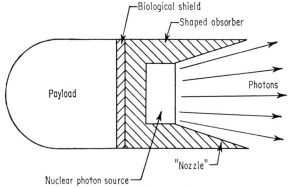

FIG. 8-1. Schematic of a photon drive. A hot nuclear power source generates a flux of photons which is shaped by photon absorbers.

the solar sail; both are photonic propulsion systems of great interest. Despite their extremely high specific impulses, it will become apparent that their immediate utility in space technology is rather limited.

8-2. Physics of Photon Engines. The photonic propulsion systems exchange momentum with their environment through the emission, absorption, and reflection of photons. Photons possess no inherent mass but do convey momentum (see Chap. 2). The word "photon"† generally applies only to quanta of visible light, but the term "quantum" applies to the entire spectrum of electromagnetic energy. The quantization of energy is described by Planck's hypothesis that energy E is transferred in discrete amounts given by

$$E = hf \tag{8-1}$$

where f = frequency of radiation
  h = Planck's constant‡
The quantity of energy possessed by any quantum or photon is, therefore, proportional to the frequency of the radiation. We also have Einstein's equation stating the equivalence of mass and energy:

$$E = mc^2 \tag{8-2}$$

---

* References are listed in the Bibliography at the back of the book.
† See Glossary of Terms at the back of the book.
‡ See Table of Symbols at the back of the book.

where m = mass
$\quad\quad c$ = velocity of light

By eliminating E and solving Eqs. (8-1) and (8-2) for mass times velocity, we obtain

$$mc = p = \frac{hf}{c} \tag{8-3}$$

The same result can be found by differentiating the energy with respect to the velocity. This crude derivation shows that the momentum carried by each quantum is hf/c or h/λ.

Although it seems, superficially, that no mass leaves the rocket as photons are emitted from the engine, a closer inspection shows that this is incorrect. As energy is created on the vehicle, through chemical or nuclear reactions, mass disappears in accordance with Eq. (8-2). Furthermore, the quanta that leave the spaceship will ultimately be absorbed by atoms somewhere in the universe, and then their energy will once again appear in the guise of mass. In this fashion, mass is actually transferred from the vehicle to its surroundings.

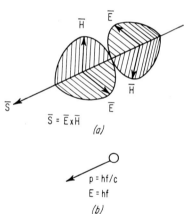

$$\bar{S} = \bar{E} \times \bar{H}$$

(a)

$p = hf/c$
$E = hf$

(b)

FIG. 8-2. (a) The wave concept of electromagnetic energy; (b) the particulate nature of light is characterized by the photon.

The description of the behavior of light in terms of photons alone is not completely satisfactory. It is found that a large class of observations are better described if light is hypothesized to be made up of waves rather than quanta. In this approach, phenomena are explained by imagining electromagnetic energy to be transmitted by the transverse vibrations of an electric intensity vector **E** and a magnetic intensity vector **H**. The amount of energy transmitted is given by the Poynting vector,

$$\mathbf{S} = \mathbf{E} \times \mathbf{H} \tag{8-4}$$

Figure 8-2 illustrates the relationship between these three important vectors.

The apparent duality of light has been a long-debated issue. Usually electromagnetic radiation becomes more particlelike as wavelengths get shorter. At the other end of the spectrum, the radio waves are almost completely wavelike in behavior. One rule of the thumb that is important in photon propulsion states that light is particlelike during absorption and emission, but wavelike during transmission. Thus, the emitter in a photon drive will best be described by quantum mechanics, but the collimators may be designed as if light were wavelike.

In photonic propulsion, there are three important classes of phenomena to be considered: emission, absorption, and reflection. Refraction and interference of light are of little practical importance in photon propulsion. Emission and absorption of photons occur when charged particles are accelerated or the planetary electrons of atoms change energy levels. The emission of radio waves from an antenna and visible light from a filament are good examples. Reflection occurs when there is a change in the index of refraction. The density of electrons in the reflecting medium is a critical quantity in describing this process. Thus, radio waves are turned back when they encounter high electron densities in the ionosphere, and light rays bounce off metallic surfaces. All of these processes must be carefully considered in the study of photonic propulsion systems.

8-3. Propulsion Parameters for Photonic Engines. The thrust exerted by a photon propulsion system is equal to the time rate change of momentum.

$$F = \frac{dp}{dt} = \frac{d}{dt}\frac{hf}{c} = \frac{1}{c}\frac{dE}{dt} = \frac{P_e}{c} \tag{8-5}$$

where P_e equals the power in the jet. It is one of the unique features of the photonic systems that the thrust is a function of the power only. It is, of course, a consequence of the constant-exhaust velocity. Note that the wavelength of the radiation has no effect on the thrust. The specific thrust thus becomes a constant.

$$F_{sp} = 3.3 \times 10^{-6} \text{ newton/kw}$$

Quite obviously, a photon rocket will require immense quantities of power for even the smallest thrusts. Even so, Eq. (8-5) and the value of the specific thrust are for ideal, perfectly collimated beams of photons only. Imperfections in the propulsion system will greatly reduce the value of specific thrust obtained above.

The thrust-to-weight ratio will depend upon the mass of the power supply, payload, and other nonpropulsive components. Considering the miniscule specific thrust of the photon propulsion systems, it is apparent that the power supply will be the dominant mass component in any photonic system. In this case

$$W = \frac{g_0 M_{sp} P_e}{1,000}$$

where W = weight

M_{sp} = power supply specific mass

The thrust-to-weight ratio is

$$\frac{F}{W} = \frac{1,000}{g_0 M_{sp} c} = \frac{3.4 \times 10^{-7}}{M_{sp}} \tag{8-6}$$

The value of M_{sp} for a specific system will vary, depending upon whether or not power is converted to electricity. The specific mass might be quite small if power can be radiated directly from a hot surface. On the other hand, it could be very large if thermal power must be converted into electricity for an arc or filament photon source. The specific mass curves developed in Chap. 4 will be applicable in many instances. Later in this chapter, two specific systems will be analyzed. According to Eq. (8-6), it will be necessary to obtain specific masses on the order of 10^{-3} kg/kw if photon propulsion systems using contained power sources are to be comparative on a thrust-to-weight basis with ion and plasma propulsion systems. External power sources, if usable, will permit the circumvention of Eq. (8-6). The solar sail is an example of a propulsion system using an external power source. This device will also be examined later in this chapter.

The specific impulse, defined by $I_{sp} = F/g_0\dot{m}$, will actually be infinite for the solar sail because no mass leaves the propulsion system. In the case of photon drives, using Eqs. (8-2) and (8-5), the specific impulse will be

$$I_{sp} = \frac{F}{g_0\dot{m}} = \frac{P_e}{c}\frac{c^2}{g_0 P_e} = \frac{c}{g_0}$$

or approximately 3.06×10^7 sec. Referring to Fig. 2-5, it is found that photon rockets are represented by a vertical line at the extreme right of the curves describing reaction engines. While imperfect focusing and the expulsion of actual mass from a practical photon drive may reduce the ideal specific impulse somewhat, the photonic propulsion systems attain specific impulses far in excess of the other propellant-carrying space engines that have been described.

8-4. Practical Aspects of Photonic Propulsion. Two fundamentally different types of photonic propulsion systems will be treated in this chapter. The first photon drive generates its own energy, converts it to photons, collimates them, and converts the generated power into thrust. The pertinent physical processes are emission, absorption, and reflection of electromagnetic quanta. The second type, the solar sail, collects solar photons and converts their energy into vehicle energy through reflection and absorption. The absorption of radiation cannot be avoided completely in either type of drive. It is related to a deterioration of propulsion system performance in the sense that energy is lost or degraded and the thrust-to-weight ratio suffers from the mass of cooling systems.

The major components of the propulsion system in the case of the photon drive are the photon source, the reflector, and the power supply. The photons created by the source are usually emitted isotropically, as in the case of the nuclear-particle emitters. Zero net thrust will result unless the photons can somehow be directed. The mechanisms available for accomplishing this are reflection and absorption. Ideally, there would be a focusing of the radiation into a perfectly collimated beam. The use of refracting devices like lenses is found to be impractical because of the small amount of absorption that inevitably occurs. The intense beams of photons required for significant thrusts would heat and melt any optical equipment involving their transmission through solid materials.

The basic problem of the photon drive is that of finding compact, high-power-level energy sources which can efficiently convert thermal or electrical energy into electromagnetic energy. An almost equally important problem is that of finding an efficient lightweight collimator of the electromagnetic energy emitted by the source.

An examination of the electromagnetic spectrum reveals a number of potential sources. At the long wavelength end, there are the radio antennas. These are notoriously large and inefficient energy converters. At the short wavelength end, nuclear reactions give off copious amounts of high-energy gamma rays. Efficient reflection and collimation of these energetic quanta are impossible because of their strong penetrating capabilities. One might conceive of hot nuclear fission or fusion-reactor cores emitting isotropic gamma fluxes which are subsequently anisotropically absorbed by properly placed shields. Figure 8-3 reveals a possible arrangement.

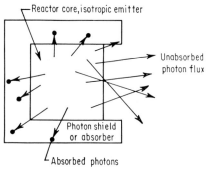

FIG. 8-3. An isotropic flux of highly penetrating photons may be shaped by absorbing material. This might be a gaseous core reactor.

Visible, ultraviolet, and infrared radiation occur near the middle of the spectrum. A great variety of sources are available to generate these wavelengths. Metallic arcs and plasma jets may operate beyond 10,000°K to produce copious quantities of photons. Ordinary tungsten filaments attain several thousand degrees Kelvin. If electrical energy is available, these sources of thermally generated photons could be incorporated into a photon drive. The common denominator of all photon sources near the visible portion of the electromagnetic spectrum is that they all rely on high temperatures to stimulate the emission of radiation. Consequently, the Stefan-Boltzmann law

$$W_r = e\sigma A T^4$$

applies. The higher the source temperature, the greater the thrust produced per unit area of source.   Unfortunately, reflection and collimation become more difficult with the decreasing wavelengths associated with high temperature (Fig. 8-4).   At higher temperatures, Wien's law states that the maximum in the spectral distribution shifts to shorter, more penetrating wavelengths.   Due to this fact, the high thrust-per-unit-area photon sources are mated with inefficient reflectors.   Obviously, the source and reflector must be chosen jointly for maximum thrust per unit area if reflection is chosen as the means of collimation.

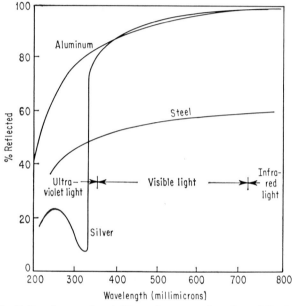

FIG. 8-4. Reflectivity of several metallic surfaces as a function of the incident wavelength.   Note the sharp decrease in reflectivity at short wavelengths.

In examining the basic elements of photon production—absorption and reflection—and their application to photon propulsion, one interesting fact emerges.   On the photon-driven vehicle, as on any other space vehicle, all power that is generated must somehow be disposed of if thermal equilibrium is to be maintained.   In outer space, the most practical means of rejecting energy is through radiation.   A small portion of the total energy, perhaps 20 per cent, may be converted into thermal energy at extremely high temperatures with arcs and filaments.   The remainder, the bulk of the power generated, must be rejected at a much lower temperature.   With the proper use of reflectors, even this photonic energy might be focused and used to provide thrust to the vehicle.   All energy that is generated may be consumed by the propulsion system.

To illustrate these ideas more clearly, imagine the following situation. A nuclear reactor produces 100 Mw of fission power. Depending upon the core, approximately 10 per cent or 10 Mw of this power appears as high-energy photons. These are the gamma rays from the fission process itself, from the subsequent decay of fission products, and from secondary neutron reactions with the materials of the reactor. By shaping the reactor components and shielding (Fig. 8-5) one might permit the escape

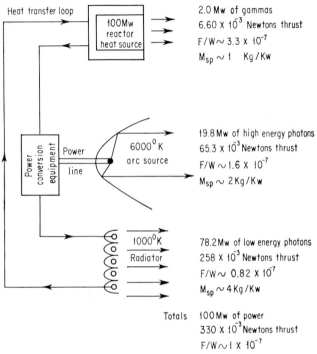

FIG. 8-5. A schematic showing the different ways in which nuclear energy may be converted into photonic energy. This does not represent a practical solution to photon propulsion.

of perhaps 2 Mw of these photons. The escaping gammas and whatever neutrons can escape through the bare reactor face will contribute to the propulsion-system thrust. The remaining 98 Mw of power will appear as thermal energy. Some of this thermal power may be upgraded to temperatures higher than those obtainable in the reactor itself. Figure 8-5 shows a 20 per cent conversion efficiency, with 19.6 Mw appearing in a 6000°K arc. The photons from the arc might be collimated by reflectors as shown. All of the rest of the power must be radiated at low temperatures. The illustration shows 78.2 Mw of energy being rejected by focusing the radiation from the radiator tubes. The objective of this example is not to provide an illustration of a practical system but rather to show the real limitations of conventional power supplies in photon rockets and the importance of the different methods of photon generation. The thrust produced by each of the photon generators in Fig. 8-5 is proportional to the power only. The importance of energetic photons is found in the smaller sources that are possible. The potential reduction in mass, however, is usually offset by the heavier reflectors needed (as in the case of a reactor) or reflector inefficiencies (as with the short wavelength arc source). The crude calculation of the thrust-to-weight ratio indicated in Fig. 8-5 demonstrates the poor performance of contemporary photon generators.

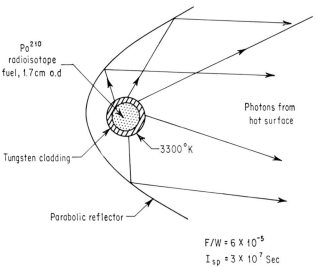

FIG. 8-6. A radioisotope photon drive.   Heat produced by the radioisotope is radiated and shaped by a reflector. The poor availability of radioisotopes limits the use of this concept.

The low performance of the photon rocket described above is due, in part, to the requirement of at least 300 Mw of power for each newton of thrust. Each kilowatt infers a certain power supply mass which enters into the thrust-to-weight ratio.

The low specific masses of the radioisotopes may improve the photon drive performance somewhat. Figure 8-6 shows a cylinder of radioisotope encased in a high melting point material like tungsten. It is placed at the focal point of a reflector. If the heat produced by the radioisotope is converted directly into radiation and the photons reflected into a collimated beam, an interesting variation of the photon rocket is obtained. With a Po-210 heat source, a thrust-to-weight ratio of 6×10^{-5} can be obtained exclusive of the reflector for the dimensions in Fig. 8-6. The practicality of radioisotope power sources is, of course, limited by their availability as discussed in Chap 4. Only a few tens of kilowatts of radioisotope power will be available for space power between 1960 and 1970. Obviously, photon rockets will require too much power for radioisotopes to be feasible sources of energy.

8-5. Evaluation of Photon Rockets. It is obvious that photon drives based on conventional power sources have little to offer in the way of usable thrust-to-weight ratios when compared to other space propulsion systems. In spite of such drawbacks, it would be unwise to completely eliminate the photon drive forever from the spectrum of practical propulsion systems. At some time in the distant future, it is conceivable that power in space will be orders of magnitude cheaper in terms of mass. It is also possible that there might be missions where the extremely high specific impulse of the photon rocket is desirable or even essential regardless of the vehicle acceleration obtainable. In contemplating the place of photon rockets in space technology, one must project his thoughts into a future where highly concentrated sources of nuclear energy radiate directional beams of photons at energy densities comparable to those observed on stellar surfaces. Most of the propulsion systems described in this book are also extrapolations of current technology. The practical photon drive is an extreme example of such projection.

In addition to the performance limitations arising from inadequate photon sources, the photon-collimation problems are far from solved. It seems to be a general rule that the desirable, compact heat sources radiate energetic and difficult-to-collimate photons. Technical break-throughs will be required to make photon propulsion feasible in the areas of both photon production and collimation.

The approximate performance of the photon drive, based upon technology available within the next decade, is shown in Fig. 8-11 at the end of this chapter.

8-6. The Operation of Solar Sails. At the earth's orbit, approximately 1,400 watts/m² of power is available for the taking. In Chap. 4, several methods of tapping this supply were described, but all involved the degradation of this photonic power to heat or the potential energy of electron-hole pairs and subsequent conversion to electricity and waste heat. Solar energy, unlike the isotropically radiated energy of nuclear particles and transportable photon sources, is highly directional by virtue of our position with respect to the sun. It would be desirable to make use of this directed solar energy without first converting it to electricity and then to the kinetic energy of propellant.

The solar sail offers this possibility. In principle, it is a complete propulsion system. A reflecting or absorbing piece of material held normal to the sun's rays will extract the radiant power, degrade it slightly, reemit the waste power, and produce a thrust on the material. The process of reflection must somehow reduce the amount of energy in the sunlight since kinetic energy is imparted to the vehicle. If complete reflection occurs, conservation of energy infers that the reflected photons are less energetic than the incident ones.

Ideally, a solar sail would be fabricated from an inert material. It would be invulnerable to serious meteoroid damage and would be easy to

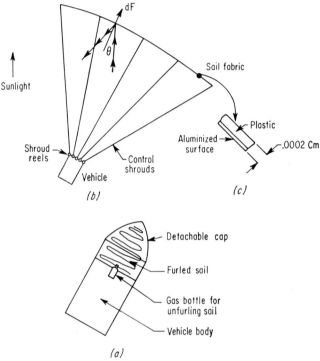

FIG. 8-7. The solar sail. (a) Launching vehicle; (b) the unfurled sail showing the thrust vector; (c) a section of typical sail fabric.

handle, package, and launch. Many of the hazards and difficulties of the other space propulsion systems appear to be alleviated with the solar sail concept, which possesses the simplicity of the environmental engine.

The thrust on the differential element of a solar sail is given by

$$dF = (1 + r) \frac{P_A}{c} \cos \theta \, dA \qquad (8-7)$$

where θ = angle between the elemental area and the radius vector from the sun

r = reflectivity

P_A = power per unit area in sunlight

A = area

Equation (8-7) must be integrated over the entire area of any sail to obtain the total thrust (Fig. 8-7). Since any real sail would be far from a plane surface, this is usually a difficult procedure. Note that the power per unit area in the sunlight varies with the distance from the sun. Using the earth's orbit as a reference, P_A may be given by

$$P_A = 1,400 \left(\frac{r}{r_E}\right)^2 \tag{8-8}$$

where r = radius from the sun
$\quad r_E$ = radius of the earth from the sun
Consequently, at the orbit of Mars, the thrust on a solar sail would be less than half that at the earth's orbit.

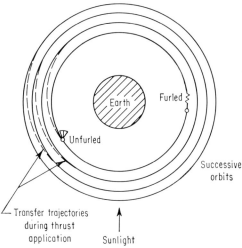

FIG. 8-8. Successive furling and unfurling of a solar sail may permit the escape from satellite orbits.

In any discussion of solar sailing, the question of maneuvering in the gravitational fields of the sun and the planets invariably arises. Of course, solar sail-driven vehicles must be launched into orbit by some other kind of propulsion system, but, once in orbit, their low thrust-to-weight ratios are sufficient to perform several maneuvers of importance.

Figure 8-8 illustrates how a solar sail vehicle with a low thrust-to-weight ratio could escape from a planet by periodically furling and unfurling the sail in the positions shown. The application of small tangential thrusts once every revolution would cause a gradual spiralling out from the planet to where escape could eventually be accomplished (Ref. 8-1). The basic mechanics of this type of maneuver are discussed in Sec. 2-14.

Once free of the gravitational influence of a planet or satellite, the sail-propelled space craft would be in an orbit about the sun similar to that of the planet it had just left. Obviously, the technique used in planetary escape can not be used here because the gravitational force and thrust-producing radiation are now parallel. Figure 8-9a shows the simplest situation, the one in which the sun is exerting only a radial force on the

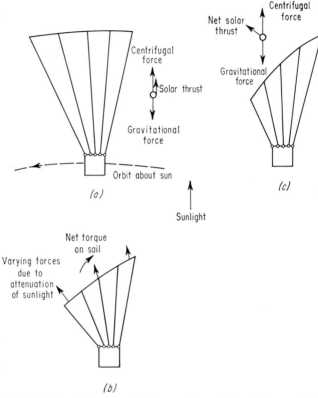

FIG. 8-9. (a) Radial thrust being exerted on a solar sail in orbit around the sun; (b) the torque produced by the diverging solar flux; (c) thrusts perpendicular to the sun's radius vector may be produced by inclination of the sail.

sail and the vehicle is strung out behind the sail much like a man attached to a parachute. The effect of the radial force will be to perturb the initial elliptical orbit into one of increasing eccentricity. If such an ellipse can be made eccentric enough, then the orbits of neighboring planets might be intersected. Such maneuvers seem to be impractically long for manned missions but might be ideal for unmanned probes sent out to explore the solar system.

From an examination of the basic solar sail configuration (Fig. 8-9b), one finds two possible torques acting upon the system. Both have their origin in the divergence of applied forces.   In one case, the decrease in gravitational force with distance from the sun causes librationlike torques. For example, the planet Mercury perpetually keeps one side facing the sun because of this effect.   The other torque is caused by the spreading out of the solar photon flux with increasing distance from the sun.   The relative magnitudes of these two torques will depend upon the configuration of the vehicle, but the torques are both in the same direction and, although very small, will tend to keep the sail in the position shown in Fig. 8-9a.

A composite radial and tangential thrust can be created, as indicated in Fig. 8-9c, by shortening and lengthening some of the shrouds connecting the space vehicle with the sail proper.   The dynamics of this maneuver and the effects of the torques have not been fully analyzed, but it appears that inward and outward spirals from planetary orbit to planetary orbit might be achieved with this type of sail operation (Sec. 2-14).

While the furling and unfurling of solar sails are controlled by the shroud lines, the sun itself will aid in the unfurling process.   Once a mass of fabric has been ejected from the vehicle just after launching, the *solar wind* will cause it to fill with radiation much as an atmospheric wind fills the sails of a ship.

The understanding of the behavior of solar sails is rudimentary.   The solar sail is not a perfect analog of the earth-bound sailing ship.   A great deal more study must be done to fill the gaps in our knowledge.   From the viewpoints of simplicity, low vulnerability, and even esthetic appeal, the solar sail is an attractive type of space propulsion system.

8-7. The Design of Solar Sails.   The key to good performance in the case of the solar sail is in finding a thin lightweight material, which is either opaque to sunlight or may be given a highly reflecting surface. Thin plastic films, like those made from Mylar, seem ideal for this purpose. They may be made with thicknesses as small as 0.0002 cm.   Mylar film can be obtained with an aluminized surface which has a high reflectivity for sunlight.

A typical sail design might call for an aluminized film 0.0002 cm thick. Even with an aluminized surface, the film would have a mass of only 5×10^{-3} kg/m^2.   The pressure or thrust on a square meter of the film, assuming normal incidence and complete reflection, would be about 10^{-5} newton/m^2.   The thrust-to-weight ratio for the sail fabric alone is thus approximately 2×10^{-4}, a very acceptable value when compared to the comparably performing but much more complex ion drives and other low-thrust propulsion engines.   The specific impulse is, of course, infinity since the propellant flow rate is zero.   In actuality, if any photons are absorbed, they will be converted into mass, giving rise to an increase in sail mass.   This will be a negligible effect.

In a practical design, the effect of the structural mass, as well as the mass of the payload, must be considered. The main structural mass would be in the shroud lines connecting the payload capsule to the sail. These lines could also be made of lightweight Mylar. Their effect upon the thrust-to-weight ratio would be negligible. The payload, however, is likely to be of the same order of magnitude as the entire sail. In practice, the thrust-to-weight ratio might be reduced by a factor of 2 or 3. In this way, the thrust-to-weight ratio would be reduced to 10^{-4} or lower. For example, a 10,000-kg payload combined with a 10,000-kg sail would collect enough sunlight to generate a thrust of 20 newtons. The sail would have an area of 2,000,000 m². If square, the sail would be 1,414 m on a side.

The dimensions given above can easily be scaled up or down. A small probe with 100 kg of instruments and a 100-kg sail might make an interesting, extraterrestrial, solar sailboat. It could be launched by 1960 and would continuously radio back data as it progresses through the solar system. It would have the same thrust-to-weight ratio (10^{-4}) and specific impulse (infinity) as the larger system. The sail would be 141 m on a side.

The design, construction, packaging, and launching of a small sail device would be very simple. Once in orbit, either about the earth or the sun, the sail could be released. Perhaps a jet of compressed gas might be used to expand it enough so that sunlight itself could finish the unfurling.

8-8. Evaluation of Solar Sails. From the standpoints of performance and design simplicity, the solar sail concept is almost ideal for space propulsion in several kinds of missions. The sail would not be used for launching, of course; however, escape from satellite orbits, interplanetary orbit transfer, and perhaps interstellar probes of the unmanned variety seem feasible. Any auxiliary power needed for maintenance of life and instrumentation would have to be provided by solar cells or separate solar turboelectric power sources.

The solar sail is not completely free from faults. Although the sail area reduction due to meteoroid penetration may be very small, it is possible that the abrasive action of cosmic dust must spoil the reflectivity of the metallized surfaces. The radiation present in space—solar protons, cosmic rays, and solar ultraviolet light—may cause the plastic in the sail to deteriorate rapidly. Finally, in the near vacuum of outer space, the plastic may sublime at a rate inconsistent with the sail's design lifetime. None of these potential disadvantages of the solar sail can be accurately ascertained at the present time. The environment of space is not well known enough to permit any final conclusions.

If the difficulties just mentioned can be overcome, then the solar sail is indeed a desirable propulsion system. Its thrust-to-weight ratio is comparable with that of the ion drive. Its specific impulse is infinity. Meteoroids will have little effect upon its performance. With no moving parts except the shroud controls, it is the simplest of all the systems examined so far. The components for the solar sail are available today; all that is required are the launching system and a realistic mission.

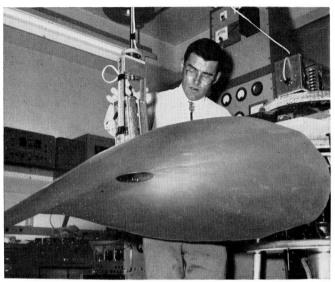

FIG. 8-10. Experiments with solar sail fabric. (*Los Alamos Scientific Laboratory, University of California.*)

Many organizations are actively studying this propulsion system. Experiments with Mylar film are also being carried out (Fig. 8-10). In many ways, the solar sail is an ideal propulsion system, particularly for unmanned explorations of interplanetary space with instrumented probes.

8-9. Summary and Evaluation of Photonic Propulsion. Two distinctly different kinds of photonic propulsion systems have been described. First, the photon drive, where power is generated internally, then converted to electromagnetic radiation, and collimated to produce thrust. The second basic type, the solar sail, extracted energy from the environment and converted a portion of it to thrust. Both systems have extremely high specific impulses, so high that propellant mass is of little importance except, perhaps, for the interstellar voyages of the distant future. Figure 8-11 summarizes the performances of each type. Note that the requirement for internal power generation forces the thrust-to-weight ratio of the photon drive to very low values if presently conceived power supplies are used. The solar sail, on the other hand, appears attractive even today, since lightweight fabrics are readily available for immediate use. It appears unlikely that the photon drive, using an internal power source, will be attractive enough for space applications until some break-through is made in the construction of small lightweight

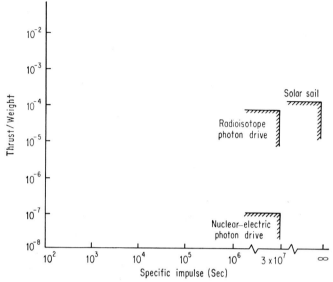

Fig. 8-11. Summary of the performance limits of photonic propulsion systems.

TABLE 8-1. SUMMARY OF PHOTONIC PROPULSION SYSTEMS

Engine type	State of the art	Major advantages and disadvantages	Applications
Photon drive.....	Rudimentary. Some knowledge of low-efficiency photon emitters and power supplies	Very low specific thrust. Very high specific impulse. Extremely low thrust-to-weight ratios	Undetermined
Solar sail........	Components are readily available. No operating experience with analogous devices. Inadequate study of potentialities	Good performance. Simple, reliable. May be sensitive to environment	Instrumented interplanetary probes

power supplies. The solar sail, however, may very likely find many demands for its special qualifications of simplicity, good performance, and reliability in the near future. Table 8-1 is included to summarize the major characteristics of each of the major types of photonic propulsion systems.

CHAPTER 9

PROPULSION SYSTEMS USING NATURAL FORCE FIELDS

9-1. Natural Force Fields. In Chap. 3, brief descriptions were given of the several naturally produced force fields that pervade outer space. The list included the gravitational, magnetic, and electrostatic fields. The propulsion systems that rely upon the expulsion of mass and energy have already been treated. It is now appropriate to study engines which exchange momentum with the primary reference frame through the use or alteration of these naturally occurring forces.

By taking exclusively the skeptical approach, this chapter could be easily written in a single page. The topics of antigravity, magnetic propulsion, and like systems can be perfunctorily dismissed by appealing to the very real absence of reliable experimental data that might lend credence to these concepts. Taking the opposite tack, one might thoroughly discuss gravitational and electromagnetic theories and fill many pages with potentially useful material. A middle course will be employed here although the resulting mixture will be more nearly like the first approach than the second.

Regardless of the means one proposes for traveling from one astronomical object to another, it will not be possible to circumvent the energy requirements stated in Chap. 2. The chemically propelled rocket and antigravity screen must both take energy from some source and transfer it to the space vehicle. There will always be some mission energy increment ΔE_M which is independent of the means of locomotion. Just as fundamental is the law of conservation of momentum. A spaceship cannot acquire a velocity without imparting an equal and opposite momentum to something else. True, these dogmatic statements are based upon the two great conservation laws of physics. These laws may eventually fail or someday be modified. To the best of our knowledge, energy and mass and momentum are conserved with great consistency and precision throughout the solar system. Therefore, we must still use these laws in guiding the design of our more radical space engines as well as the conventional chemical rockets.

The forces we shall deal with in this chapter are all of the action-at-a-distance variety. As far as we can tell, their influences predominate from atomic to galactic dimensions. Within the nucleus, the effects of short-range forces overpower the electric, magnetic, and gravitational forces. On an astronomical scale, we must extrapolate our knowledge of these action-at-a-distance forces, but there are no compelling reasons to believe that the earth-founded laws will be violated in outer space.

All action-at-a-distance forces upset our common sense to some extent. Forces are exerted between objects with no apparent physical interconnections. We cannot fully explain how this might occur in everyday terms. To many people, such phenomena are harder to comprehend than just-as-natural electrical phenomena. The physicist usually relates the observations he makes of force fields in terms of lines of force and equipotential surfaces. The lines of force map out the field in question. A tangent to a line of force represents the direction of the force acting on a test particle, while the concentration of the lines of force is proportional to the strength of the field. Equipotential surfaces are always normal to the lines of force and are the loci of points having equal potential energies in the field. All three of the fundamental action-at-a-distance force fields can be described with these simple but physically appealing techniques. In the case of a point electric charge or point mass, the lines or force extend out radially and are intersected by concentric, spherical equipotential surfaces.

In space travel, the main concern is with gravitational forces. It is necessary to overcome, nullify, weaken, or somehow modify the gravitational lines of force extending outward from a planet, star, or moon in order to achieve space travel. With the engines previously described, this is always accomplished through the use of reaction forces which oppose and cancel out the retarding gravitational forces. In this chapter, although Newton's third law, stating that action and reaction are equal and opposite is still pertinent, we shall examine the conquest of gravity through the interaction of action-at-a-distance fields and the actual modification of gravity itself. It must be admitted at the outset, however, that technology has not advanced very far in this direction.

9-2. Magnetic Fields. As far as we know, there is no direct interaction between magnetic and gravitational fields. It does not seem possible with our present knowledge to distort or nullify gravitational lines of force through the use of magnetic fields. Some speculation concerning the interrelation between the two types of fields does exist in the literature (Ref. 9-9)*; this tack, however, seems fruitless at the present time.

It is known that some astronomical objects have magnetic fields of their own. The sun and the earth are the best known examples. The precise mechanism by which their fields are generated is in doubt. It is

* References are listed in the Bibliography at the back of the book.

conceivable that propulsive effects could be produced by vehicle-generated currents which would interact with the natural magnetic fields in such a way that a force opposing that of the natural gravitational field would be set up.

In Sec. 4-11, a method for generating power on satellites which cut the earth's magnetic lines of force was suggested. It turned out that the scheme was not practical for power production, but one can easily imagine the reciprocal situation as a potential propulsion system. In Fig. 4-17, the kinetic energy of the satellite is turned into electric energy through the interaction of current-carrying elements with the earth's magnetic field. By supplying power to the satellite's windings instead, the reverse effect can be made to occur. A force on the satellite can be produced, its kinetic energy can be increased, and, potentially, satellite orbit transfer maneuvers about the earth can be attempted.

No precise calculations of the performance of such a system have been made. For a satellite velocity of 8,000 m/sec and a power plant with 100 per cent efficiency, the specific tangential thrust, calculated from $P = FV_s$, would be a maximum of 0.125 newton/kw. Using the specific mass of 10^{18} kg/kw given in Sec. 4-11, the thrust-to-weight ratio for the entire system becomes on the order of 10^{-20}. This is hardly a practical propulsion system under any circumstances. The poor performance is primarily a consequence of the very weak magnetic field possessed by the earth. The specific impulse of a magnetic satellite drive would be infinity since no propellant is used, although the loss of mass in the energy-generation process would have to be accounted for in a real design.

Away from the earth, the residual magnetic field, approximately 10^{-9} weber/m², gives little hope for magnetic interplanetary drives. It must be concluded that we do not yet know of any way to use the magnetic fields existing naturally in the universe for propulsion, nor do we see any hope that vehicle-generated magnetic fields could directly cancel out gravity. Of course, electromagnetic fields are capable of accelerating matter (Chap. 6), but we are discussing here only those propulsion systems which do not eject matter in the usual sense.

9-3. The Use of Electrostatic Fields in Space. It was mentioned in Sec. 3-10 that electrostatic fields cannot exist in space because of the high conductivity caused by the presence of interstellar protons. For this reason, we must also dispense with this type of action-at-a-distance field as an aid to propulsion. If significant interplanetary electrostatic fields did exist, then it would be conceptually possible to obtain propulsive thrusts through the use of charged spaceships. The fields would have to be strong and the charges immense for effectiveness. Such speculation is futile, however, because of the absence of significant electrostatic fields in space.

9-4. Antigravity. The mention of antigravity always brings reactions ranging from fanatic approval to implications of insanity. Naturally, there are strong opinions about a subject so controversial. Probably the deep-rooted suspicions concerning antigravity have their origin in the early science-fiction stories which relied so heavily upon the concept. The Cavorite used by H. G. Wells is a typical example. The logic of the situation goes something like this. The main obstacle to space travel is the presence of strong gravitational fields in the neighborhood of the journey's beginning and end points; therefore, the simplest solution to space travel is a device which directly negates or distorts the gravitational field itself. In fiction, antigravity devices take the form of gravitational nullifiers, shields, and *negative matter*. Although we may appreciate the objectives, it must be admitted that there is not a shred of experimental evidence to give us any hope that such machines can ever be constructed. Gravitation, however, is a poorly understood phenomenon. We cannot say arbitrarily that there will never be any hope for the taming of gravity without resorting to the crude reaction engines discussed earlier in this book. It is perhaps worthwhile to quickly review the status of gravitational research at this time (Ref. 9-1).

Examining first the all-important experimental picture, we find that numerous attempts have been made to detect deviations from Newton's law of gravitation. A typical experiment is one which measures the acceleration due to gravity for a variety of different substances. The object here is to see if g_0 really is independent of the kind of matter involved. Experiments have also been made to see if there are materials which somehow shield or distort the gravitational lines of force. To date, all such approaches have yielded negative results. Perhaps the most important and most widely accepted experiments in gravitation were those of Eotvos (Ref. 9-2). The goal of his careful series of experiments was to determine whether gravitational and inertial mass are empirically identical. The Eotvos experiments showed that they were, to one part in approximately 10^8 for the materials that were used in the tests. It is observed that meaningful experimental results in the field of gravitation are difficult to obtain, that the work that has been done to date is limited in its scope and, in too many cases, of questionable character.

The theory of gravitation is in a state where it is inundated with complex theory and intractible mathematics. As mentioned above, experiment has not yet been able to rescue the physicists from the dilemma. Still, a great deal of fascinating work is underway throughout the world. The papers given at the Conference on the Role of Gravitation in Physics held at the University of North Carolina in early 1957 are particularly rich in this respect (Ref. 9-9).

One of the foundations of Einstein's work on the theory of gravitation is the principle of equivalence. This hypothesis states that gravitational mass, as it occurs in $\mathbf{F} = -m\nabla E_p$, is identical with inertial mass, which is defined by Newton's second law. The Eotvos experiments were directed at the proof or refutation of this hypothesis. Until shown otherwise, we must regard this theorem to be substantiated by the Eotvos work. It should be added, though, that we cannot say that materials will not be found which violate the principle; nor can we rule out the possibility of negative gravitational mass since negative matter has never been subjected to the experiment (Ref. 9-9).

The white hope of the antigravity fans is *antimatter*,* which presumably has negative gravitational mass, although its inertial mass may still be positive. This situation would permit repulsive rather than attractive forces between planet and spaceship and introduce the possibility of antigravity propulsion systems. Antimatter or *contraterrene* matter is composed of negatively charged nuclei with positrons taking the places of the usual planetary electrons. The electrons, protrons, and neutrons of ordinary matter are replaced by their respective antiparticles. Experiments with antiprotons, which would show their repulsion by the earth's gravitational field, have been proposed, but such experimentation with antimatter is confounded by its tendency to disappear with a burst of energy in its mutual annihilation reaction with normal matter. Again, until experiment proves otherwise, we must regard all mass as positive and the principle of equivalence as a fact of nature. The empirical picture, however, is far from complete and we are free to speculate about antimatter falling up or down so long as we do not insist upon designing propulsion systems based on unfounded concepts.

In summary, we can find nothing in current gravitational research that permits us to seriously design antigravity propulsion systems. There is no evidence that the gravitational field can be altered or negated. The only real use that can be made of gravitation in space flight seem to be in the close brushes with gravitating bodies for space maneuvers as discussed in Sec. 2-5. But the door must be kept slightly ajar; future research will disclose many now unsuspected facts about gravitation.

9-5. Miscellaneous Concepts. Antigravity, if it ever comes to fruition, will certainly not be the end of the line. This chapter is a fitting place to touch upon the fantastic.

The first item of interest concerns the possibility of *hyperdrives* or faster-than-light drives. The stars are far away, so distant in fact that galactic exploration will want a propulsion system that either distorts time for the spaceship crew or somehow overcomes the speed limit that the special theory of relativity places on physical objects. The velocity of light can be attained only at the expense of an infinite amount of

* See Glossary of Terms at the back of the book.

energy. Thus, speeds faster than that of light do not seem possible if the special theory is an accurate portrayal of the entire universe. The obvious way around this impasse is to deny the special theory, especially its applicability in regions of space or at velocities greater than that of light where it has not been tested experimentally. Unfortunately, the special theory has a solid foundation of experimental facts. Hyperdrive adherents will have to base their hopes on some fundamentally new discovery or on the possible variation of physical laws with time or position in the universe. None of these seems intuitively likely.

Time dilatation is predicted by the special theory of relativity. It is to be expected that there will be some expansion of time on a vehicle moving rapidly relatively to some base reference frame. Time intervals on the moving reference frame will be larger than those on the reference frame where the measurements are being made by the factor $1/\sqrt{1 - V^2/c^2}$. The famous *twin paradox*, where one twin returns from an extended, high velocity space trip to find himself younger than the twin left behind, is impossible to resolve at the present time (Refs. 9-3, 9-4, 9-5, and 9-7). Even though time dilatation will occur, it may be argued that there is no preferred reference frame and that the opposite effect would occur (the traveling twin would be older) if the spaceship were taken as the reference frame from which time measurements are made. This paradox has not been explained to everyone's satisfaction.

The special theory does not apply to the acceleration phases of space trips. Here, one must resort to the general theory of relativity. Again, there is no agreement upon just what should happen in time during spaceship accelerations. It should also be pointed out that the experimental foundation of the general theory is not so substantial as that of the special theory. We may conclude that space missions which depend on relativistic time dilatation cannot be safely planned.

The wireless transmission of matter is another fascinating topic. Indeed, one can imagine a device similar to the television iconoscope scanning physical objects and transmitting data concerning the identity and position of each atom in the object to some receiving station. The receiving station would then duplicate the object from a bin of raw materials. Unfortunately, information is never transmitted perfectly. Noise will inevitably distort some of the data giving rise to an imperfect facsimile at the receiver station.

Science fiction also discusses the existence of other spatial dimensions and travel in this *hyperspace*. *Space warps* (distortions of spatial distances) are also common currency. Although hyperspace is mathematically convenient to use in the formulation of physical theory, there is no experimental evidence that there are more than three spatial dimensions. It cannot be dogmatically said that other dimensions do not exist for we might not have the abilities to sense a fourth or fifth spatial dimension.   Nor can we say that the distance to Mars might not be much less in some other dimension.   It can only be said that there is no experimental evidence to support such speculations.

Finally, the use of extrasensory perception (ESP) has been employed by several science-fiction writers for extraterrestrial transportation. Despite the multitudinous experiments in this field, no universally convincing demonstrations have been forthcoming.   Like time dilatation, ESP has created two well-established camps with opposite views. Dr. Rhine's experiments at Duke on *psychokinesis* are intriguing but not universally accepted (Ref. 9-6).   Certainly, unthought of physical laws remain to be discovered.   All that can be said at this writing, however, is that enough is not known to design propulsion systems around these concepts.

It would be grossly unfair not to credit science fiction with great foresight.   The satellites and man-in-space vehicles planned today will not suffice for the intergalactic warfare that has been imagined in fiction, but who can deny that, except for a small handful of persons, space travel was generally ridiculed before the 1957 satellites?

9-6. Evaluation of Propulsion Using Force Fields.   Even with the most optimistic assumptions, nothing has been uncovered which will permit us to utilize any of the action-at-a-distance force fields for primary propulsion in outer space.

CHAPTER 10

SUMMARY AND EVALUATION

10-1. Review of Space Propulsion Techniques. With the exception of the propulsion systems described in Chap. 9, which utilize naturally occurring force fields to accomplish the transfer of spaceships from one point to another in the cosmos, all space engines involve the acceleration and expulsion of a propellant by an engine on board the space vehicle. The propellant may be a gas, a plasma,* nuclear particles, or even photons. In this expulsion of momentum-carrying propellant, both energy and momentum must be conserved in the spaceship-propellant system. The production of thrust, of course, stems from the conservation of momentum. Since energy must also be conserved, it is necessary to provide the vehicle either with an internal power source or a means of collecting energy that is distributed in the environment. The total propulsion system includes, then, the thrust generator and the power supply. Design experience has shown that the power supply, particularly in the case of electrical space drives, dominates the performance of the whole propulsion system through its mass. The production and efficient use of power is the focal point of research and development in space propulsion.

Throughout this book, emphasis has been placed upon the importance of energy in space travel. There are three important sources of energy in space technology: chemicals, nuclear reactions, and the space environment itself. In each energy source, potential energy is released in the form of unoriented kinetic energy of physical particles or photons. To provide a propulsive thrust, this random motion in the energy source must be exchanged for oriented motion in the jet. The techniques for doing this have been the major subject of this book.

Each of the three major energy sources possesses its own special area of application. Chemical bonds are weaker than nuclear bonds; thus, chemicals have less energy content per unit mass. However, chemicals are well developed and may be used in very lightweight engines. They have specific mass advantages over nuclear fuels for short periods of application. Table 10-1 indicates these advantages and also the areas of promise for the more energetic nuclear fuels. The high energy densities

---

* See Glossary of Terms at the back of the book.

of nuclear power plants makes them attractive for applications where large amounts of power are needed for extended periods. Environmental energy is not really free when specific mass is used as a criterion since collector masses must be charged against such power sources. Environmental power sources find use at very low power levels where long periods of operation are desired.

TABLE 10-1. A SUMMARY OF IMPORTANT ENERGY SOURCES

Source	Applicability	State of the art
Chemicals.........	Short times, a few days at the most. Any power level	Off the shelf
Radioisotopes......	Low-power levels, under 10 kw. Up to several years	Now in hardware stage. Fuel scarce
Nuclear fission.....	High powers, over 1 kw. Up to several years	Much commercial experience. Space reactors now under development
Nuclear fusion.....	Questionable. Probably immense power levels only, many megawatt range	Basic reaction not yet tamed
Solar energy.......	Low-power levels, under 100 kw. Up to several years	Now under development in solar cell and focusing collector configurations

Matter may be accelerated by many techniques. Most prevalent today is the thermal engine. The combustion chamber and nozzle turn the potential energy of the chemical or nuclear bonds into the directed kinetic energy of the propellant particles. Other methods of accelerating propellant are listed in Table 10-2. It is interesting to note that only the ion and plasma propulsion systems take initially stationary matter and accelerate it unidirectionally. All of the other types generally add energy to the propellant in such a way that it first appears as random motion of the propellant particles. A nozzle, reflector, selective absorber, or shield must be added to direct the momentum of the efflux. The various methods of orienting random motion place serious limitations upon the performance of the over-all propulsion system. For example, the shaped absorbers used in photon drives are much heavier than the chemical rocket nozzles. These effects are factored into the performance estimates that are presented in the summary performance chart, Fig. 10-1.

The precise measurement of propulsion-system performance is a difficult task. In this book, the specific impulse and thrust-to-weight ratio have been adopted as the prime numerical indicators of excellence. It has also been the policy to accompany these more readily calculable measures with evaluations of the state of the art, reliability, and complexity of each major propulsion system to give a more rounded picture of the merits of each system. Through a careful analysis of both the numerical and nonnumerical performance indicators, we have a fairly accurate picture of the capabilities of each space propulsion system.

TABLE 10-2. SPACE-PROPULSION TECHNIQUES

Class	Propellant	Method of acceleration	Approximate I_{sp}	State of the art
Thermal..........	Gas, plasma	Heat addition plus nozzle	Up to 4,000 sec	Chemicals: good Nuclear: first hardware tests now underway
Electric..........	Ions, plasma, charged dust	Ionization plus electromagnetic fields	5,000 to 100,000 sec	Prototypes completed for ion and plasma types
Nuclear particles..	Ions, neutrons, electrons, etc.	Energy of nuclear reactions	10^5 to 10^7 sec	Conceptual stage
Photonic..........	Photons	Creation of heat and nuclear reactions	30,000,000 sec; solar sail, infinity	Conceptual stage
Force fields.......	Environment	Interaction with action-at-a-distance fields	Infinity	Beyond present knowledge

Space propulsion is a new and burgeoning field. It is still rife with conjectures and incompletely thought out ideas. We cannot yet pin point the exact performance of each class of space engines. Consequently, only rough areas of performance can be delimited; thus, lines and points on performance graphs become bands and small areas. This is a reflection of our ignorance about many of the phenomena occurring in these new propulsion systems and our lack of knowledge concerning the environment of outer space. The rather hazy performance estimates characterizing Fig. 10-1 will come into clearer focus as more knowledge and experience are gained.

Figure 10-1 is compounded from the summary graphs placed at the end of each chapter describing a major class of propulsion systems. Several significant features are immediately apparent. The thermal propulsion systems are all located in a group at the upper left of the $F/W-I_{sp}$ plane. This region is characterized by relatively low specific impulses and high thrust-to-weight ratios. All thermal systems convert the random thermal motion of the propellant derived from the heat source into the

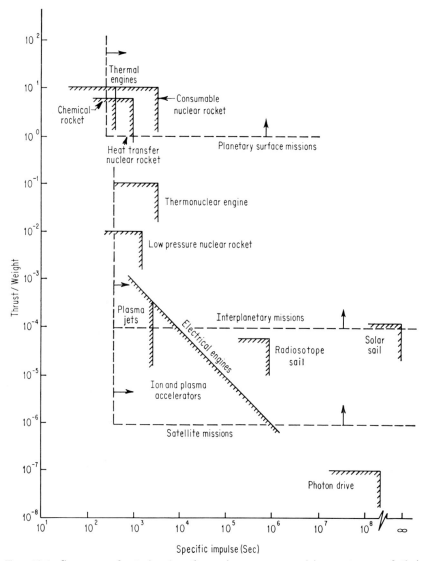

FIG. 10-1. Summary chart showing the major space propulsion systems and their approximate performance limits. The dashed lines indicate the approximate performance ranges needed for several classes of space missions.

directed jet through the action of a nozzle. No heavy conversion equipment and no vulnerable radiators are required. Separated from the high-thrust thermal engines by a discontinuity of several orders of magnitude in the thrust-to-weight ratio are the electrical propulsion systems. The discontinuity is significant for it owes its presence to the heavier conversion equipment needed by electrical space engines. The gap is more likely to be filled by the low-pressure low-thrust nuclear-heat-transfer rockets described in Sec. 5-14 than by improved electric engines. The ion and plasma engines make up for their lower thrust-to-weight ratios by extending their specific impulses far beyond those of the material-limited chemical space engines. The steady decline of the upper envelope of the electrical engines with increasing specific impulse is due to the higher power requirements per newton of thrust and, therefore, larger propulsion system masses. Although the region representing electrical space propulsion may be extended up to specific impulses of 30,000,000 sec, engines are rarely designed with such high specific impulses simply because of the extremely low thrust-to-weight ratios that result. The nuclear-particle generators and photonic propulsion systems are all at the far right of the $F/W-I_{sp}$ plane, indicating that very little mass per second is consumed for each newton of thrust. Generally speaking, the high specific impulses are purchased only at the cost of unattractively low thrust-to-weight ratios. However, some of the environmental engines, like the solar sail, also boast reasonably high thrust-to-weight ratios. The spectrum of space propulsion systems presented in Fig. 10-1 may be divided into three groups: the thermal, the electric, and the emission space engines. The emission engines differ from the others in the sense that the momentum-carrying propellants, whether particles or photons, are created directly by nuclear or atomic action rather than through the medium of nozzles or electromagnetic fields. As a final generalization from Fig. 10-1, one notes the inverse relationship between the specific impulse and the state of the art. The specific-impulse barrier in propulsion is analogous to the temperature barrier in other technologies. Large amounts of money and development effort are expended in progressing to the right across the $F/W-I_{sp}$ plane.

Again paralleling the procedure adopted in the separate chapters which treated the different propulsion systems, Table 10-3 is included here to supplement Fig. 10-1. Here are listed the other factors affecting the use of each type of propulsion system. The numerical performance indicated in Fig. 10-1 is never adequate. Reliability, complexity, state of the art, hazards, all strongly affect the choice of propulsion systems for specific applications. Table 10-3 is a crude approach to supplementing pure performance data.

10-2. Comparison of Performance and Missions Requirements. From among the different ways of providing thrust with which to orient or move a space vehicle from one position to another, how does one choose the best one for a particular application?

Each mission, in the ideal case, can be described by an optimum specific impulse and thrust-to-weight ratio. These parameters may even be functions of time for best results. Similarly, it is desirable to assign states of the art, design lifetimes, and reliabilities to the components so far as is possible. Although each mission is an entity in itself with its own special demands, it is possible to separate the four broad classes of missions described in Chap. 2. Each of these classes, like the major classes of propulsion systems, can be characterized by rough specific impulse and thrust-to-weight ratio limits. Figure 2-28 shows how this

TABLE 10-3. SUMMARY OF SPACE-PROPULSION SYSTEMS

Engine class	Typical class members	Major advantages and disadvantages	Applications
Thermal......	Chemical and nuclear rockets. Plasma jets	Low specific impulses. Well developed. Cheap and simple. High thrust-to-weight ratios. Relatively invulnerable	Planetary surface, satellite, and interplanetary missions, manned and unmanned
Electrical....	Ion and plasma drives	Low thrust-to-weight ratios. High-power requirements. Relatively vulnerable	Satellite missions. Unmanned interplanetary missions
Nuclear-particle generators	Radioisotope sail	Feasibility not shown. Space charge neutralization needed	None
Photonic......	Photon drive. Solar sail	Basic technology unknown. Solar sails are environmental engines	None, except for solar sails in unmanned probes
Force field ...	Antigravity machine	Feasibility not shown	None

can be done graphically, although this procedure is subject to exceptions and criticism of the values chosen for the limits. Ignoring the qualitative factors for the moment, it is possible to superimpose Fig. 2-28 on top of Fig. 10-1. The dotted lines in Fig. 10-1 indicate the superimposed lines. The general performance requirements of each mission class can now be compared with the capabilities of each type of space propulsion system.

Speaking only in the most general terms and looking from the specific application to the means available for accomplishing it, a number of conclusions may be derived from Fig. 10-1. Quite obviously, the planetary surface missions, except perhaps for those involving the smallest moons and asteroids, necessitate the use of thermal propulsion systems for the launching and descent maneuvers. Table 10-4 summarizes the situation for all mission classes. In satellite missions, where drag make-up, orbit adjustment, and attitude control are important, the low thrust-to-weight ratios and high specific impulses of the electrical propulsion systems are highly attractive. The solar sail is also a possibility for satellite maneuvering. Its high specific impulse is obtained by virtue of its being an environmental engine. For the interplanetary class of missions, both thermal and electric engines are competitive. The orbit-to-orbit interplanetary trip can be made either ballistically by thermal impulse engines or continuously by the low-thrust electrical systems.

TABLE 10-4. COMPARISON OF MISSION CLASSES WITH APPLICABLE
SPACE-PROPULSION SYSTEMS

Mission class	Space-propulsion systems
Planetary surface	Thermal engines for all launching and descent missions
Satellite	Thermal systems for initial applications; electrical engines may be used when better developed
Interplanetary	Initially thermal engines for all missions. Thermal engines probably always best for lunar, Mars, and Venus trips. Electrical engines for unmanned probes and eventual manned trips to farther planets. Solar sails for unmanned probes
Interstellar	Doubtful. Possibly electrical or photonic engines in the distant future

Manned trips to the moon, Mars, and Venus will first be accomplished with ballistic, thermal propulsion systems. The interplanetary orbit transfers would be combined with the launching and descent maneuvers at the end points; all maneuvers would be performed by chemical or nuclear rockets. The electrical engines, launched into orbit by thermal systems, can also perform the interplanetary orbit transfer maneuvers. Several factors enter into such a choice between thermal and electrical engines. The electric systems are heavy, vulnerable, slow, and must run continuously for years. They would also subject human passengers to long periods of exposure in the earth's radiation belts during the spiral escape and descent maneuvers. Ion and plasma drives also lag in development. The first lunar and interplanetary trips will certainly utilize thermal propulsion because it will be the only reliable kind of propulsion available when needed. The interstellar missions cannot be performed by any of the systems so far described if trips of reasonable duration are asked. Here, the time factor is even more important than it was in the case of the interplanetary missions. We cannot yet design realistic propulsion systems which can carry men to the nearest stars and back again in their lifetimes. The quantities of energy required for such trips is far beyond our present capabilities (Fig. 2-27). Some of the propulsion systems, notably the electrical drives, have enough development potential so that we might expect them eventually to be combined with fusion energy sources for interstellar expeditions.

The problem of placing *unmanned*, scientific or military vehicles in space is of an entirely different character. The vulnerability and questionable long-term reliability of the electrical drives are not so limiting for interplanetary and interstellar probe missions. The solar sail is another strong contender in this area. The elimination of human occupants so reduces the power requirements and limitations on the propulsion system that the less perfectly developed engines may well be tried and tested on such missions.

Taking the engine-oriented point of view, we can predict steady development of the thermal engines, from chemical to nuclear to thermonuclear rockets. This class of engines will undoubtedly perform the great bulk of all space propulsion tasks during the next several decades. The electrical engines will probably find their use confined to satellite missions, unmanned interplanetary and interstellar probes, and possibly manned trips, in the distant future, beyond Mars and Venus to the farther planets and the nearest stars. The particle emitters and photonic engines, except for the solar sail, show little promise. The solar sail will probably be developed to the point where it can undertake many unmanned probe-type missions. Its use in manned ventures is unlikely. The photon rocket, the radioisotope sail, and all others in this class of presently impractical space engines await the discovery of new energy sources and engineering techniques.

10-3. The Difficulties Ahead. The great bulk of the space propulsion systems described in this book have necessarily been pictured in schematic form. Photographs of operational or prototype engines have been rare. Even detailed design work is difficult to find in the literature. The reasons for this are quite clear. Space propulsion is in its infancy. Only the chemical rocket can be said to be a proven piece of hardware. Nuclear rockets, ion drives, solar sails are all in various stages of design or development, but their practical usage must be reserved for another decade. Still other concepts, like photon and thermonuclear drives, await technological break-throughs. Facts like these deserve more emphasis, for we cannot expect space propulsion to be born suddenly. It is very far— in terms of money, men, and development—from the raw concept to the finished engine which can operate reliably for long periods of time in the rigorous environment of outer space.

Imagine a space vehicle setting out for Mars. Until we possess the means by which we can utilize high-energy short-time orbit transfers, the round trip to Mars will take two years or more. During this period, hundreds, perhaps thousands of individual parts must function perfectly if the mission is to be completed successfully. How many of today's earth-bound machines will function continuously for two years? A few can. Some automobile parts, household appliances, and some stationary and shipborne power-generating equipment can function properly year in and year out. The specific masses of such equipment are very high when compared to the performance required for space vehicles.

Earth-bound journeys rarely last more than a few days. It has been possible to design machinery that will operate satisfactorily for such short missions with a high degree of probability. In the penetration of outer space, the first manned satellites will have comparable mission durations. The manned interplanetary trips, however, will extend the endurance requirements by two orders of magnitude. Here is a most critical and probably the least romantic problem in space propulsion. How can man and his accoutrements be carried safely and reliably over the immense distances between the planets. Manned missions are emphasized in this regard because the true space missions will carry man from the earth to the planets. Regardless of the logic and simplicity in listening to the beeps from probe telemetering transmitters, the transportation of man to the planets and the stars is the only satisfactory goal of astronautics. The costly complex machines that perform this task may fail for the want of a reliable relay or valve. It is a truism in rocketry that a faulty 10-cent part can cause the failure of a $10,000,000 machine.

The direct solution to this problem would be to develop more reliable and less vulnerable components. Alternatively, more powerful energy sources could be built so that the high-energy short-time trajectories between the planets could be used. Finally, for the sake of completeness, one can make a pact with probability and send out enough expeditions to ensure a good total probability of success. Probably some combination of all three approaches will be adopted, even though the third technique is morally difficult to justify.

Machinery is not made more reliable just by drawing up a new set of blueprints. Fail-safe design demands perseverance. The human component, too, if he is ever allowed to become a vital link in the space-vehicle system, will not adapt himself to space overnight. There is no simple, perfect solution to the frailty of humans and the perversity of machines. To turn the schematic figures, used so liberally in this book, into workable hardware is one of the great challenges of space technology.

This section is designed to temper enthusiasm but not to discourage enterprise in space propulsion. The literature of space technology is full of intriguing talk about the exploration of the planets, the optimization of orbits, and engines that are 100 per cent efficient. Perhaps the word "practical" has been used too liberally in these chapters, but let us acknowledge that it is at least appropriate. Space technology has become a matter-of-fact, down-to-earth business. People are trying to make money and fight wars in space.

10-4. What Lies Beyond? Just as a book dealing with space must have a few paragraphs devoted to deflating what it otherwise glorifies, so must there be a section of refuge where the author can wax romantic without too many factual restraints. This, the last section of the book, has been allotted to this function.

Many unifying trends can be found throughout human history. An apt one for use here is man's increasing mastery over energy and, consequently, over his environment. The moment a man-carrying vehicle is airborne or descends beneath the waves, great quantities of energy must be channelled into preserving the rather narrow ranges of temperature, pressure, and acceleration that man can tolerate. History has seen a steady conquest of fire, water power, chemical and nuclear energy. Each step yielded larger amounts and higher densities of energy. With each step, humans have been able to survive under more difficult environments. The invasion of space is a logical extension of this history. But all these things are well known and realized. The crucial test of the theory is its prediction of the future. Now, as we are beginning to penetrate the fringe of space, how will future developments be constrained by our abilities to obtain and control power?

It appears that each step in the conquest of space will also increase the need for energy. First, there is the difficult-to-loosen hold of the earth's gravitational field; then, there is the problem of maintaining a safe, artificial environment for man; finally, there is the desire to travel from one place to another rapidly. If we can assume unlimited amounts of energy, then all of these things can undoubtedly be done. In reality, we shall first have watts, then kilowatts, and, eventually, megawatts in space. This is not unlimited energy, and each progression into space will have to await the development of better power supplies.

Chemicals will obviously not be adequate for our ultimate purposes. Nuclear fission will be tolerated only until a safer and more abundant source of power comes along. Nuclear fusion, which appears to be the mainspring of our segment of the universe, may well satisfy our requirements for energy on interstellar flights. Environmental energy, specifically solar power, will aid materially in the conquest of the solar system. It will provide power to remote bases and spaceborne stations and perhaps generate propulsive thrust for space vehicles. Even fusion power cannot be the end result, for new laws and new ways to tap the energy resources of the universe will be discovered. The complete conversion of matter to useful energy would make interstellar flight a more reasonable objective.

The familiar timetable of space conquest begins with the present scientific satellites, proceeds to lunar and interplanetary probes, to manned satellites, and manned space exploration. We have next a vision of colonies on the planets, of a vast commerce between the few cold motes of matter in the universe where man can exist.   Each launching and descent takes large quantities of energy.   Perhaps the most logical answer for a restless mankind is to deliberately become a machine-bound space nomad.   This talk smacks of science fiction, with whole communities restricted to huge, self-sufficient space vehicles for generations, except perhaps forbrief fo rays to planets and asteroids for raw materials.   One recalls Jules Verne's novel "Twenty Thousand Leagues Under the Sea" and the submarine Nautilus, which extracted most of its needs from the sea itself.   We can also conceive of a space colony absorbing the sun's energy, ingesting the low density matter between the planets, and being completely independent of the vicissitudes of planetary surfaces.   We will not argue the desirability of such a future, but we can say that energy, through its use in conveying and sustaining man in outer space, is the key to making this or any other plans of space conquest become a reality.

How can one end a book on space travel except on a note of optimism? Ton-size satellites are already in orbit; million-pound thrust engines are being built; thousands of engineers and scientists are laboring on ion drives and thermonuclear power.   There is an urgency in astronautics, stimulated to some degree by the military potentialities of space.   There is even a sense of destiny among many of those working in the field.   We are on the brink of true space exploration.   The engines described in this book will be built, and the journeys charted will take place.

GLOSSARY OF TERMS

In space technology, a number of terms associated with space propulsion have evolved which have unusual or special meanings. Many of these words have been used in the text of this book. To aid in the understanding of the subject matter, a glossary is presented in this section.

accelerate-decelerate principle In ion propulsion, the technique of first accelerating the ions to velocities higher than necessary to increase current densities in the presence of space charge. Subsequent deceleration reduces the ion velocities to the desired value.

afterheat The heat evolved in nuclear-reactor cores after the chain reaction has been stopped. This heat originates from the decay of radioisotopes produced in the fission process.

air-breathing engine An engine which derives oxidizer and propellant from the atmosphere. The ram jet and turbojet are typical examples.

antigravity A term associated with any device which directly negates or alters the force due to gravity (Chap. 9).

antimatter Atoms where the neutrons, protons, and electrons have been replaced by their antiparticles—antineutrons, negatrons (antiprotons), and positrons in this instance (Chap. 9).

atmospheric braking The deceleration of spaceships during landing by the frictional effects of the atmosphere.

ballistic trajectory A trajectory initiated by an impulse as opposed to continuous-thrust propulsion. The vehicle will travel in a conic section after the thrust has been cut off (Chap. 2).

Bremsstrahlung (literally, *braking radiation*) Created when charged particles are decelerated rapidly by electrostatic fields in their passage through matter.

capture maneuver The space maneuver which takes a spaceship out of an orbit and places it under the gravitational influence of a planet or other astronomical object.

cavity reactor A nuclear-fission reactor with a gaseous core but normal density reflector. Used in plasma-core nuclear rockets (Chap. 5).

consumable rocket A rocket where part of the solid structure is expelled with the propellant in order to achieve high temperatures (Chap. 5).

contact potential ion source An ion source which utilizes the fact that a hot metallic surface made from a material with a high work function will ionize atoms with low first-ionization potentials upon contact (Chap. 6).

contraterrene matter See **antimatter.**

conversion equipment Rotating equipment or solid-state devices which convert heat or light into electricity. Turbomachinery, generators, and solar cells are examples.

cosmic dust Very small meteoroids which erode and abrade materials and surfaces in space (Chap. 3).

cosmos The universe.

direct conversion The conversion of heat or light into electricity without the use of rotating machinery. Solar cells, thermocouples, and fuel cells are examples (Chap. 4).

drive A general term applied to any space propulsion system. Any reaction engine.

electric propulsion Propulsion which utilizes electrostatic or electro-magnetic fields to accelerate ions or plasma.

endurance The ability of equipment to operate successfully for long time periods.

environment In space, all things which interact with space vehicles. Collectively, the meteoroids, radiations, vacuum, and action-at-a distance fields (Chap. 3).

environmental engine A reaction engine which extracts part or all of its propellant from the environment or surroundings. The solar sail and recombination ram jet are examples.

escape maneuver The maneuver which releases a space vehicle from the gravitational control of a planet or other astronomical object (Chap. 2).

exotic Any object, concept, or component which is highly advanced in approach or design.

extrasensory perception (ESP) Physical events which cannot be explained by any of the accepted physical laws (Chap. 9).

fizzler A slow-burning nuclear bomb or consumable nuclear rocket (Chap. 5).

flexibility The characteristic of a space engine which permits it to be readily modified to perform other missions.

hardware Physical equipment as opposed to paper designs.

Hohmann ellipse The minimum-energy, maximum-time interplanetary transfer orbit (Chap. 2).

hyperdrive Any propulsion system which can achieve velocities greater than that of light. A science-fiction term.

hyperspace Space with more than three dimensions.

impulse maneuver A maneuver accomplished by a burst of thrust rather than a continuous application of force.

ion drive A propulsion system which accelerates ions electrostatically to produce thrust.

magnetic mirror A plasma-containment device utilizing magnetic fields to reflect charged particles from the ends of a magnetic bottle (Chap. 6).

magnetohydrodynamics, MHD The discipline created by the welding of electrodynamics and gas dynamics (Chap. 6).

maneuver Any adjustment or orbital position, trajectories, or vehicle attitude (Chap. 2).

meteor bumper A thin sheet of protective material placed over radiator surfaces to fragment meteoroids into ineffectual pieces (Chap. 4).

mission In space propulsion, a space trip with prescribed objectives (Chap. 2).

neutralizer A source of charged particles designed to neutralize space charges built up because of the expulsion of charged particles from spaceships. Used in ion drive (Chap. 6).

orbit The repetitive path taken by an object in space, as opposed to trajectories which are not closed paths.

orbit transfer A space maneuver which takes a space vehicle from one orbit to another. Example: changes in satellite altitude (Chap. 2).

orbit trimming The changing of the eccentricity or plane of rotation of an orbit.

packaging In space propulsion, the reduction of large areas or volumes (solar sails) to small packages suitable for launching into space in rockets.

payload The useful contents of a launching vehicle. For example, instrumentation, fuel in orbit, men.

performance A term descriptive of the ability of a space engine to perform its mission for a minimum cost as measured by some figure of merit. Example figures of merit, specific mass, thrust-to-weight ratio (Chap. 2).

photon drive A rocket using collimated beams of photons to produce thrust.

plasma A mixture of electrons, ions, and neutral atoms.

plasma core rocket A nuclear rocket with the fissions occurring in the working fluid. Containment may be through the action of vortices or electromagnetic fields (Chap. 5).

plasma jet A space engine which uses the heat produced by an electric arc to raise propellant temperatures to extreme values (Chap. 5).

plasmoid gun A pulsed propulsion system which shoots small bunches of plasma (plasmoids) at high velocities (Chap. 6).

potential well A schematic representation of the gravitational potential energy associated with an astronomical object (Chap. 2).

powered descent The use of propulsion system braking in the descent to a planet surface, as opposed to atmospheric braking.

probe An unmanned space vehicle containing instrumentation for measurement of physical phenomena that occur in space and close to astronomical bodies.

propellant The matter which is expelled from the propulsion system to produce thrust. It may be composed of atoms, ions, plasma, or photons.

propulsion system The thrust-producing unit plus the power source. Included are heat sources, conversion equipment, radiators, and the mass accelerators (Chap. 2).

psychokinesis The influencing of motion and position of physical objects through the use of the mind (Chap. 9).

radioisotope sail A thin sheet of radioisotopes which produces thrust through the emission of nuclear particles (Chap. 7).

reaction engine Any propulsion system which generates thrust through the expulsion of matter in an anisotropic fashion.   Photons may also be included in the jet.

recombination ram jet A propulsion system deriving thrust from the recombination of dissociated molecules in the atmosphere (Chap. 5).

reentry The process of approaching the surface of a planet using atmospheric braking.

relativistic effects Phenomena occurring at high relative velocities. When the velocity of light is approached, mass is observed to increase on the moving reference frame, for example (Chap. 2).

rocket Any propulsion system which obtains thrust through the expulsion of matter.

Rover The U.S. nuclear-rocket program (Chap. 5).

selective surface A specially prepared surface (white paint or blackened metal), which enhances or hampers the radiation of thermal energy (Chap. 4).

shadow shielding In reactor technology, the placement of radiation shields in the line of sight only, as opposed to 4π shielding (Chap. 4).

Snap The systems for Nuclear Auxiliary Power program sponsored by the AEC (Chap. 4).

solar sail A propulsion system using the pressure of sunlight to produce thrust (Chap. 8).

sophisticated Well-developed, as opposed to unrefined.

space charge The charge residing in a cloud or beam of ions.

space propulsion The art of propelling objects from one place to another in outer space.

space warps Distortions in the structure of space. A science-fiction term (Chap. 9).

specific impulse A measure of the propellant economy of an engine. Thrust per unit propellant-weight flow (Chap. 2).

specific mass The mass of power-generating equipment needed to produce 1 kw of power (Chap. 4).

state of the art The time period when a component or system is expected to be operational (Chap. 2).

teleportation The movement of objects by mental means.

thermal engine A propulsion system that relies upon the addition of heat and expansion of a propellant through a nozzle for the production of thrust.

thrust-to-weight-ratio Propulsion-system thrust per system weight. A measure of the accelerating capabilities of a spaceship (Chap. 2).

time dilatation The apparent slowing down of time aboard a rapidly moving space vehicle (Chap. 9).

trajectory The nonrepetitive path in space taken by a space vehicle. See also **orbit**.

transfer ellipse An orbit connecting the initial and the target orbits.

twin paradox The possible disparity between the ages of space travelers and nonspace travelers due to relativistic time dilatation (Chap. 9).

vehicle The spaceship.

velocity increment The change in velocity needed to complete some space maneuver.

vulnerability The sensitivity of the space vehicle and propulsion system to the environment (Chap. 2).

waste heat Energy that must be rejected by the spaceship. It includes all energy generated not appearing in the jet.

working fluid The matter which does work on the spaceship or on power conversion machinery.

TABLE OF SYMBOLS

A common set of symbols has been used throughout this book.   In the few duplications that occur, it is immediately evident from the context which meaning has been given to the symbol.   A complete list of symbols used follows.

Symbol	Definition	Unit
A	Atomic weight	g/mole
A	Constant in Richardson equation	amp/m^2-$^\circ$K^2
A	Area	m^2
A_c	Collector area	m^2
A_r	Radiating area	m^2
A_v	Vehicle area	m^2
B	Magnetic induction	weber/m^2
D	Displacement	coulomb/m^2
D	Drag	newtons
E	Energy	joules
E	Electric intensity	volt/m
E_i	Ionization potential	ev
E_k	Kinetic energy	joule
E_p	Potential energy	joule
E_t	Total energy	joule
ΔE_M	Mission energy increment	joule
ΔE_V	Vehicle energy increment	joule
ΔE_{PS}	Propulsion-system energy increment	joule
F	Thrust, force	newton
F_A	Thrust per unit area	newton/m^2
F_{sp}	Specific thrust	newton/kw
H	Magnetic intensity	amp/m
I	Electric current	amp
I_{sp}	Specific impulse	sec
J	Current density	amp/m^2
J_c	Cathode current density	amp/m^2
K	Conduction losses	watts/m^2
K	Modulus of elasticity	kg/cm^2
K_0	Reference modulus of elasticity (7×10^4)	kg/cm^2
L	Lead losses	watt/m^2
M	Vehicle mass	kg
M	Molecular weight	g/mole

Symbol	Definition	Unit
M_{PL}	Payload mass	kg
M_{PP}	Propellant mass	kg
M_{ST}	Structural mass	kg
M_{PS}	Propulsion-system mass	kg
M_{bo}	Burn-out mass	kg
M_0	Initial vehicle mass	kg
M_p	Planetary mass	kg
M_s	Sun's mass (1.99×10^{30})	kg
M_{sp}	Specific mass of power supply	kg/kw
N	Particles per unit volume	$1/m^3$
N_0	Avogadro's number (6.02×10^{23})	atom/mole
P	Power level of source	kw
P_e	Directed power in jet	kw
P_0	Initial power level	kw
P_v	Power diverted to auxiliaries	kw
P_A	Power per unit area	kw/m^2
Q	Charge	coulomb
Q	Heat added or subtracted	joule
R	Radius of earth (6.38×10^6)	m
R	Universal gas constant (8.31)	joule/mole-°K
R	Radiation losses	$watt/m^2$
S	Poynting vector	$watt/m^2$
T	Temperature	°K
T_c	Cathode temperature	°K
T_0	Effective sink temperature of space	°K
T_p	Planet surface temperature	°K
T_s	Sun's surface temperature (5720)	°K
$T_{1/2}$	Half-life	sec
T_{eff}	Effective radiator temperature	°K
U	Volume of meteoroid crater	m^3
V	Vehicle velocity	m/sec
V	Voltage	volt
V_a	Anode voltage	volt
V_c	Cathode voltage	volt
V_e	Escape velocity	m/sec
V_0	Initial vehicle velocity in orbit	m/sec
V_0	Output voltage	volt
V_s	Satellite velocity	m/sec
ΔV	Velocity increment	m/sec
W	Weight of entire vehicle	newton
W_r	Radiant emittance	$watt/m^2$
Z	Ionization losses	$watt/m^2$
a	Acceleration	m/sec^2
a	Constant	varies
b	Constant	varies
c	Velocity of light (2.99×10^8)	m/sec
c_P	Specific heat at constant pressure	joule/kg-°K
c_V	Specific heat at constant volume	joule/kg-°K

Symbol	Definition	Unit
d	Differential operator	none
e	Thermal efficiency of power supply	none
e	emissivity	none
e'	Efficiency of propulsion unit	none
f	Frequency	sec^{-1}
g_0	Acceleration due to gravity at the Earth's surface (9.80)	m/sec^2
h	Planck's constant (6.62×10^{-34})	joule-sec
k	Boltzmann's constant (1.37×10^{-23})	joule/atom-°K
m	Particle mass	kg
m_α	Alpha particle mass (6.68×10^{-27})	kg
m_0	Rest mass of particle	kg
$\dot{m}$	Mass flow rate of propellant	kg/sec
$\dot{m}_A$	Mass flow rate per unit area	kg/sec-m^2
n	Number of charge units of particle	none
n	Ratio of final orbit radius to initial orbit radius	none
p	Pressure	newton/m^2
p	Momentum	kg-m/sec
q	Charge on the electron (1.60×10^{-19})	coulomb
r	Radius	m
r	Reflectivity	none
r_0	Initial radius	m
r_E	Radius of the earth's orbit (1.49×10^{11})	m
t	Time	sec
t_s	Satellite period	sec
u	Ratio of semimajor axis of the ellipse of the transfer orbit to the initial planet orbit radius	none
v	Particle velocity	m/sec
v_e	Exhaust velocity	m/sec
x	Distance	cm
x_i	Fraction of atoms ionized	none
α	Angle with the horizontal	
γ	Constant of gravitation (6.67×10^{-11})	newton-m^2/kg^2
γ	Ratio of specific heats	none
ϵ	Eccentricity	none
ϵ_0	Permittivity of free space (8.85×10^{-12})	coulomb^2/newton-m^2
θ	Angle	degrees
λ	Wavelength	m^{-1}
λ	Radioactive decay constant	sec^{-1}
μ_0	Permeability of free space (1.26×10^{-6})	newton-sec^2/coulomb^2
μ_1	Viscosity	poise
ρ	Mass density	kg/m^3
ρ_e	Charge density	coulomb/m^3
ρ_E	Energy density	joule/m^3
σ	Stefan-Boltzmann constant (5.67×10^{-8})	watt/m^2-°K^4
σ	Conductivity	1/ohm-meter
Φ	Magnetic flux	weber

Symbol	Definition	Unit
ϕ_a	Anode work function	volt
ϕ_c	Cathode work function	volt
ϕ_p	Plasma drop in thermionic converters	volt
ϕ_k	Kinetic energy of electrons	volt
ω_s	Solid angle subtended by sun	steradian
ω_p	Solid angle subtended by planet	steradian
$\mathcal{E}$	Electromotive force	volt
∂	Partial differential operator	none
∇	Gradient operator	

BIBLIOGRAPHY

The literature of space propulsion is extensive. Thanks to the emphasis placed on this field by political and military exigencies, the amount of reference material available has multiplied severalfold in recent years. It is impossible in this book to include all of the references that are available. The policy adopted here is that of listing the sources specifically cited in the text and only those additional references that are especially valuable because of the new concepts they introduce, their comprehensiveness, or other special qualities.

The bibliography is divided into categories which parallel the chapter material in the body of the book. The general references on space flight are included in the first section of the bibliography.

While there is no really comprehensive compilation of space abstracts issued regularly, there are several excellent listings of current references on the subject of space flight. A list of these follows.

Abstracts of Classified Reports, United States Atomic Energy Commission, Technical Information Service Extension, Oak Ridge, Tennessee. Secret-Restricted Data. Abstracts all work of a classified nature on nuclear rockets and secondary nuclear auxiliary power.

Aero/Space Engineering, Aeronautical Review Section, Institute of Aeronautical Sciences, 2 E. 64th St., New York 24, N.Y. A fairly complete listing of all space-flight literature with brief abstracts.

NASA Publications Announcements, National Aeronautics and Space Administration, 1520 H. St., N.W., Washington 25, D.C., Confidential. Lists and abstracts all publications originated by the NASA.

Nuclear Science Abstracts, United States Atomic Energy Commission, Technical Information Service Extension, Oak Ridge, Tenn. Abstracts all unclassified work completed by government contractors of a nuclear nature. Some periodicals are also covered.

Technical Abstract Bulletin, Armed Services Technical Information Agency (ASTIA), Arlington Hall Station, Arlington 12, Va. Presents abstracts of reports submitted by government contractors.

Today, there are many periodicals which frequently include articles of interest to space technology. The most prominent of these are given in the following list.

Aero/Space Engineering, Institute of the Aeronautical Sciences, 2 E. 64th St., New York 21, N.Y.

ARS Journal, formerly *Jet Propulsion*, American Rocket Society, 500 Fifth Ave., New York 36, N.Y.

Astronautica Acta, Molkerbastei 5, Vienna, Austria. Organ of the International Astronautical Federation.

Astronautics, American Rocket Society, 500 Fifth Ave., New York 36, N.Y.

Aviation Week, McGraw-Hill Publishing Company, Inc., 330 W. 42nd St., New York 36, N.Y.

Journal of the Aero/Space Sciences, Institute of the Aeronautical Sciences, 2 E. 64th St., New York 21, N.Y.

Journal of the Astronautical Sciences, American Astronautical Society, 516 Fifth Ave., New York 36, N.Y.

Journal of the British Interplanetary Society, British Interplanetary Society, 12 Bessborough Gardens, London S.W.1, England.

Missiles and Rockets, 1001 Vermont Ave., N.W., Washington 5, D.C.

Missile Design and Development, 140 E. 40th St., New York 16, N.Y.

Nucleonics, McGraw-Hill Publishing Company, Inc., 330 W. 42nd St., New York 36, N.Y.

Raketentechnik und Raumfahrtforschung, Deutsche Gesellschaft fur Raketentechnik und Raumfahrt, Neuensteiner Strasse 19, Stuttgart-Zuffenhausen, Germany.

Spaceflight, British Interplanetary Society, 12 Bessborough Gardens, London S.W.1, England.

Space Journal, Box 94, Nashville, Tenn.

Space Technology, McGraw-Hill Publishing Company, Inc., 330 W. 42nd St., New York 36, N.Y.

1. General References

1-1. Adams, C. C.: "Space Flight," McGraw-Hill Book Company, Inc., New York, 1958.

1-2. Allen, C. W.: "Astrophysical Quantities," The Athlone Press, University of London, London, 1955.

1-3. Alperin, M., M. Stern, and H. Wooster (eds.): "Vistas in Astronautics," Pergamon Press, New York, vol. 1, 1958, vol. 2, 1959.

1-4. Bizony, M. T., and R. Griffin (eds.): "The Space Encyclopedia," E. P. Dutton & Co., Inc., New York, 1957.

1-5. Bowman, N. J.: "The Handbook of Rockets and Guided Missiles," Perastadion Press, Chicago, 1957.

1-6. Carter, L. J. (ed.): "Realities of Space Travel," McGraw-Hill Book Company, Inc., New York, 1957.

1-7. Clarke, A. C.: "The Exploration of Space," Harper & Brothers, New York, 1951.

1-8. Clarke, A. C.: "Interplanetary Flight," Temple Press, Ltd., London, 1950.

1-9. Dillaway, R. B.: Propulsion Systems for Space Flight, *Aeronaut. Eng. Rev.*, **17,** 42 (April 1958).

1-10. Keieger, F. J.: "A Casebook on Soviet Astronautics," parts I and II, Rand Corporation, RM-1760 and RM-1922.

1-11. Ley, W.: "Rockets, Missiles and Space Travel," The Viking Press, Inc., New York, 1958.

1-12. Ley, W.: "The Conquest of Space," The Viking Press, Inc., New York, 1949.

1-13. Ley, W., and W. von Braun: "The Exploration of Mars," The Viking Press, Inc., New York, 1956.

1-14. Moeckel, W. E.: "Propulsion Methods in Astronautics," Paper presented at the First International Congress of Aeronautical Sciences, Madrid, Spain, 1958.

1-14a. Puckett, A. E., and S. Ramo: "Guided Missile Engineering," McGraw-Hill Book Company, Inc., New York, 1958.

1-15. Sanger, E.: "The Attainability of the Fixed Stars," Paper given at the International Astronautical Federation Meeting, Rome, Italy, 1956.

1-16. Sutton, G. P.: "Rocket Propulsion Elements," 2d ed., John Wiley & Sons, Inc., New York, 1956.

1-17. von Braun, W.: "The Mars Project," University of Illinois Press, Urbana, Ill., 1953.

1-18. von Braun, W., et al: "Conquest of the Moon," The Viking Press, Inc., New York, 1953.

1-19. "Space Flight Problems," *Proceedings of the Fourth International Astronautical Congress*, Zurich, Switzerland, 1953.

1-20. "Advanced Propulsion Systems Symposium, Compilation of Papers," Rocketdyne Division of North American Aviation, Los Angeles, 1957. Confidential.

2. Propulsion-system Performance and Missions Analysis

2-1. Camac, M.: "Reduction of Flight Time and Propellant Requirements of Satellites with Electrical Propulsion by the Use of Stored Electrical Energy," American Rocket Society Preprint 721–58.

2-2. Clarke, A. C.: The Dynamics of Space Flight, *J. Brit. Interplanet. Soc.*, **8,** 71 (Mar. 1949). Also in Ref. 1-6.

2-3. Demetriades, S. T., and C. B. Kretschmer: "A Preliminary Investigation of an Atomic Oxygen Powerplant," ASTIA Document

154229, also Air Force Office of Scientific Research TN-58-325. This report describes a typical environmental engine.

2-3a. Ehricke, K. A.: "Space Flight," vol. 1, D. Van Nostrand Company, Inc., Princeton, N.J., 1960.

2-4. Ehricke, K. A.: The Satelloid, *Astronaut. Acta*, **2**, 63 (1956).

2-5. Ehricke, K. A.: "Instrumented Comets—Astronautics of Solar and Planetary Probes," American Rocket Society Preprint 493-57.

2-6. Ferebee, F. M.: "Flight Mechanics of Low Thrust, High Energy Space Vehicles," American Rocket Society Preprint 605-58.

2-7. Haviland, R. P.: "The Communication Satellite," American Rocket Society Preprint 487-57.

2-8. Herrick, S.: "Astrodynamics," D. Van Nostrand Company, Inc., Princeton, N.J., to be published.

2-9. Irving, J. H., and E. K. Blum: "Comparative Performance of Ballistic and Low-thrust Vehicles for Flight to Mars," Presented at the Second Annual Air Force Office of Scientific Research Astronautics Symposium, Denver, Colorado, April 1958.

2-10. Irving, J. H.: Power-limited Flight—Optimization in Gravitational Fields, Lecture 5B, University of California Space Technology Course, Berkeley, Calif., 1958.

2-11. Klemperer, W. B., and R. M. Baker, Jr.: Satellite Librations, *Astronaut. Acta*, **3**, 16 (1957).

2-12. Kooy, J. M. J., and J. W. H. Uytenbogaart: "Ballistics of the Future," McGraw-Hill Book Company, Inc., New York, 1946.

2-13. Lawden, D. F.: Orbital Transfer Via Tangential Ellipses, *J. Brit. Interplanet. Soc.*, **11**, 278 (1952).

2-14. Malina, F. J., and M. Summerfield: The Problem of Escape from the Earth by Rocket, *J. Aeronaut. Sci.*, **14**, 471 (1947).

2-15. Moeckel, W. E.: "Interplanetary Trajectories with Excess Energy," Presented before the International Astronautical Federation, Amsterdam, Netherlands, 1958.

2-16. Moulton, F. R.: "Celestial Mechanics," The Macmillan Company, New York, 1914.

2-17. Preston-Thomas, H.: Generalized Interplanetary Orbits, *J. Brit. Interplanet. Soc.*, **11**, 76 (1952).

2-18. Roberson, R. E.: "Torques on a Satellite from Internal Moving Parts," American Society of Mechanical Engineers Preprint 57-A-39.

2-19. Roberson, R. E.: "A Unified Analytical Description of Satellite Attitude Motions," American Rocket Society Preprint 722-58.

2-20. Romick, D. C., R. E. Knight, and S. Black: "Meteor Junior: A Preliminary Design Investigation of a Minimum Sized Rocket Vehicle of the Meteor Concept," American Rocket Society Preprint 504-57.

2-21. Rosser, J. B., R. R. Newton, and G. L. Gross: "Mathematical

Theory of Rocket Flight," McGraw-Hill Book Company, Inc., New York, 1947.

2-22. Shepherd, L. R.: Interstellar Flight, *J. Brit. Interplanet. Soc.*, **11,** 19 (1952).

2-23 Spitzer, L.: Interplanetary Travel between Satellite Orbits, *J. Brit. Interplanet. Soc.*, **10,** 249 (1951).

2-24. Tsien, H. S.: Take-off from Satellite Orbits, *J. Am. Rocket Soc.*, **23,** 233 (1953).

2-25. Van Allen, J. A. (ed.): "Scientific Uses of Earth Satellites," University of Michigan Press, Ann Arbor, Mich., 1956.

2-26. Vertregt, M.: Interplanetary Orbits, *J. Brit. Interplanet. Soc.*, **16,** 326 (1958).

2-27. "Earth Satellites as Research Vehicles," Monograph No. 2, The Franklin Institute, Lancaster, 1956.

2-28. Orbital Data and Preliminary Analyses of Satellites 1957α and 1957β *Smithsonian Cont. to Astrophysics*, **2,** 10 (1958).

2-29. "Space Handbook: Astronautics and Its Applications," U.S. Government Printing Office, 1959. Prepared by the Rand Corp.

3. The Space Environment

3-1. Alfven, H.: "Cosmical Electrodynamics," Oxford University Press, New York, 1950.

3-2. Baker, R. H.: "Astronomy," D. Van Nostrand Company, Inc., Princeton, N.J., 1938.

3-3. Bates, D. R.: "The Earth and Its Atmosphere," Basic Books, Inc., New York, 1957.

3-4. Bates, D. R., and L. Spitzer: Density of Molecules in Interstellar Space, *Astrophys. J.*, **113,** 441 (1951).

3-5. Beard, D. B.: "Interplanetary Dust Distribution and Erosion Effects," American Astronautical Society Preprint 58-23.

3-6. Curtis, H.: "Effect of the Primary Cosmic Radiation on Matter," Air Force Surveys in Geophysics No. 78, 1956.

3-7. Korff, S. A.: The Origin and Implications of the Cosmic Radiation, *Am. Scientist*, **45,** 281 (1957).

3-8. Kornhauser, M.: "Estimates of the Penetration of the Skin of a Satellite by Meteoroids," Applied Mechanics Memo 50, Missile and Ordnance Systems Dept., General Electric Company, Inc., April 25, 1958.

3-9. Kuiper, G. P.: "The Atmospheres of the Earth and Planets," rev. ed., University of Chicago Press, Chicago, 1952.

3-10. Kuiper, G. P., et al: A Survey of the Asteroids, *Astrophys. J. Supplement No.* 32, vol. III, 1958.

3-11. Minzner, R. A., and W. S. Ripley: "The ARDC Model Atmosphere," Air Force Surveys in Geophysics No. 86. Also ASTIA Document 110233.

3-12. Opik, E. J.: Problems in the Physics of Meteors, *Am. J. Phys.*, **26,** 70 (1958).

3-13. Ovenden, M. W.: Meteor Hazards to Space Stations, *J. Brit. Interplanet. Soc.*, **10,** 275 (1951).

3-14. Partridge, W. S., H. B. Vanfleet, and C. R. Whited, Crater Formation in Metallic Targets, *J. App. Phys.*, **29,** 1332 (1958).

3-15. Singer, S. F.: The Effect of Meteoric Particles on a Satellite, *Jet Propulsion*, **26,** 1071 (1956).

3-16. Singer, S. F.: "Some Consequences of a Theory of the Radiation Belt," Presented at the meeting of the International Astronautical Federation, Amsterdam, Netherlands, 1958.

3-17. Singer, S. F.: Measurements of Interplanetary Dust, in J. A. Van Allen (ed.), "Scientific Uses of Earth Satellites," University of Michigan Press, Ann Arbor, Mich., 1956.

3-18. Singer, S. F.: Radiation Belt and Trapped Cosmic Ray Albedo, *Phys. Rev. Letters*, **1,** 171 (1958).

3-19. Van Allen, J. A., et al: "The Observation of High Intensity Radiation by Satellites 1958 Alpha and Gamma," IGY Satellite Report Series No. 3, 1958, p. 73.

3-20. Van Allen, J. A., C. E. McIlwain, and G. H. Ludwig: "Radiation Observations with Satellite 1958 Epsilon," State University of Iowa Report SUI-58-10, Iowa City, Iowa.

3-21. Van Allen, J. A., C. E. McIlwain, and G. H. Ludwig: "Radiation Measurements from Explorer IV," State University of Iowa Report SUI-58-8, Iowa City, Iowa.

3-22. Van Valkenburg, M. E., W. G. Clay, and J. H. Huth: Impact Phenomenon at High Speeds, *J. Appl. Phy.*, **27,** 1123 (1956).

3-23. Whipple, F. L.: "The Meteoric Risk to Space Vehicles," American Rocket Society Preprint 499-57.

3-24. White, C. S., and O. O. Benson (eds.): "Physics and Medicine of the Upper Atmosphere," University of New Mexico Press, Albuquerque, N.M., 1952.

3-25. Summaries of Radiation Belt Data, *Aviation Week*, Jan. 5, 1959.

4. Space Power

4-1. Adams, A. M.: Recent Developments in Fuel Cells, *J. Inst. Fuel*, **27,** 366 (1954).

4-2. Baldwin, L. V., and P. L. Blackshear: "Preliminary Survey of Propulsion Using Chemical Energy Stored in the Upper Atmosphere," NACA, TN 4267.

4-3. Bedford, B. D.: "Systems for Producing Large Pulses of Electrical Power," General Electric Company, Inc., 57GL126.

4-4. Bussard, R., and R. M. Kiehn: "Small Power Plants for Satellites," Atomic Energy Commission, TID-2023. Secret.

4-5. Colgate, S. A.: Plasma Reactor Promises Direct Electric Power, *Nucleonics*, **15,** 50 (1957).

4-6. Cross, C. A.: The Fundamental Basis of Power Generation in a Satellite Vehicle, *J. Brit. Interplanet. Soc.*, **11,** 117 (1952).

4-7. Daniels, F., and J. A. Duffie: "Solar Energy Research," University of Wisconsin Press, Madison, Wis., 1955.

4-8. Ehricke, K. A.: "On the Application of Solar Power in Space Flight," ASTIA Document 106928, 1955.

4-9. Gale, A. J.: Electrostatic Generators, in "Advanced Propulsion Systems Symposium, Compilation of Papers," Rocketdyne Division of North American Aviation, Los Angeles, Calif., 1957. Confidential.

4-10. Glasstone, S.: "Principles of Nuclear Reactor Engineering," D. Van Nostrand Company, Inc., Princeton, N.J., 1955.

4-11. Goldsmid, H. J.: Use of Semiconductors in Thermoelectric Generators, *Research*, **8,** 172 (1955).

4-12. Goldstein, B., and L. Pensak: High Voltage Photovoltaic Effect, *J. Appl. Phy.*, **30,** 155 (1959).

4-13. Hatsopoulos, G. N., and J. Kaye: Measured Thermal Efficiencies of a Diode Configuration of a Thermo Electron Engine, *J. Appl. Phy.*, **29,** 1124 (1958).

4-14. Hellund, E. J.: "Fundamental Investigation of Electrical Power Sources for Electric Thrust Devices, Morphology," ASTIA Document 202223, also Air Force Office of Scientific Research TN 58-790, 1958.

4-15. Hernqvist, K. G.: Thermionic Energy Converters, *RCA Review*, **19,** 244 (1958).

4-16. Huth, J. A.: Direct Power Conversion, see Ref. 4-9.

4-17. Keller, C.: Closed cycle Gas Turbine, *Trans, ASME*, **72,** 835 (1950).

4-18. Kovacik, V. P., and D. P. Ross: "Performance of Nuclear Electric Propulsion Systems," Institute of Aeronautical Sciences Report 59-25.

4-19. Linden, D., and A. F. Daniel: New Batteries for the Space Age, *Electronics*, **31,** 59 (1958).

4-20. Morehouse, C. K., R. Glicksman, and G. S. Lozier: Batteries, *Proc. IRE*, **46,** 1462 (1958).

4-21. Moteff, J.: "Miscellaneous Data for Shielding Calculations," Atomic Energy Commission APEX-176.

4-22. Peterson, R. E., and G. A. Newby: An Unreflected U-235 Critical Assembly, *Nuclear Sci. and Eng.*, **1,** 112 (1956).

4-23. Post, R. E.: Controlled Fusion Research—An Application of the Physics of High Temperature Plasmas, *Rev. Modern Phys.*, **28,** 338 (1956).

4-24. Prince, M. B.: Silicon Solar Generators, *J. Appl. Phy.*, **26,** 534 (1955).

4-25. Raisbeck, G.: Solar Battery, *Sci. American*, **193,** 102 (1955).

4-26. Rappaport, P., J. J. Lofersky, and E. G. Linder, The Electron-voltaic Effect in Germanium and Silicon P–N Junctions, *RCA Review*, **17,** 100 (1956).

4-27. Rauch, S. E., and L. J. Johnson: High Frequency Alternators, *Elec. Eng.*, **73,** 735 (1954).

4-28. Rochlin, R. S.: "Radioisotope Power Sources for Space Vehicles," General Electric Company, Inc., 58GL243.

4-29. Rosenblum, L.: Small Power Plants for Use in Space, *Aero. Space Eng.*, **17,** 30 (1958).

4-30. Rockwell, T.: "Reactor Shielding Design Manual," Atomic Energy Commission TID-7004, 1956.

4-31. Schnetzer, E. and W. R. Corliss: "A One Megawatt Nuclear Power Package for Applications in Outer Space," American Nuclear Society Paper, December 1958.

4-32. Spedding, F. H.: "The Molten-metal-fuel Reactor," Atomic Energy Commission, ISC-318, 1953.

4-33. Stephenson, R.: "Introduction to Nuclear Engineering," McGraw-Hill Book Company, Inc., New York, 1954.

4-34. Telkes, M.: The Efficiency of Thermoelectric Generators, *J. Appl. Phy.*, **18,** 1116 (1947).

4-35. Telkes, M.: Solar Thermoelectric Generators, *J. Appl. Phy.*, **25,** 765 (1954).

4-36. Teller, E.: General Problems of the Controlled Thermonuclear Process, *Nuclear Sci. and Eng.*, **1,** 313 (1956).

4-37. Thomas, A.: Nuclear Batteries: Types and Possible Uses, *Nucleonics*, **13,** 129 (1955).

4-38. Thompson, A. S.: "Liquid Vapor Power Cycle," Atomic Energy Commission NAA-SR-26 and AECU-135, 1949.

4-39. Webster, H. F.: Calculation of the Performance of a High Vacuum Thermionic Energy Converter, *J. Appl. Phy.*, **30,** 488, (1959).

4-40. Wesling, G. C., and H. Brown: "Thermodynamics of Space Power Plants," General Electric Company, Inc., R59AGT16.

4-41. Wilson, V. C.: Conversion of Heat to Electricity by Thermionic Emission, *J. Appl. Phy.*, **30,** 475, (1959).

4-42. "Proceedings of the World Symposium on Applied Solar Energy, Phoenix, Arizona, 1955," Jorgenson & Co., San Francisco, Calif., 1956.

4-43. "Outer Space Propulsion by Nuclear Energy," Hearings before Subcommittees of the Joint Committee on Atomic Energy, Congress of the United States, Government Printing Office, Washington, D.C., 1958.

5. Thermal-propulsion Systems

5-1. Bussard, R. W.: "Some Boundary Conditions for the Use of Nuclear Energy in Rocket Propulsion," American Rocket Society Preprint 690-58.

5-2. Bussard, R. W., and R. D. DeLauer: "Nuclear Rocket Propulsion," McGraw-Hill Book Company, Inc., New York, 1958.

5-3. Clauser, M. U.: Feasibility of Fusion Propulsion, in Heinz Fischer (ed.), "Conference on Extremely High Temperatures," John Wiley & Sons, Inc., New York, 1958.

5-4. Ducati, A. C., and G. L. Cann: "Propulsive Properties of High Intensity Plasma Jets," Air Force Office of Scientific Research TN-57-748.

5-5. Giannini, G. M.: The Plasma Jet, *Sci. American*, **197,** 80 (1957).

5-6. Green, L., Jr., and J. M. Carter: "Performance Calculations for Hybrid Nuclear–Chemical Rocket Propulsion System," American Rocket Society Preprint 595-58.

5-7. Kaeppeler, H. J.: Zur Verwendung von Kernenergie fur Staustrahltriebwerke, *Astronaut. Acta*, **2,** 48 (1956).

5-8. Levoy, M. M. and J. J. Newgard: Rocket Reactor Design, *Nucleonics*, **16,** 66 (1958).

5-9. Mark, S. D. (ed.): "High Intensity Arc Symposium," The Carborundum Co., Niagara Falls, N.Y.

5-10. Post, R. F.: Fusion Power, *Sci. American*, **197,** 73 (1957).

5-10a. Rom, F. E., and P. G. Johnson: "Nuclear Rockets for Interplanetary Propulsion," Society of Automotive Engineers Preprint 63R, 1959.

5-11. Rosenblum, M. H., W. T. Rinehart, and T. L. Thompson, "Rocket Propulsion with Nuclear Energy," American Rocket Society Preprint 559-57.

5-12. Safonov, G.: "The Criticality and Some Potentialities of Cavity Reactors," Rand Report RM-1835, July 17, 1955. Also ASTIA Document 112410.

5-13. Sanger, E.: Steady Nuclear Combustion in Rockets, *Astronaut. Acta*, **1,** 61 (1955). Also NACA TM 1405.

5-14. Sanger-Bredt, I.: Thermodynamics of Working Gases in Atomic Rockets, *J. Brit. Interplanet. Soc.*, **15,** 233 (1956).

5-15. Schrieber, R. E.: "Nuclear Rocket Propulsion at Los Alamos," American Rocket Society Preprint 689-58.

5-16. Shepherd, L. R., and A. V. Cleaver: The Atomic Rocket, in

L. J. Carter (ed.), "Realities of Space Travel," McGraw-Hill Book Company, Inc., New York, 1957.

5-17. Shepherd, L. R.: Note on Shielding of Atomic Rockets, *J. Brit. Interplanet. Soc.*, **8**, 149 (1949).

5-18. Tormey, J. F.: Liquid Rocket Propellants—Is There an Energy Limit? *Ind. and Eng. Chem.*, **49** (1): 339 (1957).

5-19. Tsien, H. S.: Rockets and Other Thermal Jets Using Nuclear Energy, in C. Goodman (ed.), "The Science and Engineering of Nuclear Power," vol. 2, Addison-Wesley Publishing Company, Reading, Mass., 1949.

5-20. Winterberg, F.: "Die Erreichung von Ausstromgeschwindigkeiten bis 20,000 m/s durch isotherme Expansion in Kernraketen," Paper before the International Astronautical Federation, Amsterdam, Netherlands, 1958.

5-21. Yaffee, M.: First Mono-atomic Ramjet Vehicle Designed for 59 Mi. Altitude, *Aviation Week*, April 7, 1958.

5-22. Zucrow, M. J.: "Principles of Jet Propulsion and Gas Turbines," John Wiley & Sons, New York, 1948.

6. Electrical-propulsion Systems

6-1. Allis, W. P., et al: "Series of Lectures on the Physics of Ionized Gases," Atomic Energy Commission LA-2055, 1956.

6-2. Barnes, A. H., S. M. MacNeille, and C. Starr: "Problems of Physics in the Ion Source," Atomic Energy Commission TID-5219, 1951.

6-3. Boden, R. H.: "The Ion Rocket Engine," Society of Automotive Engineers Preprint 41D, 1958.

6-4. Bostick, W. H.: "Plasma Motors," Atomic Energy Commission NYO-7737.

6-5. Bostick, W. H.: Plasmoids, *Sci. American*, **197**, 87 (1957).

6-6. Bostick, W. H.: Experimental Study of Plasmoids, *Phys. Rev.*, **106**, 404 (1957).

6-7. Bussard, R. W.: A Nuclear-electric Propulsion System, *J. Brit. Interplanet. Soc.*, **15**, 297 (1956).

6-8. Butz, J. S., Jr.: Magnetohydrodynamics: Hope for Space, reprint from *Aviation Week*, 1958.

6-9. Clauser, M. U.: "Magnetohydrodynamics," Lecture 17B, University of California Space Technology Course, Berkeley, Calif., 1958.

6-10. Cobine, J. D.: "Gaseous Conductors," McGraw-Hill Book Company, Inc., New York, 1941.

6-11. Cowling, G. G.: "Magnetohydrodynamics," Interscience Publishers, Inc., New York, 1957.

6-12. Edwards, R. N., T. M. Dickinson, and L. J. Goldberg: "Electrical Propulsion Units for Space Flight, Report of 1957 Study," General Electric Company, Inc., 57GL395.

6-13. Edwards, R. N., and G. Kuskevics: "Cesium Ion Rocket Research Studies," American Society of Mechanical Engineers Preprint 59-AV-32.

6-14. Forrester, A. T.: "Problems Associated with the Testing of Ion Thrust Chambers," American Society of Mechanical Engineers Preprint 59-AV-35.

6-15. Fox, R.: "Preliminary Studies on Electrical Propulsion Systems for Space Travel," American Rocket Society Preprint 708-58.

6-16. James, G. S., and R. M. Patrick: "Production of High Temperature Gas by Magnetic Acceleration," AVCO Research Report No. 27, 1958.

6-17. Kolb, A. C.: Production of High Energy Plasmas by Magnetically Driven Shock Waves, *Phys. Rev.*, **107**, 345 (1957).

6-18. Landshoff, R. K. M. (ed.): "Magnetohydrodynamics," Stanford University Press, Stanford, Calif., 1957.

6-19. Langmuir, D.: "Problems of Thrust Production by Electrostatic Fields," Paper presented to the Second Air Force Office of Scientific Research Astronautics Symposium, Denver, April 1958.

6-20. Marshall, J.: "Acceleration of Plasma into Vacuum," Paper presented at the 1958 Geneva Conference on the Peaceful Uses of Atomic Energy, Atomic Energy Commission A/CONF. 15/P/355.

6-21. Mixson, D. M.: "The Feasibility of the Nuclear Powered Ion Propelled Space Vehicle, "Thesis, Air Force Institute of Technology, ASTIA Document 125194.

6-22. Patrick, R. M.: "A Description of a Propulsive Device Which Employs a Magnetic Field as the Driving Force," AVCO Research Report No. 28, 1958.

6-23. Resler, E. L., Jr., and W. R. Sears: Prospects for Magneto-Aerodynamics, *J. Aeronaut Sci.*, **25**, 235 (1958).

6-24. Spitzer, L.: "Physics of Fully Ionized Gases," Interscience Publishers, Inc., New York, 1956.

6-25. Steketee, J. A.: "An Introduction to the Equations of Magnetogasdynamics," University of Toronto, Toronto, Ontario, Canada, UTIA Review No. 9, 1957. Also ASTIA Document 140424.

6-26. Stuhlinger, E.: Electrical Propulsion System for Space Ships with Nuclear Power Source, *J. Astronaut.*, Winter 1955, Spring 1956, and Summer 1956.

6-27. Willinski, M. I., and E. C. Orr: "Project Snooper: A Program for Reconnaisance of the Solar System with Ion Propelled Vehicles," American Rocket Society Preprint 419-57.

6-28. "Research on Power from Fusion and Other Major Activities in the Atomic Energy Programs, January–June 1958," Atomic Energy Commission. Available at the Government Printing Office, Washington, D.C.

7. Nuclear-particle Emitters

No important references in this area.

8. Photonic Propulsion

8-1. Garwin, R. L.: Solar Sailing—A Practical Method of Propulsion Within the Solar System, *Jet Propulsion*, **28**, 188 (1958).

8-2. Sanger, E.: "On the Mechanics of Photonic Jet Propulsion," Martin Company Report ER 8868-7. Also ASTIA Document 121060, 1956.

8-3. Sanger, E.: "Sources of Radiation for Photonic Jet Propulsion," Paper presented before the International Astronautical Federation Meeting, Amsterdam, Netherlands, 1958.

8-4. Sanger, E.: On Directing Intense Photonic Beams by Electron Gas Mirrors, *Astronaut. Acta*, **5**, 266 (1959).

9. Miscellaneous Topics

9-1. DeWitt, B. S.: Principle Directions of Current Research Activity in the Theory of Gravitation, *J. Astronaut.*, Summer 1957.

9-2. Eotvos, R. v.: Inertia and Gravity, *Ann. Physik*, **68**, 11 (1922).

9-3. McMillan, E. M.: The Clock Paradox in Space Flight, *Science*, **126**, 381 (1957).

9-4. McCrea, W. H.: Time Paradox, *Nature*, **167**, 680 (1951).

9-5. Milne, E. A.: Time Paradox, *Phil. Mag.*, **40**, 1244 (1949).

9-6. Rhine, J. B.: "The Reach of the Mind," William Sloane Associates, New York.

9-7. Stehling, K. R.: Space Travel and Relativity, *Jet Propulsion*, **26**, 1105 (1956).

9-8. Wittry, D. B., et al.: Essays on Gravity, Gravity Research Foundation, New Boston, N.H., 1955.

9-9. Conference on the Role of Gravitation in Physics, *Rev. Modern Phys.*, **29** (1957). Also ASTIA Document 118180 and WADC TR 57-216.

INDEX

Accelerate-decelerate principle, 202–205, 273
Accelerators (*see* Ion drives; Plasma accelerators)
Ackeret, J., 182
Action-at-a-distance fields, 8, 12, 69, 256
  (*See also* Gravitational fields)
AICBM weapons, 159
Air-breathing boost, 138–144, 273
  performance of, 142, 143, 183–185
  recovery of first stage in, 140
  turbojet capabilities in, 139–141
Air-breathing engines (*see* Environmental engines)
Alternator (*see* Generators)
Antigravity, 9, 12, 13, 258–259, 273
Antimatter, 258, 259, 273
Arc jet (*see* Plasma jets)
Artificial gravity, 10
Asteroids, physical data for, 30, 55–57
  utility of, in space flight, 13, 55–57
Atlas, 34
Atmosphere of earth, 64, 65
Atmospheres of planets, utilization of, 64–66
Atmospheric braking, 26
Attitude control, 8, 10, 24, 26, 40, 41, 90, 91

Baldwin, L. V., 147, 150
Ballistic trajectories (*see* Trajectories)
Balloon-type solar mirror, 92, 93
Batteries, 119, 120, 131, 132
  for energy storage, 87, 93
Blackshear, P. L., 141, 150
Bomb propulsion, 167–169, 183–185
Booster rockets, 28–34
  performance table for, 34
  (*See also* Nuclear rockets)
Bostick, W., 217
Brayton cycle, 100–108, 131–133
  compared to Rankine cycle, 101–106, 129–133
  working fluids for, 105
Burnup of nuclear cores, 85, 166
Button type of plasmoid gun, 217, 218

Calutron, 197
Capture maneuver, 273
Cavity-reactor rocket, 164–166, 273
  (*See also* Consumable nuclear rockets)
Characteristic energy increment, 26
  (*See also* Energy increment)
Characteristic velocity increment (*see* Velocity increment)
Chemical power, 74–76
  batteries, 119, 120
  compared to nuclear power, 74–77, 130, 131
  fuel cell, 118, 119
  (*See also* Chemical rockets)
Chemical rockets, 144–147, 183–185
Child's law, 202
Clauser, M. U., 192
Collectors, energy, 88–98
  solar mirror, 92–95
Collimation, ion, 204
  magnetic, 235, 236
  photon, 243
Colloidal propulsion, 211
  (*See also* Ion drives)
Consumable nuclear rockets, 161–167, 273
  fuel retention in, 166, 167
  hazards of, 165, 166
  liquid, 164–166
  performance of, 166–167, 183–185
  solid, 162–164
  using bomb propulsion, 167–169
Contact-potential ion source, 197–200, 274
Continuous thrust performance, 26, 46, 47
  (*See also* Trajectories, spiral)
Contraterrene matter, 258, 259, 274
Cosmic dust (*see* Meteoroids)
Cosmic rays, 62–64

Demetriades, S. T., 147
Descent maneuver, 26–28, 64, 276
Direct conversion, 111–122, 274
  batteries, 119, 120

Direct conversion, devices, compared
    with electromechanical, 112, 130
    performance of, 131
    fuel cells, 118, 119
    solar cells, 120–122
    thermionic, 113–116
    thermoelectric, 116–118
Dissociation, effects on specific impulse,
    138
    in nuclear rockets, 161, 162
    in ionosphere, 64, 95
    utilization of (*see* Environmental
        engines)
Drag compensation, 8, 24, 32, 40
Dribble effect in plasma drives, 225
Dynamic conversion (*see* Electro-
    mechanical conversion)

E ✕ H accelerators, 222–223
Earth, atmosphere of, 64, 65
    magnetic field of, 69
    orbit of, 44
    physical data for, 30
    radiation belts of, 63
Efficiency, of propulsion unit, 17, 18
    of space engine, 16–18
    optimization of, 101
Einstein, A., 11, 12, 239
Electrical propulsion, 186–228
    performance in, 19, 21, 24, 226–228,
        264–266
    summary chart, 226
    power requirements, 72
    (*See also* Ion drives; Plasma accelera-
        tors)
Electromagnetic bottle, 170–173, 188–
    190
Electromagnetic energy, in space, 66–69
    transmission of, 97, 98
    (*See also* Photon drives; Radiators)
Electromagnetic generators, 108–111
Electromagnetic theory of light, 238–241
Electromechanical conversion, 73, 98–
    111, 129–133
    Brayton cycle, 100–108
    compared with direct conversion, 112
    comparison of cycles for, 101–106,
        129–133
    electrical generators for, 108–111
    Rankine cycle, 100–108
    reliability of, 103, 104
    Stirling cycle, 106
    thermodynamics of, 100–106
    turbomachinery for, 106–108
    vapor cycle, 100–108
Electrostatic accelerators (*see* Ion
    drives)

Electrostatic fields in space, 69, 257
Electrostatic generators, 108–111
Emitter, ion, 196–200
Energy increment, 18–51
    interplanetary mission, 42–47
    interstellar mission, 49, 50
    planetary-surface mission, 28–34
    satellite maneuver, 35
Energy-level diagrams, 24–51
    for earth escape, 31
    generalized, 27
    for interplanetary missions, 43
    for interstellar missions, 50
    for lunar trip, 41
    for satellite maneuvers, 35
    for various mission classes, 50
Energy storage, 87, 88, 123
    (*See also* Batteries)
Environment of space, 54–70
    effect, on propulsion system, 3, 13
        on radiators, 126–129
        on solar cells, 122
        on solar collectors, 94, 95
    temperature, 67, 68, 124, 125
    utilization (*see* Environmental energy
        sources; Environmental engines)
Environmental energy sources, 73,
    88–98, 263
Environmental engines, 13, 16, 88, 274
    interstellar ram jet, 66
    particulate mass, 65, 66
    recombination ram jet, 64–66, 95, 96,
        147–152
    solar sail, 247–253, 264–267
    turbojet, 138–144
Environmental power, 88–98
    collectors, 89–93, 97, 98
    free-radical, 95
    magnetic field, 96–97
    orientation requirements for, 90, 91
    solar, 90–95
    (*See also* Environmental engines)
Eotvos, R. von, 258, 259
Erosion, by cosmic dust, 61, 62
    of solar cells, 122
    of solar collectors, 94, 95
    by solar protons, 63
Escape maneuver, 23, 28–34, 274
Escape velocity, 28, 30, 36
ESP, 261, 274
Exhaust velocity, 8, 11–15
    (*See also* Specific impulse)
Extrasensory perception, 261, 274

Faster-than-light drives, 6, 49, 259, 260
Fission energy (*see* Nuclear reactors)
Fission-fragment propulsion, 230, 231

Fission-product sail (*see* Radioisotope sail)
Fizzler nuclear rocket, 162–167, 274
  (*See also* Consumable nuclear rockets)
Focusing (*see* Collimation)
Free radicals, in atmosphere, 64–66
  for power, 75, 95
  (*See also* Recombination ram jet)
Fusion (*see* Thermonuclear energy)
Fuel cells, 118, 119, 131

Gale, A. J., 111
Generators, electric, 108–111
  nuclear-particle, 229–237
Gerdien, H., 173
Goddard, R. H., 2
Gravitational fields, 12, 13, 28, 69
  artificial, 24
  overcoming, 23, 28–34, 46
  use of, in propulsion, 13, 258, 259
  (*See also* Antigravity)
Gyroscopic effects, 10, 24, 40, 41

Harteck, P., 147, 150
Heat engines (*see* Electromechanical conversion; Thermal engines)
Heat rejection (*see* Radiators)
Heat-transfer nuclear rockets (*see* Nuclear heat-transfer rockets)
Hermann, R., 147
History of space flight, 2, 3
Hohmann ellipse, 27, 44, 274
  (*See also* Trajectories, minimum energy)
Huth, J., 118
Hyperbolic orbits, 36, 44
  (*See also* Trajectories, fast)
Hyperdrives, 259, 274
Hypeasyace, 6, 260, 274

ICBM, 34, 47
Impulse maneuver, 275
  (*See also* Trajectories, ballistic)
Interplanetary missions, 24, 42–48
Interstellar missions, 24, 48–51
Interstellar ram jet, 66
Ion drives, 9, 10, 195–215, 275
  accelerate-decelerate principle, 202–205
  accelerator design for, 195, 200–205
  applications of, 195, 215
  colloidal, 211
  compared to plasma drives, 196, 226–228
  emitters for, 195–200
  evaluation of, 214, 215, 227, 228
  focusing in, 203

Ion drives, neutralization in, 195, 204–206
  performance of, 208–213, 226–228, 264–267
  summary graph, 209
  principles of, 195–206
Ion gun, ion propulsion (*see* Ion drives)
Ion sources, 195–206
Ionospheric ram jet (*see* Recombination ram jet)
Irving, J. H., 47
Isothermal nuclear rockets, 161–163

Jet engine (*see* Reaction engine)
Jet power, 12–19, 72, 241
Jupiter-C, 34

KIWI-A, 160, 161
Kolb tube, 223, 224
Kretschmer, C., 147

Leakage caused by meteoroids, 94, 127
Leaky magnetic bottle, 172, 173
Ley, W., 2
Low-pressure nuclear rocket, 161, 162
Lunar trip, 23, 24, 41, 42

Magnetic bottle, 170–173, 188–190
Magnetic fields, of earth, 69
  in space, 69
  utilization of, for power, 96, 97
  for propulsion, 256, 257
Magnetic mirrors, 170–173, 188–190, 221, 275
Magnetohydrodynamics, 181, 187–194, 275
  equations of, 191–193
  in plasma acceleration, 215–226
Maneuverable satellites, 34–42, 161
Metastable atoms, 75
Meteoroids, 57–62
  bumpers for, 61, 62, 128
  composition of, 58
  densities of, 58
  distribution of, 58–62
  earth shielding of, 58, 60
  effects of, on radiators, 61, 126–129
    on solar cells, 122
    on solar collectors, 94, 95
  frequency of, 59–62
  kinetic energy of, 60
  masses of, 58–60
  methods of observation on, 58
  reliability of, 57, 58
MHD (*see* Magnetohydrodynamics)
Micrometeoroids (*see* Meteoroids)
Midcourse corrections, 24

Minimum energy trajectory, 27, 44, 45
    (See also Trajectories, ballistic)
Mirrors, magnetic (see Magnetic
    mirrors)
    in solar power, 92–95
Missions, space, 7, 23–53
    interplanetary, 24, 42–48
    interstellar, 24, 48–51
    list of, 23, 24
    minimum performance require-
        ments for, 52
    satellite, 24, 34–42, 52
Moeckel, W. E., 45
Momentum (see Reaction engine)
Moon, trip to, 23, 41, 42

Neutralization of space charge (see
    Space charge)
Neutralizer of ion drive, 205, 206
Newton, I., 2
Nova booster class, 34
Nuclear heat-transfer rockets, 153–161,
    183–185, 264–267
    evaluation of, 145, 159–160, 183–185,
        264–267
    low-pressure, 161, 162
        isothermal expansion in, 161–163
    materials for, 156, 157
Nuclear-particle generators, 229–237
    summary of, 236–237
Nuclear reactors, 81–87
    burnup limitations in, 85
    comparative performance of, 130, 131
    control of, 85
    coolants for, 82, 83
    criticality limitations on, 76, 81, 84,
        86
    description of, 81–84
    fuels for, 81–84
    heat-transfer limitations on, 81, 84, 86
    particles emitted by, 230–231
    shielding of, 85–87
    SNAP program on, 87
Nuclear rockets, 152–173
    consumable, 161–169
    heat-transfer (see Nuclear heat-
        transfer rockets)

Orbit transfer (see Interplanetary
    missions; Satellites, missions)
Orbit trimming, 24, 35–42, 275
Orion, Project, 169
    (See also Bomb propulsion)

Parameters, propulsion, 16–20
    optimization of, 20–23
Particulate mass in space, 55–66

Patrick, R. M., 220
Payload-to-gross-mass ratio, maximiz-
    ing, 20–23
Penetrations by meteoroids, 59–62
    leakage due to, 94, 127
    in stainless steel, 61
Performance of space engines, definition,
    16–18, 275
    factors in, 17, 18
    summary chart and tables, 264–267
Photon drives, 11, 12, 16, 239–247, 275
    collimation in, 243
    evaluation of, 241–247, 253, 254,
        264–267
Photons, 10–12
    pressure from, 68, 238–241
    in space, 66–69
    thrust from, 12, 238–241, 264–267
    (See also Photon drives; Solar sails)
Pierce gun, 204
Pinch effect, 170, 175, 193, 194
Planck, M., 239
Planets, atmospheres of, 64–66
    escape velocities of, 30
    gravitational well depths of, 29, 30
    orbital data for, 44
    physical data for, 30
    use of, in propulsion, 13
Plasma, definition, 190, 275
    in thermonuclear reactors, 170
    (See also Magnetohydrodynamics;
        Plasma accelerators)
Plasma accelerators, 215–228, 264–267
    dribble effect in, 225
    E × H, 222–223
    evaluation of, 217, 225–228, 264–267
    Kolb tube, 223–224
    plasmoid gun, 217–220
        button type, 217, 218
        coaxial-cylinder type, 220
        rail type, 218, 219
    transient-magnetic-field, 225
    traveling-wave, 220–222
Plasma-core rocket, 164–166, 275
    (See also Consumable nuclear rockets)
Plasma jets, 173–183, 264–267, 275
    effects of dissociation and ionization
        on, 176–179
    evaluation of, 180–185, 264–267
    lifetime of, 175, 182
    MHD booster for, 181
    thermal equilibrium in, 178
Plasmoid guns (see Plasma accelerators)
Plasmoids, 217
Post, R. E., 170
Potential-energy wells, 29, 30, 276
    of planets, 30
Power, for electrical engines, 72

Power, in jet, 12–19
  in photon drives, 241
Power generation, 71–133
  role in space flight, 4, 262, 263
  summary performance graphs, 130, 131
Power-plant components, 73
Powered descent, 64, 276
Propellants, for chemical rockets, 146
  for ion drives, 198, 199
  for nuclear heat-transfer rockets, 158, 160
  for plasma jets, 177–179
  for thermonuclear rockets, 169, 171
Propulsion system, definition of, 3, 4
  generalized schematic for, 3, 9
  selection of, 51–53
    summary data for, 264–268
Propulsive efficiency, 25
Psychokinesis, 261, 276

Quantum mechanics, 238–241
  (See also Photons)

Radiation belts (see Van Allen belts)
Radiators, 73, 122–129
  effects of coatings on, 91, 92, 124, 125
  finning for, 126, 127
  influence of sun on, 124, 125
  performance of, 128
  physical construction of, 125–127
  specific mass chart for, 128
  temperature problem in, 67, 68, 123
  vulnerability of, to meteoroids, 126–129
Radioisotope sail, 76, 231–235, 264–267, 276
Radioisotopes, 76–81
  availability and cost of, 78–81
  comparative performance of, 130–132
  methods of heat removal from, 79–81
  particle sources, 231–235
  properties of, 78
  shielding of, 77, 78
  SNAP programs on, 80, 81
  specific mass graph for, 80
  (See also Radioisotope sail)
Rail plasmoid gun, 218, 219
Ram jets (see Environmental engines; Recombination ram jet)
Rankine cycle, 100–108, 131–133
  comparison of, with Brayton cycle, 101–106, 129–133
  effect of zero gravity on, 108
  turbomachinery for, 106, 107
  working fluids for, 105
Reaction engine, 7–16, 263, 264, 276
  generalized performance chart for, 14

Reaction engine, photon, 241, 242
  relativistic, 10, 12
Reactors, fission (see Nuclear reactors)
Recombination ram jet, 147–152, 264–267, 276
  energy source for, 95, 96
  evaluation of, 149–152, 183–185
  thermodynamics of, 150–151
  use of catalyst in, 150
Reentry, 64, 276
Relativity, 10, 11, 48, 259, 276
  general theory of, 260
  special theory of, 11, 260
Reliability, 5, 17, 72, 269, 270
Rendezvous maneuver, 24
Rhine, J. B., 261
Rotating equipment (see Electro-mechanical conversion)
ROVER program, 152, 160, 276

Saha's equation, 176
Sanger, E., 239
Satellites, missions, 24, 34–42, 52
  propulsion, 34–42
  staging platforms, 23, 34
  velocity, 30
Saturn booster rockets, 34
Selection of propulsion systems, 51–53
  summary data for, 264–268
Selective absorption, 91, 92, 125, 276
Shadow shielding (see Shielding)
Sherwood project, 172
Shielding, for nuclear reactors, 85–87
  for nuclear rockets, 152, 158, 159
  for radioisotopes, 77, 78
  shadow, 85, 86
  for thermonuclear rockets, 171
SNAP programs, SNAP-I, 80
  SNAP-II, 87
  SNAP-VIII, 87
Solar cells, 120–122
  erosion of, 61, 63, 122
  performance of, 122, 131
Solar collectors, 88–95
Solar constant, 66
Solar mirrors, 92–95
Solar power, 90–95
  balloons in, 92–94
  concentrators, 92
  effects of meteoroids on, 94
  flat-plate collectors for, 91, 92
  selective absorption in, 91, 92
  solar cells, 120–122
Solar sails, 13, 16, 247–253, 264–267, 276
  construction of, 248
  evaluation of, 248–254, 264–267
  operation of, 249–251
  radiation pressure on, 68, 238–241

Solar spectrum, 66, 67
Sources, ion, 195–200
Space charge, in ion propulsion, 195, 200, 205, 206
  in nuclear-particle generators, 230, 231, 234
  in thermionic converters, 113–115
Space warps, 260, 277
Specific impulse, 15, 16, 277
  effect of variable, 47
  optimization, 21, 22
Specific mass, importance of, 4, 73
  power plant, 17, 18, 21, 73, 277
   summary chart of, 130, 131
Specific thrust, 17, 19
  of ion drive, 212
  of photon drive, 241
  of plasma jet, 179
Specific weight (see Specific mass)
Sputtering of ion drive electrodes, 203, 204
Stars, mass spectrum, 55
  physical characteristics, 55–57
  (See also Interstellar missions)
State of the art, 5, 17
Stellerator, 172
Stirling engine, 106
Sunlight, contribution to environment temperature, 68
  effects of, 67
  pressure of, 68
  (See also Solar power)
Sustainer nuclear rockets, 161

Teleportation, 6, 49, 277
Teller, E., 170
Temperature of space, 67, 68, 123, 124
Thermal engines, 134–185, 277
  performance summary for, 183–185, 264–267
  specific impulse, 138
  techniques for isolating heat sources in, 135, 136
  thermodynamics of, 136–138
  thrust of, 138
Thermionic converters, 113–116
  performance of, 116, 131
  as topping devices, 115, 116
  vacuum, 114, 115, 201
  vapor-filled, 115
Thermodynamics, of space power plants, 100–106
  of thermal engines, 136–138
Thermoelectric generators, 116–118, 131
Thermonuclear energy, 87, 169–173
  evaluation of, 173, 183–185
  for power plants, 87
  for rockets, 169–173

Thor, 34
Thrust, 8, 17
  circumferential, 37–39
  equations for, 8, 11, 12, 15
  Newton's second law, 8
  specific (see Specific thrust)
  tangential, 37–39
  variable, 23, 47
Thrust-to-weight ratio, 19, 23, 24, 74, 277
  effect of electrical generating equipment on, 99
  in interstellar flight, 48–51
  in launching missions, 32
  in mission constraints, 52, 53
  in orbit transfer, 38
Time dilatation, 48, 260, 277
Titan, 34
Trajectories, ballistic, 24, 26, 273
  comparison with continuous-thrust trajectories, 46, 47
  correction of, 24
  fast, 27, 31, 36, 41–44
  minimum energy, 27, 44, 45
  spiral, 38, 39
Transient-magnetic-field accelerator, 225
Transportable energy sources, 73–88
Traveling-wave accelerator, 220–222
Turbojet engine (see Air-breathing boost)
Turbomachinery for space power, 106–108
  specific mass of, 108
Twin paradox, 260, 277

Van Allen belts, 63, 64
  impact, on low thrust-to-weight-ratio engines, 64
  on space flight, 63, 64
  shielding for, 158
Vanguard, 34, 144, 145
Vapor cycle (see Rankine cycle)
Velocity increment, 17, 25–28, 32, 277
  (See also Energy increment)
Verne, J., 2, 272
Vertregt, M., 45
Vulnerability of space vehicle to meteoroids, 5, 17, 23, 72, 126–129, 269, 270, 277
  effect of penetration frequency on, 60, 128

Waste-heat rejection (see Radiators)
Wells, H. G., 2, 258
Whipple, F. L., 59
Wireless transmission of power, 97, 98

Ziolkowski, K., 2